Handbook of
Heating, Ventilating
and
Air Conditioning

Eighth edition

F. Porges
LL.B. BSc(Eng), CEng, FIMechE, MIEE, FIHVE

Butterworths
London Boston Sydney Wellington Durban Toronto

First published 1942
Second edition 1946
Third edition 1952
Fourth edition 1960
Fifth edition 1964
Sixth edition 1971
Seventh edition 1976
    Reprinted 1979
Eighth edition 1982
    Reprinted 1986

© Fred Porges, 1982

British Library Cataloguing in Publication Data

Porges, F,
Handbook of heating, ventilating and air conditioning — 8th ed.

1. Heating — Equipment and supplies — Tables
2. Ventilation — Equipment and supplies — Tables
3. Air conditioning — Equipment and supplies — Tables
697   TH 7011   80-41195
ISBN 0-408-00519-X

Typeset by Tunbridge Wells Typesetting Services Limited
Printed in England by The Camelot Press Ltd., Southampton

Preface

This book contains in a readily available form the data, charts and tables which are required by the heating engineer many times during his daily work.

The data is presented in a concise manner in order to facilitate the work of the heating and ventilating engineer. The book is designed for daily use and a comprehensive bibliography has been included for the benefit of those who wish to pursue the theoretical side of any particular branch.

Previous editions of this well-known book have been written by my father, the late John Porges, whose name was associated with the heating and ventilating industry for many years. This eighth edition has been completely rewritten in order to bring it up-to-date with current practice and the most recent data available. Some of the sections have also been re-arranged to give a more consistent presentation and thus make it easier to find relevant information.

A large part of the industry's work is concerned with modifications and alterations to existing buildings. Records and drawings of these are inevitably in Imperial units and engineers who are faced with such information may need other data in the same units. The policy has therefore been continued of giving tabulated data in both SI and Imperial units although theoretical expressions are generally given only in SI units.

F. Porges

Contents

1

Abbreviations, symbols and conversions

Symbols for units

m	metre	s	second	st	stoke
mm	millimetre	min	minute	J	joule
μm	micrometre	h	hour	kWh	kilowatt hour
	(formerly	d	day	cal	calorie
	micron)	a	year	Btu	British
in	inch	kg	kilogram		thermal unit
ft	foot	t	tonne	W	watt
yd	yard	lb	pound	V	volt
m^2	square metre	gr	grain	A	ampere
mm^2	square	cwt	hundred-	VA	volt ampere
	millimetre		weight	K	kelvin
a	are	N	newton	°C	degree
ha	hectare	kgf	kilogram		Celsius
in^2	square inch		force	°F	degree
ft^2	square foot	pdl	poundal		Fahrenheit
m^3	cubic metre	lbf	pound force	°R	degree
l	litre	Pa	pascal		Rankine
in^3	cubic inch	m^2/s	metre	dB	decibel
ft^3	cubic foot		squared per		
gal	gallon		second		

Symbols for physical quantities

l	length	α	attenuation	T	thermo-
h	height		coefficient		dynamic
b	width	β	phase		temperature
r	radius		coefficient	θt	common
d	diameter	m	mass		temperature
AS	area	ρ	density	C_p	specific heat
V	volume	d	relative		capacity at
t	time		density		constant
T	period (time	F	force		pressure
	of one cycle)	W	weight	C_v	specific heat
uvw	velocity	M	moment		capacity at
ω	angular	h	pressure		constant
	velocity	w	work		volume
a	acceleration	p	power	U	thermal
g	acceleration	η	efficiency		trans-
	due to	ν	kinematic		mittance
	gravity		viscosity	k	thermal
					conductivity

1

Multiples and sub-multiples

$\times 10^{12}$	tera	T	$\times 10^{-1}$	deci	d
$\times 10^{9}$	giga	G	$\times 10^{-2}$	centi	c
$\times 10^{6}$	mega	M	$\times 10^{-3}$	milli	m
$\times 10^{3}$	kilo	k	$\times 10^{-6}$	micro	μ
			$\times 10^{-9}$	nano	n
			$\times 10^{-12}$	pico	p

Abbreviations used on drawings

BBOE	bottom bottom opposite ends (radiator connections)	LSV	lockshield valve
		MV	mixing valve
CF	cold feed	MW	mains water
CW	cold water	NB	nominal bore
DC	drain cock	NTS	not to scale
EC	emptying cock	PR	primary (hot water flow)
F	flow	R	return
FA	from above	SEC	secondary
TA	to above	TA	to above
FS	fire service	TB	to below
FTA	from and to above	TBOE	top bottom opposite ends (radiator connections)
FTB	from and to below		
FW	fresh water	TBSE	top bottom same end
GV	gate valve	TW	tank water
HTG	heating	TWDS	tank water down service

Standard sizes of drawing sheets

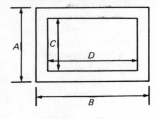

Designation	Size of sheet		Size of frame	
	A	B	C	D
	mm	mm	mm	mm
A0	841	1189	791	1139
A1	594	841	554	804
A2	420	594	380	554
A3	297	420	267	390
A4	210	297	180	267

Recommended scales for drawings

1:1	1:10	1:100	1:1000
1:2	1:20	1:200	
1:5	1:50	1:500	

Representation of screw threads

THREAD DETAIL   *CONVENTION*

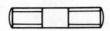

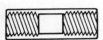
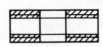

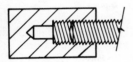
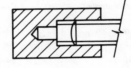

Symbols on drawings (based on BS 1853)

———————	Pipe		Angle relief valve
– – – – –	Pipe below ground		Non-return valve
— · — · —	Pipe at high level		Three-way valve
/////////////	Existing pipe to be removed		Four-way valve
	Crossing, unconnected		Float operated in line valve
	Junction, connected		Globe valve
——→	Indication of flow direction		Ball valve
fall 1 : 200	Indication of fall		Bellows
========	Heated or cooled		Strainer or filter
	Jacketed		Tundish
	Guide		Open vent
	Anchor		
	In line valve (any type)		
	Angle valve		
	Relief valve		

Symbols on drawings *(continued)*

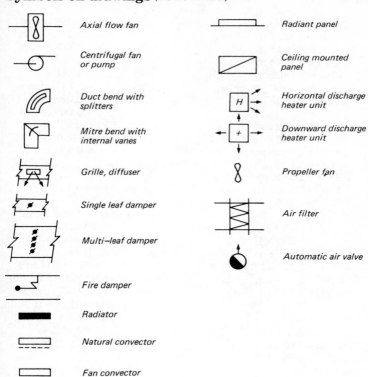

Axial flow fan	Radiant panel
Centrifugal fan or pump	Ceiling mounted panel
Duct bend with splitters	Horizontal discharge heater unit
Mitre bend with internal vanes	Downward discharge heater unit
Grille, diffuser	Propeller fan
Single leaf damper	Air filter
Multi–leaf damper	Automatic air valve
Fire damper	
Radiator	
Natural convector	
Fan convector	

Conversions

Length

1 in = 25.4 mm
= 0.0254 m
1 ft = 0.3048 m
1 yd = 0.9144 m
1 m = 3.2809 ft
= 1.0936 yd
1 mm = 0.03937 in

Area

$1 \text{ in}^2 = 6.452 \text{ cm}^2$
$= 6.452 \times 10^{-4} \text{ m}^2$
$1 \text{ ft}^2 = 0.0929 \text{ m}^2$
$1 \text{ yd}^2 = 0.836 \text{ m}^2$
$1 \text{ mm}^2 = 1.55 \times 10^{-5} \text{ in}^2$
$1 \text{ m}^2 = 10.764 \text{ ft}^2$
$= 1.196 \text{ yd}^2$

Volume

$1 \text{ in}^3 = 16.39 \text{ cm}^3$
$= 1.639 \times 10^{-5} \text{ m}^3$
$1 \text{ ft}^3 = 0.0283 \text{ m}^3$
$= 6.23 \text{ gal}$
$1 \text{ yd}^3 = 0.7646 \text{ m}^3$
$1 \text{ gal} = 4.546 \text{ l}$
$= 4.546 \times 10^{-3} \text{ m}^3$
$= 0.16 \text{ ft}^3$
1 pint = 0.568 l
1 U.S. gal = 0.83 Imperial gal
$1 \text{ cm}^3 = 0.061 \text{ in}^2$
$1 \text{ m}^3 = 35.31 \text{ ft}^3$
$= 1.308 \text{ yd}^3$
= 219.98 gal
1 l = 0.21998 gal

Mass

1 grain = 0.000143 lb
= 0.0648 g
1 lb = 7000 grains
= 0.4536 kg
= 453.6 g
1 g = 15.43 grains
= 0.0353 oz
= 0.002205 lb
1 kg = 2.205 lb
1 tonne = 1000 kg
= 0.984 tons

Content by weight

1 g/kg = 7.0 gr/lb
1 gr/lb = 0.143 g/kg

Density

$1 \text{ lb/ft}^3 = 16.02 \text{ kg/m}^3$
$1 \text{ kg/l} = 62.425 \text{ lb/ft}^3$
$1 \text{ kg/m}^3 = 0.0624 \text{ lb/ft}^3$

Velocity and volume flow

1 ft/min = 0.00441 m/s
1 m/s = 226.85 ft/min
1 kg/s (water) = 13.23 gal/min
$1 \text{ m}^3/\text{s} = 2118.6 \text{ ft}^3/\text{min}$
$1 \text{ ft}^3/\text{min} = 1.7 \text{ m}^3/\text{h}$
= 0.47 l/s
1 l/s = 791.9 gal/h

Conversions *(continued)*

Pressure

1 atm = 1.033×10^4 kg/m^2
= 1.033 kg/cm^2
= 1.013×10^2 kN/m^2
= 1.013 bar
= 14.7 lb/in^2
= 407.69 in water at 62°F
= 10.33 m water at 62°F
= 30 in mercury at 62°F
= 760 mm mercury at 62°F

1 lb/in^2 = 6895 N/m^2
= 6.895×10^{-2} bar
= 27.71 in water at 62°F
= 703.6 mm water at 62°F
= 2.0416 in mercury at 62°F
= 51.8 mm mercury at 62°F
= 703.6 kg/m^2
= 0.068 atm

1 kg/m^2 = 1.422×10^{-3} lb/in^2
= 9.80 N/m^2
= 0.0394 in water
= 1 mm water
= 0.0736 mm mercury
= 0.9677×10^{-4} atm

1 N/m^2 = 0.1452×10^{-3} lb/in^2
= 1×10^{-5} bar
= 4.03×10^{-3} in water
= 0.336×10^{-3} ft water
= 0.1024 mm water
= 0.295×10^{-3} in mercury
= 7.55×10^{-3} mm mercury
= 0.1024 kg/m^2
= 0.993×10^{-5} atm

1 in water = 0.0361 lb/in^2
= 249 N/m^2
= 25.4 kg/m^2
= 0.0739 in mercury

1 mm water = 1.42×10^{-3} lb/in^2
= 9.80 N/m^2
= 1 kg/m^2
= 0.0736 mm mercury
= 0.9677×10^{-4} atm

1 in mercury = 0.49 lb/in^2
= 3378 N/m^2
= 12.8 in water

1 mm mercury = 0.0193 lb/in^2
= 133 N/m^2
= 12.8 mm water

1 bar = 1×10^5 N/m^2
= 14.52 lb/in^2

1 Pa = 1 N/m^2

Energy and heat

1 joule = 1 watt second
= 1 Nm
= 0.74 ft lb
= 9.699×10^{-4} Btu

1 Btu = 1.055×10^3 joule
= 0.252 kcal
= 778.5 ft lb
= 0.293 watt hour

1 kcal = 3.9683 Btu
= 427 kg m
= 4.183×10^3 joule

1 ft lb = 0.1383 kg m
= 0.001286 Btu
= 1.356 joule

1 kg m = 7.233 ft lb
= 0.009301 Btu
= 9.807 joule

Conversions *(continued)*

Heat flow

1 Btu/h$=$0.293 watt

1 kW$=$1000 J/s

$=$3.6$\times$10^6 J/h

$=$1.358 metric
   horse power

$=$737 ft lb/s

$=$3412 Btu/h

$=$860 kcal/h

1 kcal/h$=$1.16$\times$10^{-3} kW

1 Btu/ft^2$=$2.713 kcal/m^2

$=$1.136$\times$10^{-4} J/m^2

1 Btu/ft^2 h$=$3.155 W/m^2

1 Btu/ft^3 h$=$10.35 W/m^3

1 Btu/ft^2 °F$=$4.88 kcal/m^2 K

$=$2.043$\times$10^4 J/m^2 K

1 Btu/ft^3$=$8.9 kcal/m^3

$=$3.727$\times$10^4 J/m^3

1 Btu/lb$=$0.556 kcal/kg

$=$2326 J/kg

1 kcal/m^2$=$0.369 Btu/ft^2

1 kcal/m^2 K$=$0.205 Btu/ft^2 °F

1 kcal/m^3$=$0.1125 Btu/ft^3

1 kcal/kg$=$1.800 Btu/lb

1 ton
refrigeration$=$12.000 Btu/h

$=$3.516 kw

1 ft^2 h °F/Btu in$=$0.18 m^2 K/w

1 ft^2 h °F/Btu in $=$ 6.9 m K/w

1 Btu/h ft^2°F $=$5.68 W/m^2 K

Power

1 watt $=$ 1 Nm/s

1 horse power$=$550 ft lb/s

$=$33,000 ft lb/m

$=$1.0139 metric
   horse power

$=$746 W

$=$2545 Btu/h

1 metric horse power$=$735.56 W

$=$75 kg m/s

$=$0.986 English
   horse power

Temperatures

°F$=$($\frac{9}{5}$ °C)$+$32

°C$=$$\frac{5}{9}$(°F$-$32)

1 deg F$=$0.555 deg C

1 deg C$=$1.8 deg F

Viscosity

1 poise$=$0.1 kg m/s

$=$0.1 N s/m^2

1 stoke$=$1$\times$10^{-4} m^2/s

Force

1 N $=$ 0.2248 lbf

1 lbf $=$ 4.449 N

A mass of 1 kg has a weight of 1 kp

1 kp$=$9.81 N

Acceleration due to gravity

in London$=$32.2 ft/s^2

$=$9.81 m/s^2

at Equator$=$32.1 ft/s^2

$=$9.78 m/s^2

Conversion tables

Temperature conversion table. Degrees Fahrenheit to Degrees Centigrade (Figures in italics represent negative values on the Centigrade Scale)

Degrees F	0	1	2	3	4	5	6	7	8	9
	°C	°C	°C	°C	°C	°C	°C	°C	°C	°C
0	*17.8*	*17.2*	*16.7*	*16.1*	*15.6*	*15.0*	*14.4*	*13.9*	*13.3*	*12.8*
10	*12.2*	*11.7*	*11.1*	*10.6*	*10.0*	*9.4*	*8.9*	*8.3*	*7.8*	*7.2*
20	*6.7*	*6.1*	*5.6*	*5.0*	*4.4*	*3.9*	*3.3*	*2.8*	*2.2*	*1.7*
30	*1.1*	*0.6*	—	—	—	—	—	—	—	—

	0	1	2	3	4	5	6	7	8	9
30	—	0	0	0.6	1.1	1.7	2.2	2.8	3.3	3.9
40	4.4	5.0	5.6	6.1	6.7	7.2	7.8	8.3	8.9	9.4
50	10.0	10.6	11.1	11.7	12.2	12.8	13.3	13.9	14.4	15.0
60	15.6	16.1	16.7	17.2	17.8	18.3	18.9	19.4	20.0	20.6
70	21.1	21.7	22.2	22.8	23.3	23.9	24.4	25.0	25.6	26.1
80	26.7	27.2	27.8	28.3	28.9	29.4	30.0	30.6	31.1	31.7
90	32.2	32.8	33.3	33.9	34.4	35.0	35.6	36.1	36.7	37.2
100	37.8	38.3	38.9	39.4	40.0	40.6	41.1	42.7	42.2	42.8
110	43.3	43.9	44.4	45.0	45.6	46.1	46.7	47.2	47.8	48.3
120	48.9	49.4	50.0	50.6	51.1	51.7	52.2	52.8	53.3	53.9
130	54.4	55.0	55.6	56.1	56.7	57.2	57.8	58.3	58.9	59.4
140	60.0	60.6	61.1	61.7	62.2	62.8	63.3	63.9	64.4	65.0
150	65.6	66.1	66.7	67.2	67.8	68.3	68.9	69.4	70.0	70.6
160	71.1	71.7	72.2	72.8	73.3	73.9	74.4	75.0	75.6	76.1
170	76.7	77.2	77.8	78.3	78.9	79.4	80.0	80.6	81.1	81.7
180	82.2	82.8	83.3	83.9	84.4	85.0	85.6	86.1	86.7	87.2
190	87.8	88.3	88.9	89.4	90.0	90.6	91.1	91.7	92.2	92.8
200	93.3	93.9	94.4	95.0	95.6	96.1	96.7	97.2	97.8	98.3
210	98.9	99.4	100.0	100.6	101.1	101.7	102.2	102.8	103.3	103.9
220	104.4	105.0	105.6	106.1	106.7	107.2	107.8	108.3	108.9	109.4
230	110.0	110.6	111.1	111.7	112.2	112.8	113.3	113.9	114.4	115.0
240	115.6	116.1	116.7	117.2	117.8	118.3	118.9	119.4	120.0	120.6
250	121.1	121.7	122.2	122.8	123.3	123.9	124.4	125.0	125.6	126.1

$F = (C \times 1.8) + 32$

Temperature conversion table. Degrees Fahrenheit to Degrees Centigrade *(continued)*

Degrees F	0	1	2	3	4	5	6	7	8	9
	°C	°C	°C	°C	°C	°C	°C	°C	°C	°C
260	126.7	127.2	127.8	128.3	128.9	129.4	130.0	130.6	131.1	131.7
270	132.2	132.8	133.3	133.9	134.4	135.0	135.6	136.1	136.7	137.2
280	137.8	138.3	138.9	139.4	140.0	140.6	141.1	141.7	142.2	142.8
290	143.3	143.9	144.5	145.0	145.6	146.1	146.7	147.2	147.8	148.3
300	148.9	149.4	150.0	150.6	151.1	151.7	152.2	152.8	153.3	153.9
310	154.4	155.0	155.6	156.1	156.7	157.2	157.8	158.3	158.9	159.4
320	160.0	160.6	161.1	161.7	162.2	162.8	163.3	163.9	164.4	165.0
330	165.6	166.1	166.7	167.2	167.8	168.3	168.9	169.4	170.0	170.6
340	171.1	171.7	172.2	172.8	173.2	173.9	174.4	175.0	175.6	176.1
350	176.7	177.2	177.8	178.3	178.9	179.4	180.0	180.6	181.1	181.7
360	182.2	182.8	183.3	183.9	184.4	185.0	185.6	186.1	186.7	187.2
370	187.8	188.3	188.9	189.4	190.0	190.6	191.1	191.7	192.2	192.8
380	193.3	193.9	194.4	195.0	195.6	196.1	196.7	197.2	197.8	198.3
390	198.9	199.4	200.0	200.6	201.1	201.7	202.2	202.8	203.3	203.9
400	204.4	205.0	205.6	206.1	206.7	207.2	207.8	208.3	208.9	209.4
410	210.0	210.6	211.1	211.7	212.2	212.8	213.3	213.9	214.4	215.0
420	215.6	216.1	216.7	217.2	217.8	218.3	218.9	219.4	220.2	220.6
430	221.1	221.7	222.2	222.8	223.3	223.9	224.4	225.0	225.6	226.1
440	226.7	227.2	227.8	228.3	228.9	229.4	230.0	230.6	231.1	231.7
450	232.2	232.8	233.3	233.9	234.4	235.0	235.6	236.1	236.7	237.2
460	237.8	238.3	238.9	239.4	240.0	240.6	241.1	241.7	242.2	242.8
470	243.3	243.9	244.4	245.0	245.6	246.1	246.7	247.2	247.8	248.3
480	248.9	249.4	250.0	250.6	251.1	251.7	252.2	252.8	253.3	253.9
490	254.4	255.0	255.6	256.1	256.7	257.2	257.8	258.3	258.9	259.4
500	260.0	—	—	—	—	—	—	—	—	—

$F = (C \times 1.8) + 32$

Temperature conversion table. Degrees Centigrade to Degrees Fahrenheit

Degrees C	0	1	2	3	4	5	6	7	8	9
	°F	°F	°F	°F	°F	°F	°F	°F	°F	°F
0	32.0	33.8	35.6	37.4	39.2	41.0	42.8	44.6	46.4	48.2
10	50.0	51.8	53.6	55.4	57.2	59.0	60.8	62.6	64.4	66.2
20	68.0	69.8	71.6	73.4	75.2	77.0	78.8	80.6	82.4	84.2
30	86.0	87.8	89.6	91.4	93.2	95.0	96.8	98.6	101.4	102.2
40	104.0	105.8	107.6	109.4	111.2	113.0	114.8	116.6	118.4	120.2
50	122.0	123.8	125.6	127.4	129.2	131.0	132.8	134.6	136.4	138.2
60	140.0	141.8	143.6	145.4	147.2	149.0	150.8	152.6	154.4	156.2
70	158.0	159.8	161.6	163.4	165.2	167.0	168.8	170.6	172.4	174.2
80	176.0	177.8	179.6	181.4	183.2	185.0	186.8	188.6	190.4	192.2
90	194.0	195.8	197.6	199.4	201.2	203.0	204.2	206.6	208.4	210.2
100	212.0	213.8	215.6	217.4	219.2	221.0	222.8	224.6	226.4	228.2
110	230.0	231.8	233.6	235.4	237.2	239.0	240.8	242.6	244.4	246.2
120	248.0	249.8	251.6	253.4	255.2	257.0	258.8	260.6	262.4	264.2
130	266.0	267.8	269.6	271.4	273.2	275.0	276.8	278.6	280.4	282.2
140	284.0	285.8	287.6	289.4	291.2	293.0	294.8	296.6	298.4	300.2
150	302.0	303.8	305.6	307.4	309.2	311.0	312.8	314.6	316.4	318.2
160	320.0	321.8	323.6	325.4	327.2	329.0	330.8	332.6	334.4	336.2
170	338.0	339.8	341.6	343.4	345.2	347.0	348.8	350.6	352.4	354.2
180	356.0	357.8	359.6	361.4	363.2	365.0	366.8	368.6	370.4	372.2
190	374.0	375.8	377.6	379.4	381.2	383.0	384.8	386.6	388.4	390.2
200	392.0	393.8	395.6	397.4	399.2	401.0	402.8	404.6	406.4	408.2
210	410.0	411.8	413.6	415.4	417.2	419.0	420.8	422.6	424.4	426.2
220	428.0	429.8	431.6	433.4	435.2	437.0	438.8	440.6	442.4	444.2
230	446.0	447.8	449.6	451.4	453.2	455.0	456.8	458.6	460.4	462.2
240	464.0	465.8	467.6	469.4	471.2	473.0	474.8	476.6	478.4	480.2
250	482.0	483.8	485.6	487.4	489.2	491.0	492.8	494.6	496.4	498.2
260	500.0	501.8	503.6	505.4	507.2	509.0	510.8	512.6	514.4	516.2
270	518.0	519.8	521.6	523.4	525.2	527.0	528.8	530.6	532.4	534.2
280	536.0	537.8	539.6	541.4	543.2	545.0	546.8	548.6	550.4	552.2
290	554.0	555.8	557.6	559.4	561.2	563.0	563.8	566.6	568.4	570.2
300	572.0	573.8	575.6	577.4	579.2	581.0	582.8	584.6	586.4	588.2

$C = (F-32) \div 1.8$

Conversion table. Fractions of an inch. (With decimal and metric equivalents)

Fraction		Decimal	Milli-metres		Fraction		Decimal	Milli-metres
	1/64	0.015625	0.397			33/64	0.515625	13.097
1/32		0.03125	0.794		17/32		0.53125	13.494
	3/64	0.046875	1.191			35/64	0.546875	13.891
1/16		0.0625	1.587		9/16		0.5625	14.287
	5/64	0.078125	1.984			37/64	0.578125	14.684
3/32		0.09375	2.381		19/32		0.59375	15.081
	7/64	0.109375	2.778			39/64	0.609375	15.478
1/8		0.125	3.175	5/8			0.625	15.874
	9/64	0.140625	3.572			41/64	0.640625	16.272
5/32		0.15625	3.969		21/32		0.65625	16.669
	11/64	0.171875	4.366			43/64	0.671875	17.066
3/16		0.1875	4.762		11/16		0.6875	17.462
	13/64	0.203125	5.160			45/64	0.703125	17.859
7/32		0.21875	5.556		23/32		0.71875	18.256
	15/64	0.234375	5.953			47/64	0.734375	18.653
1/4		0.25	6.349	3/4			0.75	19.049
	17/64	0.265625	6.747			49/64	0.765625	19.477
9/32		0.28125	7.144		25/32		0.78125	19.844
	19/64	0.296875	7.541			51/64	0.796875	20.241
5/16		0.3125	7.937		13/16		0.8125	20.637
	21/64	0.328125	8.333			53/64	0.828125	21.034
11/32		0.34375	8.731		27/32		0.84375	21.431
	23/64	0.359375	9.128			55/64	0.859375	21.828
3/8		0.375	9.524	7/8			0.875	22.224
	25/64	0.390625	9.922			57/64	0.890625	22.622
13/32		0.40625	10.319		29/32		0.90625	23.019
	27/64	0.421875	10.716			59/64	0.921875	23.416
7/16		0.4375	11.112		15/16		0.9375	23.812
	29/64	0.453125	11.509			61/64	0.953125	24.209
15/32		0.46875	11.906		31/32		0.96875	24.606
	31/64	0.484375	12.303			63/64	0.984375	25.003
1/2		0.50	12.699	1			1.00	25.400

Areas and circumferences of circle

Dia.	Circum.	Area	Dia.	Circum.	Area	Dia.	Circum.	Area
1/16	0.1963	0.00307	2 5/16	7.2649	4.2	6 1/4	19.63	30.67
1/8	0.3927	0.01227	2 3/8	7.4613	4.4302	6 1/2	20.42	33.18
3/16	0.589	0.02761	2 7/16	7.6576	4.6664	6 3/4	21.20	35.78
1/4	0.7854	0.04909	2 1/2	7.854	4.9087	7	21.99	38.48
5/16	0.9817	0.0767	2 9/16	8.0503	5.1573	7 1/4	22.77	41.28
3/8	1.1781	0.1104	2 5/8	8.2467	5.4119	7 1/2	23.56	44.17
7/16	1.3744	0.1503	2 11/16	8.443	5.6723	7 3/4	24.34	47.17
1/2	1.5708	0.1963	2 3/4	8.6394	5.9395	8	25.13	50.26
9/16	1.7771	0.2485	2 13/16	8.8357	6.2126	8 1/4	25.91	53.45
5/8	1.9635	0.3068	2 7/8	9.0321	6.4918	8 1/2	26.70	56.74
11/16	2.1598	0.3712	2 15/16	9.2284	6.7772	8 3/4	27.49	60.13
3/4	2.3562	0.4417	3	9.4248	7.0686	9	28.27	63.62
13/16	2.5525	0.5185	3 1/8	9.8175	7.6699	9 1/4	29.06	67.20
7/8	2.7489	0.6013	3 1/4	10.21	8.2957	9 1/2	29.84	70.88
15/16	2.9452	0.6903	3 3/8	10.602	8.9462	9 3/4	30.63	74.66
1	3.1416	0.7854	3 1/2	10.995	9.6211	10	31.41	78.54
1 1/16	3.3379	0.8866	3 5/8	11.388	10.32	10 1/2	32.98	86.59
1 1/8	3.5343	0.994	3 3/4	11.781	11.044	11	34.56	95.03
1 3/16	3.7306	1.1075	3 7/8	12.173	11.793	11 1/2	36.13	103.87
1 1/4	3.927	1.2271	4	12.566	12.566	12	37.69	113.09
1 5/16	4.1233	1.353	4 1/8	12.959	13.364	12 1/2	39.27	122.71
1 3/8	4.3197	1.4848	4 1/4	13.351	14.186	13	40.84	132.73
1 7/16	4.516	1.6229	4 3/8	13.744	15.033	13 1/2	42.41	143.13
1 1/2	4.7124	1.7671	4 1/2	14.137	15.904	14	43.98	153.93
1 9/16	4.9087	1.9175	4 5/8	14.529	16.8	14 1/2	45.55	165.13
1 5/8	5.1051	2.0739	4 3/4	14.922	17.72	15	47.12	176.71
1 11/16	5.3014	2.2365	4 7/8	15.315	18.665	15 1/2	48.69	188.69
1 3/4	5.4978	2.4052	5	15.708	19.635	16	50.26	201.06
1 13/16	5.6941	2.58	5 1/8	16.1	20.629	16 1/2	51.83	213.82
1 7/8	5.8905	2.7611	5 1/4	16.493	21.647	17	53.40	226.98
1 15/16	6.0868	2.9483	5 3/8	16.886	22.69	17 1/2	54.97	240.52
2	6.2832	3.1416	5 1/2	17.278	23.758	18	56.54	254.47
2 1/16	6.4795	3.3410	5 5/8	17.671	24.85	18 1/2	58.12	268.80
2 1/8	6.6759	3.5465	5 3/4	18.064	25.967	19	59.69	283.53
2 3/16	6.8722	3.7584	5 7/8	18.457	27.108	19 1/2	61.26	298.64
2 1/4	7.0686	3.976	6	18.85	28.27	20	62.83	314.16

Conversion table. Feet and inches to metres

Feet \ Inches	0	1	2	3	4	5	6	7	8	9	10	11
	m	m	m	m	m	m	m	m	m	m	m	m
0	—	0.0254	0.0508	0.0762	0.1016	0.1270	0.1524	0.1778	0.2032	0.2286	0.2540	0.2794
1	0.3048	0.3302	0.3556	0.3810	0.4064	0.4318	0.4572	0.4826	0.5080	0.5334	0.5588	0.5842
2	0.6096	0.6350	0.6604	0.6858	0.7112	0.7366	0.7620	0.7874	0.8128	0.8382	0.8636	0.8890
3	0.9144	0.9398	0.9652	0.9906	1.0160	1.0414	1.0668	1.0922	1.1176	1.1430	1.1684	1.1938
4	1.2192	1.2446	1.2700	1.2954	1.3208	1.3462	1.3716	1.3970	1.4224	1.4478	1.4732	1.4986
5	1.5240	1.5494	1.5748	1.6002	1.6256	1.6510	1.6764	1.7018	1.7272	1.7526	1.7780	1.8034
6	1.8288	1.8542	1.8796	1.9050	1.9304	1.9558	1.9812	2.0066	2.0320	2.0574	2.0828	2.1082
7	2.1336	2.1590	2.1844	2.2098	2.2352	2.2606	2.2860	2.3114	2.3368	2.3622	2.3876	2.4130
8	2.4384	2.4638	2.4892	2.5146	2.5400	2.5654	2.5908	2.6162	2.6416	2.6670	2.6924	2.7178
9	2.7432	2.7686	2.7940	2.8194	2.8448	2.8702	2.8956	2.9210	2.9464	2.9718	2.9972	3.0226
10	3.0480	3.0734	3.0988	3.1242	3.1496	3.1750	3.2004	3.2258	3.2512	3.2766	3.3020	3.3274
11	3.3528	3.3782	3.4036	3.4290	3.4544	3.4798	3.5052	3.5306	3.5560	3.5814	3.6068	3.6322
12	3.6576	3.6830	3.7084	3.7338	3.7592	3.7846	3.8100	3.8354	3.8608	3.8862	3.9116	3.9370
13	3.9624	3.9878	4.0132	4.0386	4.0640	4.0894	4.1148	4.1402	4.1656	4.1910	4.2164	4.2418
14	4.2672	4.2926	4.3180	4.3434	4.3688	4.3942	4.4196	4.4450	4.4704	4.4958	4.5212	4.5466
15	4.5720	4.5974	4.6228	4.6482	4.6736	4.6990	4.7244	4.7498	4.7752	4.8006	4.8260	4.8514
16	4.8768	4.9022	4.9276	4.9530	4.9784	5.0038	5.0292	5.0546	5.0800	5.1054	5.1308	5.1562
17	5.1816	5.2070	5.2324	5.2578	5.2832	5.3086	5.3340	5.3594	5.3848	5.4102	5.4356	5.4610
18	5.4864	5.5118	5.5372	5.5626	5.5880	5.6134	5.6388	5.6642	5.6896	5.7150	5.7404	5.7658
19	5.7912	5.8166	5.8420	5.8674	5.8928	5.9182	5.9436	5.9690	5.9944	6.0198	6.0452	6.0706
20	6.0960	6.1214	6.1468	6.1722	6.1976	6.2230	6.2484	6.2738	6.2992	6.3246	6.3500	6.3754

	0	1	2	3	4	5	6	7	8	9	10	11
30	9.1440	9.1694	9.1948	9.2202	9.2456	9.2710	9.2964	9.3218	9.3472	9.3726	9.3980	9.4234
40	12.1920	12.2174	12.2428	12.2682	12.2936	12.3190	12.3444	12.3698	12.3952	12.4206	12.4460	12.4714
50	15.2400	15.2654	15.2908	15.3162	15.3416	15.3670	15.3924	15.4178	15.4432	15.4686	15.4940	15.5194
60	18.2880	18.3134	18.3388	18.3642	18.3896	18.4150	18.4404	18.4658	18.4912	18.5166	18.5420	18.5674
70	21.3360	21.3614	21.3868	21.4122	21.4376	21.4630	21.4884	21.5138	21.5392	21.5646	21.5900	21.6154
80	24.3840	24.4094	24.4348	24.4602	24.4856	24.5110	25.5364	24.5618	24.5872	24.6126	24.6380	24.6634
90	27.4320	27.4574	27.4828	27.5082	27.5336	27.5590	27.5844	27.6098	27.6352	27.6606	27.6860	27.7114
100	30.4800											

Metres to feet

Metres	0	1	2	3	4	5	6	7	8	9
0	—	3.281	6.562	9.843	13.123	16.404	19.685	22.966	26.247	29.528
10	32.808	36.089	39.370	42.651	45.932	49.213	52.493	55.774	59.055	62.336
20	65.617	68.898	72.179	75.459	78.740	82.023	85.302	88.583	91.864	95.144
30	98.425	101.706	104.987	108.268	111.549	114.829	118.110	121.391	124.672	127.953
40	131.234	134.515	137.795	141.076	144.357	147.638	150.919	154.200	157.480	160.761
50	164.042	167.323	170.604	173.885	177.166	180.446	183.727	187.008	190.289	193.570
60	196.851	200.131	203.412	206.693	209.974	213.255	216.536	219.816	223.097	226.378
70	229.659	232.940	236.221	239.502	242.782	246.063	249.344	252.625	255.906	259.187
80	262.467	265.748	269.029	272.310	275.591	278.872	282.152	285.433	288.714	291.995
90	295.276	298.557	301.838	305.118	308.399	311.680	314.961	318.242	321.523	324.803
100	328.08									

Conversion table. Cubic feet to cubic metres

ft³	0	1	2	3	4	5	6	7	8	9
	m^3	m^3	m^3	m^3	m^3	m^3	m^3	m^3	m^3	m^3
0	—	0.0283	0.0566	0.0850	0.1133	0.1416	0.1699	0.1982	0.2265	0.2549
10	0.2832	0.3115	0.3398	0.3681	0.3964	0.4248	0.4531	0.4814	0.5097	0.5380
20	0.5663	0.5947	0.6230	0.6583	0.6796	0.7079	0.7362	0.7646	0.7929	0.8212
30	0.8495	0.8778	0.9061	0.9345	0.9628	0.9911	1.0194	1.0477	1.0760	1.1044
40	1.1327	1.1610	1.1893	1.2176	1.2459	1.2743	1.3026	1.3369	1.3592	1.3875
50	1.4158	1.4442	1.4725	1.5008	1.5291	1.5574	1.5857	1.6141	1.6424	1.6707
60	1.6990	1.7273	1.7556	1.7840	1.8123	1.8406	1.8689	1.8972	1.9255	1.9539
70	1.9822	2.0105	2.0388	2.0671	2.0954	2.1238	2.1521	2.1804	2.2087	2.2370
80	2.2653	2.2937	2.3220	2.3503	2.3786	2.4069	2.4352	2.4636	2.4919	2.5202
90	2.5485	2.5768	2.6051	2.6335	2.6618	2.6901	2.7184	2.7467	2.7750	2.8034
100	2.8317	—	—	—	—	—	—	—	—	—

Conversion table. Cubic metres to cubic feet

m³	0	1	2	3	4	5	6	7	8	9
	ft³	ft³	ft³	ft³	ft³	ft³	ft³	ft³	ft³	ft³
0	—	35.3148	70.6295	105.9443	141.2590	176.5738	211.8885	247.2033	282.5181	317.8328
10	353.1476	388.4623	423.7771	459.0918	494.4066	529.7214	565.0361	600.3509	635.6656	670.9804
20	706.2951	741.6099	776.9247	812.2394	847.5542	882.8689	918.1837	953.4984	988.8132	1024.1280
30	1059.4427	1094.7575	1130.0722	1165.3870	1200.7017	1236.0165	1271.3313	1306.6460	1341.9608	1377.2755
40	1412.5903	1447.9050	1483.2198	1518.5346	1553.8493	1589.1641	1624.4788	1659.7936	1695.1083	1730.4231
50	1765.7379	1801.0526	1836.3674	1871.6821	1906.9969	1942.3116	1977.6264	2012.9411	2048.2559	2083.5707
60	2118.8854	2154.2002	2189.5149	2224.8297	2260.1444	2295.4592	2330.7740	2366.0887	2401.4035	2436.7182
70	2472.0330	2507.3477	2542.6625	2577.9773	2613.2920	2648.6068	2683.9215	2719.2363	2754.5510	2789.8658
80	2825.1806	2860.4953	2895.8101	2931.1248	2966.4396	3001.7543	3037.0691	3072.3839	3107.6986	3143.0134
90	3178.3281	3213.6429	3248.9576	3284.2724	3319.5872	3354.9019	3390.2167	3425.5314	3460.8462	3496.1609
100	3531.47	—	—	—	—	—	—	—	—	—

Gallons to litres [1 litre=10^{-3} m³]

gal	0	1	2	3	4	5	6	7	8	9
	litres	litres	litres	litres	litres	litres	litres	litres	litres	litres
0	—	4.546	9.092	13.638	18.184	22.730	27.276	31.822	36.368	40.914
10	45.460	50.006	54.552	59.098	63.643	68.189	72.735	77.281	81.827	86.373
20	90.919	95.465	100.011	104.557	109.103	113.649	118.195	122.741	127.287	131.833
30	136.379	140.925	145.471	150.017	154.563	159.109	163.655	168.201	172.747	177.293
40	181.839	186.384	190.930	195.476	200.022	204.568	209.114	213.660	218.206	222.752
50	227.298	231.844	236.390	240.936	245.482	250.028	254.574	259.120	263.666	268.212
60	272.758	277.304	281.850	286.396	290.942	295.488	300.034	304.580	309.125	313.671
70	318.217	322.763	327.309	331.855	336.401	340.947	345.493	350.039	354.585	359.131
80	363.677	368.223	372.769	377.315	381.861	386.407	390.953	395.499	400.045	404.591
90	409.137	413.683	418.229	422.775	427.321	431.866	436.412	440.958	445.504	450.050
100	454.596	—	—	—	—	—	—	—	—	—

Litres to gallons [1 litre=10^{-3} m³]

litres	0	1	2	3	4	5	6	7	8	9
	gal	gal	gal	gal	gal	gal	gal	gal	gal	gal
0	—	0.2200	0.4400	0.6600	0.8800	1.1000	1.3199	1.5398	1.7598	1.9798
10	2.1998	2.4197	2.6397	2.8597	3.0797	3.2996	3.5196	3.7396	3.9596	4.1795
20	4.3995	4.6195	4.8395	5.0594	5.2794	5.4994	5.7194	5.9393	6.1593	6.3793
30	6.5993	6.8192	7.0392	7.2592	7.4792	7.6991	7.9191	8.1391	8.3591	8.5790
40	8.7990	9.0190	9.2390	9.4589	9.6789	9.8989	10.1189	10.3388	10.5588	10.7788
50	10.9988	11.2187	11.4387	11.6587	11.8787	12.0986	12.3186	12.5386	12.7586	12.9785
60	13.1985	13.4185	13.6385	13.8584	14.0784	14.2984	14.5184	14.7384	14.9583	15.1783
70	15.3983	15.6183	15.8382	16.0582	16.2782	16.4982	16.7181	16.9381	17.1581	17.3781
80	17.5980	17.8180	18.0380	18.2580	18.4779	18.6979	18.9179	19.1379	19.3578	19.5778
90	19.7978	20.0178	20.2377	20.4577	20.6777	20.8977	21.1176	21.3376	21.5576	21.7776
100	21.9975	—	—	—	—	—	—	—	—	—

Pounds to kilogrammes

lb	0	1	2	3	4	5	6	7	8	9
	kg	kg	kg	kg	kg	kg	kg	kg	kg	kg
0	—	0.4535	0.9071	1.3607	1.8143	2.2679	2.7215	3.1751	3.6287	4.0823
10	4.5359	4.9895	5.4431	5.8967	6.3503	6.8039	7.2575	7.7111	8.1647	8.6183
20	9.0718	9.5254	9.9790	10.4326	10.8862	11.3398	11.7934	12.2470	12.7006	13.1542
30	13.6078	14.0614	14.5150	14.9686	15.4221	15.8757	16.3293	16.7829	17.2365	17.6901
40	18.1437	18.5973	19.0509	19.5045	19.9581	20.4117	20.8653	21.3188	21.7724	22.2260
50	22.6796	23.1332	23.5868	24.0404	24.4940	24.9476	25.4012	25.8548	26.3084	26.7620
60	27.2155	27.6691	28.1227	28.5763	29.0299	29.4835	29.9371	30.3907	30.8443	31.2979
70	31.7515	32.2051	32.6587	33.1122	33.5658	34.0194	34.4730	34.9266	35.3802	35.8338
80	36.2874	36.7410	37.1946	37.6482	38.1018	38.5554	39.0089	39.4625	39.9161	40.3697
90	40.8233	41.2769	41.7305	42.1841	42.6377	43.0913	43.5449	43.9985	44.4521	44.9057
100	45.3592	—	—	—	—	—	—	—	—	—

Kilogrammes to pounds

kg	0	1	2	3	4	5	6	7	8	9
	lb	lb	lb	lb	lb	lb	lb	lb	lb	lb
0	—	2.204	4.409	6.613	8.818	11.023	13.227	15.432	17.637	19.841
10	22.0462	24.250	26.455	28.660	30.864	33.069	35.273	37.478	39.683	41.887
20	44.0924	46.297	48.502	50.706	52.911	55.116	57.320	59.525	61.729	63.934
30	66.139	68.343	70.548	72.753	74.957	77.162	79.366	81.571	83.776	85.980
40	88.185	90.389	92.594	94.799	97.003	99.208	101.413	103.617	105.822	108.026
50	110.231	112.436	114.640	116.845	119.050	121.254	123.459	125.663	127.868	130.073
60	132.277	134.482	136.686	138.891	141.096	143.300	145.505	147.710	149.914	152.119
70	154.324	156.528	158.733	160.937	163.142	165.347	167.551	169.756	171.960	174.165
80	176.370	178.574	180.779	182.984	185.188	187.393	189.597	191.802	194.007	196.211
90	198.416	200.620	202.825	205.030	207.234	209.439	211.644	213.848	216.053	218.258
100	220.462	—	—	—	—	—	—	—	—	—

Pounds per square inch to kilonewtons per square metre

lb/in^2	0	1	2	3	4	5	6	7	8	9
0	—	6.895	13.79	20.68	27.58	34.47	41.37	48.25	55.16	62.04
10	68.95	75.85	82.74	89.63	96.53	103.4	110.3	117.2	124.1	131.0
20	137.9	144.8	151.7	158.6	165.5	172.4	179.3	186.2	193.1	199.9
30	206.8	213.7	220.6	227.5	234.4	241.3	248.2	255.1	262.0	268.8
40	275.8	282.7	289.6	296.5	303.4	310.3	317.2	324.1	331.0	337.8
50	344.7	351.6	358.5	365.4	372.3	379.2	386.1	393.0	399.9	406.7
60	413.7	420.6	427.5	434.4	441.3	448.2	455.1	462.0	468.9	475.7
70	482.7	489.5	496.4	503.3	510.2	517.1	524.0	530.9	537.8	544.7
80	551.6	558.5	565.4	572.3	579.0	586.1	593.0	599.9	606.8	613.6
90	620.4	627.3	634.2	641.1	648.0	654.9	661.8	668.7	675.6	682.4
100	689.5	—	—	—	—	—	—	—	—	—

Kilonewtons per square metre to pounds per square inch

kN/m^2	0	1	2	3	4	5	6	7	8	9
0	—	0.145	0.290	0.435	0.580	0.725	0.871	1.02	1.16	1.31
10	1.45	1.60	1.74	1.89	2.03	2.18	2.32	2.47	2.61	2.76
20	2.90	3.05	3.19	3.34	3.48	3.63	3.77	3.92	4.06	4.21
30	4.35	4.50	4.64	4.79	4.93	5.08	5.22	5.37	5.52	5.66
40	5.80	5.94	6.09	6.23	6.38	6.52	6.67	6.81	6.96	7.10
50	7.25	7.40	7.54	7.69	7.83	7.98	8.12	8.27	8.41	8.56
60	8.71	8.85	9.00	9.14	9.28	9.43	9.58	9.72	9.87	10.01
70	10.15	10.30	10.44	10.59	10.73	10.88	11.02	11.17	11.31	11.46
80	11.61	11.76	11.90	12.05	12.19	12.33	12.48	12.63	12.77	12.92
90	13.05	13.20	13.34	13.49	13.63	13.78	13.92	14.07	14.21	14.36
100	14.51	—	—	—	—	—	—	—	—	—

British thermal units to kilojoules

Btu	0	1	2	3	4	5	6	7	8	9
0	—	1.05	2.11	3.17	4.22	5.28	6.33	7.39	8.44	9.50
10	10.55	11.61	12.66	13.72	14.77	15.83	16.88	17.94	18.99	20.05
20	21.10	22.16	23.21	24.27	25.32	26.38	27.43	28.49	29.54	30.60
30	31.65	32.71	33.76	34.82	35.87	36.93	37.98	39.03	40.09	41.15
40	42.21	43.26	44.31	45.37	46.42	47.48	48.53	49.59	50.64	51.70
50	52.76	53.81	54.86	55.92	56.97	58.03	59.08	60.14	61.19	62.25
60	63.31	64.36	65.41	66.46	67.52	68.58	69.63	70.69	71.74	72.80
70	73.86	74.91	75.96	77.02	78.07	79.13	80.18	81.24	82.29	83.35
80	84.41	85.46	86.51	87.57	88.62	89.68	90.73	91.79	92.84	93.90
90	94.95	96.01	97.06	98.12	99.17	100.23	101.28	102.34	103.40	104.45
100	105.5	—	—	—	—	—	—	—	—	—

Kilojoules to British thermal units

kJ	0	1	2	3	4	5	6	7	8	9
0	—	0.95	1.90	2.84	3.79	4.74	5.69	6.63	7.58	8.53
10	9.48	10.42	11.37	12.32	13.27	14.22	15.16	16.11	17.06	18.01
20	18.95	19.90	20.85	21.80	22.74	23.69	24.64	25.59	26.54	27.48
30	28.43	29.38	30.33	31.27	32.22	33.17	34.12	35.06	36.01	36.96
40	37.91	38.86	39.80	40.75	41.70	42.65	43.59	44.54	45.49	46.44
50	47.39	48.33	49.28	50.23	51.18	52.12	53.07	54.02	54.97	55.91
60	56.86	57.81	58.76	59.71	60.65	61.60	62.55	63.50	64.44	65.39
70	66.34	67.29	68.23	69.18	70.13	71.08	72.03	72.97	73.92	74.87
80	75.82	76.76	77.71	78.66	79.61	80.55	81.50	82.45	83.40	84.35
90	85.29	86.24	87.19	88.14	89.08	90.03	90.98	91.93	92.87	93.82
100	94.77	—	—	—	—	—	—	—	—	—

British thermal units per square foot to kilojoules per square metre

Btu/ft²	0	1	2	3	4	5	6	7	8	9
	kJ/m²	kJ/m²	kJ/m²	kJ/m²	kJ/m²	kJ/m²	kJ/m²	kJ/m²	kJ/m²	kJ/m²
0	—	11.36	22.72	34.08	45.44	56.80	68.16	75.52	90.88	102.2
10	113.6	125.0	136.3	147.7	159.0	170.4	181.8	193.1	204.5	215.8
20	227.2	238.6	245.0	261.3	272.6	284.0	295.4	306.7	318.1	329.4
30	340.8	352.2	363.5	374.9	386.2	297.6	409.0	420.3	431.7	443.0
40	454.4	465.8	477.1	488.5	499.8	511.2	522.6	533.9	545.3	556.6
50	568.0	579.4	590.7	602.1	613.4	624.8	636.1	647.5	658.9	670.2
60	681.6	693.0	704.3	715.7	727.0	738.4	749.8	761.1	772.5	783.8
70	795.2	806.6	817.9	829.3	840.6	852.0	863.4	874.7	886.1	897.4
80	908.8	920.2	931.5	942.9	954.2	965.6	977.0	988.3	999.7	1011.0
90	1022.4	1033.8	1045.1	1056.5	1067.8	1079.2	1090.6	1101.9	1113.3	1124.6
100	1136.0	—	—	—	—	—	—	—	—	—

Kilojoules per square metre to British thermal units per square foot

kJ/m²	0	1	2	3	4	5	6	7	8	9
	Btu/ft²	Btu/ft²	Btu/ft²	Btu/ft²	Btu/ft²	Btu/ft²	Btu/ft²	Btu/ft²	Btu/ft²	Btu/ft²
0	—	0.088	0.176	0.264	0.352	0.440	0.528	0.616	0.704	0.792
10	0.880	0.968	1.056	1.144	1.232	1.320	1.408	1.496	1.584	1.672
20	1.760	1.848	1.936	2.024	2.113	2.201	2.289	2.377	2.465	2.553
30	2.641	2.729	2.817	2.905	2.993	3.081	3.169	3.257	3.345	3.433
40	3.521	3.609	3.697	3.785	3.873	3.961	4.049	4.137	4.225	4.313
50	4.401	4.489	4.577	4.665	4.753	4.841	4.929	5.017	5.105	5.193
60	5.281	5.369	5.457	5.545	5.633	5.721	5.809	5.897	5.986	6.073
70	6.161	6.249	6.337	6.425	6.514	6.602	6.690	6.778	6.866	6.954
80	7.042	7.130	7.218	7.306	7.394	7.482	7.570	7.658	7.746	7.834
90	7.922	8.010	8.098	8.186	8.274	8.362	8.450	8.538	8.626	8.714
100	8.802	—	—	—	—	—	—	—	—	—

Btu/ft² °F to kJ/m² °C

Btu/ft² °F	0	1	2	3	4	5	6	7	8	9
	kJ/m²K	kJ/m²K	kJ/m²K	kJ/m²K	kJ/m²K	kJ/m²K	kJ/m²K	kJ/m²K	kJ/m²K	kJ/m²K
0	—	20.44	40.88	61.32	81.76	102.21	122.65	143.09	163.53	183.97
10	204.41	224.85	245.29	265.73	286.17	306.62	327.06	347.50	367.94	388.38
20	408.82	429.26	449.70	470.14	490.58	511.03	531.47	551.91	572.35	592.79
30	613.23	633.67	654.11	674.55	694.99	715.44	735.88	756.32	776.76	797.20
40	817.64	838.08	858.52	878.97	899.40	918.85	940.29	960.73	981.17	1001.6
50	1022.1	1042.5	1062.9	1083.4	1103.8	1124.3	1144.7	1165.2	1185.6	1206.0
60	1226.5	1246.9	1267.3	1287.8	1308.2	1328.7	1349.1	1369.5	1390.0	1410.4
70	1430.9	1451.3	1471.8	1492.2	1512.6	1533.1	1553.5	1574.0	1594.4	1614.9
80	1635.3	1655.7	1676.2	1696.6	1717.0	1737.5	1757.9	1778.4	1798.8	1819.2
90	1839.7	1860.1	1880.6	1901.0	1921.5	1941.9	1962.3	1982.8	2003.2	2023.7
100	2044.1	—								

kJ/m² °C to Btu/ft²

kJ/m² °C	0	1	2	3	4	5	6	7	8	9
	Btu/ft²°F	Btu/ft²°F	Btu/ft²°F	Btu/ft²°F	Btu/ft²°F	Btu/ft²°F	Btu/ft²°F	Btu/ft²°F	Btu/ft²°F	Btu/ft²°F
0	—	0.049	0.098	0.147	0.195	0.244	0.293	0.342	0.391	0.440
10	0.489	0.538	0.586	0.635	0.684	0.733	0.782	0.831	0.880	0.929
20	0.977	1.026	1.075	1.124	1.173	1.222	1.271	1.320	1.368	1.417
30	1.466	1.515	1.564	1.613	1.662	1.710	1.760	1.808	1.857	1.906
40	1.959	2.004	2.053	2.101	2.150	2.199	2.248	2.297	2.346	2.395
50	2.444	2.492	2.541	2.590	2.639	2.688	2.737	2.786	2.835	2.883
60	2.932	2.981	3.030	3.079	3.128	3.177	3.225	3.274	3.323	3.372
70	3.421	3.470	3.519	3.568	3.616	3.665	3.714	3.763	3.812	3.861
80	3.910	3.959	4.007	4.056	4.105	4.154	4.203	4.252	4.301	4.349
90	4.398	4.447	4.496	4.545	4.594	4.643	4.692	4.740	4.789	4.838
100	4.887	—								

2 Standards for materials

Feed and expansion cisterns to BS 417

Imperial sizes

Reference Nos.	Length in	Width in	Depth in	Capacity gal	Thickness Body B.G.	Loose cover B.G.
SC 10	18	12	12	4	16	20
15	24	12	15	8	16	20
20	24	16	15	12	16	20
25	24	17	17	15	16	20
30	24	18	19	19	16	20
40	27	20	20	25	16	20
50	29	22	22	35	14	20
60	30	23	24	42	14	20
70	36	24	23	50	14	20
80	36	26	24	58	14	20
100/2	38	27	27	74	14	20
125	38	30	31	93	12	18
150	43	34	29	108	12	18
200	46	35	35	156	12	18
250	60	36	32	185	12	18
350	60	45	36	270	$\frac{1}{8}$ in	16
500	72	48	40	380	$\frac{1}{8}$ in	16
600	72	48	48	470	$\frac{1}{8}$ in	16
1000	96	60	48	740	$\frac{3}{16}$ in	16

Metric sizes

Reference No.	Length mm	Width mm	Depth mm	Capacity litres	Thickness Body mm	Loose cover mm
SCM 45	457	305	305	18	1.6	1.0
70	610	305	381	36	1.6	1.0
90	610	406	381	54	1.6	1.0
110	610	432	432	68	1.6	1.0
135	610	457	482	86	1.6	1.0
180	686	508	508	114	1.6	1.0
230	736	559	559	159	2.0	1.0
270	762	584	610	191	2.0	1.0
320	914	610	584	227	2.0	1.0
360	914	660	610	264	2.0	1.0
450/1	1219	610	610	327	2.0	1.0
450/2	965	686	686	336	2.0	1.0
570	965	762	787	423	2.5	1.2
680	1092	864	736	491	2.5	1.2
910	1168	889	889	709	2.5	1.2
1130	1524	914	813	841	2.5	1.2
1600	1524	1143	914	1227	3.2	1.6
2270	1829	1219	1016	1727	3.2	1.6
2720	1829	1219	1219	2137	3.2	1.6
4540	2438	1524	1219	3364	4.8	1.6

Closed tanks to BS 417

Imperial sizes

Reference No.	Length in	Width in	Depth in	Capacity gal	Thickness in
T25/1	24	17	17	21	$\frac{1}{8}$
25/2	24	24	12	21	$\frac{1}{8}$
30/1	24	18	19	25	$\frac{1}{8}$
30/2	24	24	15	27	$\frac{1}{8}$
40	27	20	20	34	$\frac{1}{8}$

Metric sizes

Reference No.	Length mm	Width mm	Depth mm	Capacity litres	Thickness mm
TM114/1	610	432	432	95	3.2
114/2	610	610	305	95	3.2
136/1	610	457	482	114	3.2
136/2	610	610	381	123	3.2
182	690	508	508	155	3.2

Copper indirect cylinders
To BS 1566:1972

Reference No.	Diameter mm	Height mm	Capacity litres	Heating Surface annular type m^2	Surface coil type m^2
1	350	900	72	0.40	0.27
2	400	900	96	0.52	0.35
3	400	1050	114	0.63	0.42
4	450	675	84	0.46	0.31
5	450	750	95	0.52	0.35
6	450	825	106	0.60	0.40
7	450	900	117	0.66	0.44
8	450	1050	140	0.78	0.52
9	450	1200	162	0.91	0.61
10	500	1200	190	1.13	0.75
11	500	1500	245	1.30	0.87
12	600	1200	280	1.60	1.10
13	600	1500	360	2.10	1.40
14	600	1800	440	2.50	1.70

Copper direct cylinders
To BS 699:1972

Reference No.	Diameter mm	Height mm	Capacity litres
1	350	900	74
2	400	900	98
3	400	1050	116
4	450	675	86
5	450	750	98
6	450	825	109
7	450	900	120
8	450	1050	144
9	450	1200	166
10	500	1200	200
11	500	1500	255
12	600	1200	290
13	600	1500	370
14	600	1800	450

Sheet and wire gauges

Standard Wire Gauge No.	Birmingham Gauge No.	German Sheet Gauge No. (DIN 1541)	ISO Metric R20 Preferred Series mm	Thickness or Diameter		Weight of Sheet	
				in	mm	lb/ft²	kg/m²
30	—	—	0.315	0.0124	0.315	0.48	2.5
—	—	27	—	0.0126	0.32	0.52	2.5
29	—	—	—	0.0136	0.345	0.52	2.7
—	29	—	—	0.0139	0.354	0.56	2.8
—	—	—	0.355	0.140	0.355	0.56	2.8
28	—	—	—	0.0148	0.376	0.56	2.9
—	28	—	—	0.0156	0.397	0.63	3.1
—	—	26	—	0.0150	0.38	0.62	3.0
—	—	—	0.400	0.0158	0.400	0.64	3.1
27	—	—	—	0.0164	0.417	0.64	3.2
—	27	—	—	0.0175	0.443	0.71	3.5
—	—	25	—	0.0172	0.44	0.70	3.5
—	—	—	0.450	0.0177	0.450	0.72	3.5
26	—	—	—	0.018	0.457	0.72	3.6
—	26	—	—	0.0196	0.498	0.79	3.9
—	—	24	0.500	0.0197	0.500	0.80	3.9
25	—	—	—	0.020	0.508	0.80	4.0
24	—	—	—	0.022	0.559	0.88	4.4
—	25	—	—	0.022	0.560	0.89	4.4
—	—	23	0.560	0.0221	0.560	0.91	4.4
23	—	—	—	0.024	0.610	1.00	4.8
—	24	—	—	0.025	0.629	1.00	4.9
—	—	22	0.630	0.0248	0.630	1.02	4.9
—	23	—	—	0.028	0.707	1.13	5.5
—	—	—	0.710	0.0280	0.710	1.14	5.6
22	—	—	—	0.028	0.711	1.12	5.6
—	—	21	—	0.0295	0.75	1.21	5.9
—	22	—	—	0.031	0.794	1.27	6.2
—	—	—	0.800	0.0315	0.800	1.28	6.3
21	—	—	—	0.032	0.813	1.28	6.3
—	—	20	—	0.0346	0.88	1.41	6.9
—	21	—	—	0.035	0.887	1.41	7.0
—	—	—	0.900	0.0354	0.900	1.42	7.1
20	—	—	—	0.036	0.914	1.42	7.2
—	20	—	—	0.039	0.996	1.59	7.8
—	—	19	1.000	0.0394	1.000	1.61	7.8
19	—	—	—	0.040	1.016	1.68	8.0
—	19	—	—	0.044	1.12	1.78	8.8
—	—	—	1.12	0.0441	1.12	1.80	8.8
—	—	18	—	0.0443	1.13	1.81	8.9

Sheet and wire gauges *(continued)*

Standard Wire Gauge No.	Birmingham Gauge No.	German Sheet Gauge No. (DIN 1541)	ISO Metric R20 Preferred Series mm.	Thickness or Diameter		Weight of Sheet	
				in	*mm*	*lb/ft²*	*kg/m²*
18	—	—	—	0.048	1.219	1.96	9.6
—	—	17	1.25	0.0492	1.25	2.00	9.8
—	18	—	—	0.050	1.26	2.00	9.9
—	—	16	—	0.0543	1.38	2.22	10.8
—	—	—	1.40	0.0551	1.40	2.25	11.0
—	17	—	—	0.056	1.41	2.25	11.1
17	—	—	—	0.056	1.422	2.32	11.1
—	—	15	—	0.0591	1.50	2.42	11.7
—	16	—	—	0.063	1.59	2.53	12.4
—	—	—	1.60	0.0630	1.60	2.58	12.5
16	—	—	—	0.064	1.626	2.60	12.7
—	—	14	—	0.0689	1.75	2.82	13.7
—	15	—	—	0.070	1.78	2.83	13.9
—	—	—	1.80	0.0709	1.80	2.90	14.1
15	—	—	—	0.072	1.829	2.94	14.3
—	14	—	—	0.079	1.99	3.18	15.6
—	—	13	2.00	0.0787	2.00	3.18	15.7
14	—	—	—	0.080	2.032	3.32	15.9
—	—	—	—	—	—	—	—
—	13	—	2.24	0.088	2.24	3.57	17.6
—	—	12	—	0.0886	2.25	3.59	17.6
13	—	—	—	0.092	2.337	3.80	18.3
—	—	11	2.50	0.0984	2.50	3.98	19.6
—	12	—	—	0.099	2.52	4.01	19.7
12	—	—	—	0.104	2.642	4.36	20.7
—	—	10	—	0.1083	2.75	4.38	21.6
—	—	—	2.80	0.1102	2.80	4.46	22.0
—	11	—	—	0.111	2.83	4.51	22.2
11	—	—	—	0.116	2.946	4.80	23.1
—	—	9	—	0.1181	3.00	4.56	23.5
—	—	—	3.15	0.1240	3.15	5.02	24.7
—	10	—	—	0.125	3.18	5.06	24.8
—	—	8	—	0.1279	3.25	5.18	25.5
10	—	—	—	0.128	3.251	5.36	25.4
—	—	7	—	0.1378	3.50	5.58	27.4
—	9	—	3.55	0.140	3.55	5.66	27.8
9	—	—	—	0.144	3.658	5.92	28.7
—	—	6	—	0.1476	3.75	5.98	29.4
—	8	—	—	0.157	3.99	6.36	31.3

Sheet and wire gauges *(continued)*

Standard Wire Gauge No.	Birmingham Gauge No.	German Sheet Gauge No. (DIN 1541)	ISO Metric R20 Preferred Series mm	Thickness or Diameter		Weight of Sheet	
				in	mm	lb/ft²	kg/m²
—	—	5	4.0	0.1575	4.0	6.38	31.4
8	—	—	—	0.160	4.064	6.60	31.9
—	—	4	—	0.1673	4.25	6.77	33.3
7	—	—	—	0.176	4.470	7.12	35.1
—	7	—	—	0.176	4.48	7.14	35.1
—	—	3	4.5	0.1772	4.50	7.17	35.3
6	—	—	—	0.192	4.877	7.80	38.2
—	—	2	5.0	0.1969	5.00	7.97	39.2
—	6	—	—	0.198	5.032	8.02	39.5
5	—	—	—	0.212	5.385	8.80	42.2
—	—	1	—	0.2165	5.50	8.77	43.1
—	—	—	5.6	0.2205	5.6	8.93	43.9
—	5	—	—	0.222	5.66	9.01	44.4
4	—	—	—	0.232	5.893	9.52	46.2
—	—	—	6.30	0.2480	6.30	10.04	49.4
—	4	—	—	0.250	6.35	10.12	49.9
3	—	—	—	0.252	6.401	10.36	50.2
2	—	—	—	0.276	7.010	11.17	55.0
—	—	—	7.10	0.2795	7.10	11.32	55.7
—	3	—	—	0.280	7.13	11.34	55.9
1	—	—	—	0.300	7.620	12.0	59.7
—	2	—	—	0.315	8.00	12.74	62.7
—	—	—	8.00	0.3150	8.00	12.74	62.7
0	—	—	—	0.324	8.229	13.1	63.9
2/0	—	—	—	0.348	8.839	13.9	69.3
—	1	—	—	0.353	8.98	14.30	70.4
—	—	—	9.00	0.3543	9.00	14.3	70.6
3/0	—	—	—	0.372	9.449	14.9	74.1
—	—	—	10.00	0.3937	10.00	15.9	78.4
—	0	—	—	0.396	10.07	16.0	78.9
4/0	—	—	—	0.400	10.160	16.0	79.7
5/0	—	—	—	0.432	10.973	17.3	86.0
—	—	—	11.2	0.4409	11.2	17.8	87.8
—	2/0	—	—	0.445	11.3	18.0	88.6
6/0	—	—	—	0.464	11.785	18.6	92.4
—	—	—	12.5	0.4921	12.5	19.9	98.0
7/0	3/0	—	—	0.500	12.700	20.0	99.5

Weight of steel bar and sheet

Thickness or Dia. mm	*Weight in kg of*		
	Sheet per m²	*Square per m*	*Round per m*
5	39.25	0.196	0.154
6	47.10	0.283	0.222
8	62.80	0.502	0.395
10	78.50	0.785	0.617
12	94.20	1.130	0.888
14	109.90	1.539	1.208
16	125.60	2.010	1.578
18	141.30	2.543	1.998
20	157.00	3.140	2.466
22	172.70	3.799	2.984
24	188.40	4.522	3.551
26	204.10	5.307	4.168
28	219.80	6.154	4.834
30	235.50	7.065	5.549
32	251.20	8.038	6.313
34	266.90	9.075	7.127
36	282.60	10.174	7.990
38	298.30	11.335	8.903
40	314.00	12.560	9.865
42	329.70	13.847	10.876
44	345.40	15.198	11.936
46	361.10	16.611	13.046
48	376.80	18.086	14.205
50	392.50	19.625	15.413
52	408.20	21.226	16.671
54	423.90	22.891	17.978
56	439.60	24.618	19.335
58	455.30	26.407	20.740
60	471.00	28.260	22.195
62	486.70	30.175	23.700
64	502.40	32.154	25.253
66	518.10	34.195	26.856

Thickness or Dia. mm	*Weight in kg of*		
	Sheet per m²	*Square per m*	*Round per m*
68	533.80	36.298	28.509
70	569.50	36.465	30.210
72	585.20	40.694	31.961
74	600.90	42.987	33.762
76	616.60	45.342	35.611
78	632.30	47.759	37.510
80	628.00	50.240	39.458
85	667.25	56.716	44.545
90	706.50	63.585	49.940
95	745.75	70.846	55.643
100	785.00	78.500	61.654
105	824.25	86.546	67.973
110	863.5	94.985	74.601
115	902.75	103.816	81.537
120	942.0	113.040	88.781
125	981.2	122.656	96.334
130	1020	132.665	104.195
135	1060	143.006	112.364
140	1099	153.860	120.841
145	1138	165.046	129.627
150	1178	176.625	138.721
155	1217	188.596	148.123
160	1256	200.960	157.834
165	1295	213.716	167.852
170	1355	226.865	178.179
175	1394	240.406	188.815
180	1413	254.340	199.758
185	1452	268.666	211.010
190	1492	283.385	222.570
195	1511	298.496	234.438
200	1570	314.000	246.615

Thickness or Dia. in	*Weight in lb of*		
	Sheet per ft²	*Square per ft*	*Round per ft*
$\frac{1}{8}$	5.10	0.053	0.042
$\frac{3}{16}$	7.65	0.120	0.094
$\frac{1}{4}$	10.20	0.213	0.167
$\frac{5}{16}$	12.75	0.332	0.261
$\frac{3}{8}$	15.30	0.479	0.376
$\frac{7}{16}$	17.85	0.651	0.511
$\frac{1}{2}$	20.40	0.851	0.658
$\frac{9}{16}$	22.95	1.08	0.845
$\frac{5}{8}$	25.50	1.33	1.04
$\frac{11}{16}$	28.05	1.61	1.29
$\frac{3}{4}$	30.60	1.91	1.50
$\frac{13}{16}$	33.15	2.25	1.77
$\frac{7}{8}$	35.70	2.61	2.04
$\frac{15}{16}$	38.25	2.99	2.35

Thickness or Dia. mm	*Weight in lb of*		
	Sheet per ft²	*Square per ft*	*Round per ft*
1	40.80	3.40	2.68
$1\frac{1}{8}$	45.9	4.31	3.38
$1\frac{1}{4}$	51.0	5.32	4.17
$1\frac{3}{8}$	56.1	6.43	5.05
$1\frac{1}{2}$	61.2	7.71	6.01
$1\frac{5}{8}$	66.3	8.99	7.05
$1\frac{3}{4}$	71.4	10.4	8.19
$1\frac{7}{8}$	76.5	12.0	9.39
2	81.6	13.6	10.7
$2\frac{1}{2}$	102.2	21.3	16.8
3	122.4	30.6	24.1
4	163.2	54.4	42.8
5	204.0	85.1	66.9
6	324.8	122.5	96.2

British Standard tables of pipe flanges (for land use)

Table D (superseding Table 1 of Report No. 10-1904). Flanges for pipes, valves, and fittings for working steam pressures up to 50 lb/in^2

1	1a	2	3	4	5	6(a)	6(b)	6(c)
Nominal Pipe Size	Actual Outside Dia. of Wrought Pipe	Dia. of Flange	Dia. of Bolt Circle	Number of Bolts	Diam. of Bolts	Thickness of Flange		
						Cast Iron	Cast Steel	Iron or Steel (stamped or forged) screwed or riveted on with boss or welded on with fillet
in	in	in	in		in	in	in	in
$\frac{1}{2}$	$\frac{27}{32}$	$3\frac{1}{4}$	$2\frac{5}{8}$	4	$\frac{1}{2}$	$\frac{1}{2}$	$\frac{3}{8}$	$\frac{3}{16}$
$\frac{3}{4}$	$1\frac{1}{16}$	4	$2\frac{7}{8}$	4	$\frac{1}{2}$	$\frac{1}{2}$	$\frac{3}{8}$	$\frac{3}{16}$
1	$1\frac{11}{32}$	$4\frac{1}{2}$	$3\frac{1}{4}$	4	$\frac{1}{2}$	$\frac{1}{2}$	$\frac{3}{8}$	$\frac{3}{16}$
$1\frac{1}{4}$	$1\frac{11}{16}$	$4\frac{3}{4}$	$3\frac{7}{16}$	4	$\frac{1}{2}$	$\frac{5}{8}$	$\frac{1}{2}$	$\frac{1}{4}$
$1\frac{1}{2}$	$1\frac{29}{32}$	$5\frac{1}{4}$	$3\frac{7}{8}$	4	$\frac{1}{2}$	$\frac{5}{8}$	$\frac{1}{2}$	$\frac{1}{4}$
2	$2\frac{3}{8}$	6	$4\frac{1}{2}$	4	$\frac{5}{8}$	$\frac{11}{16}$	$\frac{9}{16}$	$\frac{5}{16}$
$2\frac{1}{2}$	3	$6\frac{1}{2}$	5	4	$\frac{5}{8}$	$\frac{11}{16}$	$\frac{9}{16}$	$\frac{5}{16}$
3	$3\frac{1}{2}$	$7\frac{1}{4}$	$5\frac{3}{4}$	4	$\frac{5}{8}$	$\frac{3}{4}$	$\frac{9}{16}$	$\frac{3}{8}$
$3\frac{1}{2}$	4	8	$6\frac{1}{2}$	4	$\frac{3}{4}$	$\frac{3}{4}$	$\frac{9}{16}$	$\frac{3}{8}$
4	$4\frac{1}{2}$	$8\frac{1}{2}$	7	4	$\frac{5}{8}$	$\frac{3}{4}$	$\frac{11}{16}$	$\frac{3}{8}$
5	$5\frac{1}{2}$	10	$8\frac{1}{4}$	8	$\frac{5}{8}$	$\frac{13}{16}$	$\frac{11}{16}$	$\frac{1}{2}$
6	$6\frac{1}{2}$	11	$9\frac{1}{4}$	8	$\frac{5}{8}$	$\frac{13}{16}$	$\frac{11}{16}$	$\frac{1}{2}$
7	$7\frac{5}{8}$	12	$10\frac{1}{4}$	8	$\frac{5}{8}$	$\frac{7}{8}$	$\frac{3}{4}$	$\frac{1}{2}$
8	$8\frac{5}{8}$	$13\frac{1}{4}$	$11\frac{1}{2}$	8	$\frac{5}{8}$	$\frac{7}{8}$	$\frac{3}{4}$	$\frac{1}{2}$
9	$9\frac{5}{8}$	$14\frac{1}{2}$	$12\frac{1}{4}$	8	$\frac{5}{8}$	$\frac{7}{8}$	$\frac{3}{4}$	$\frac{5}{8}$
10	$10\frac{3}{4}$	16	14	8	$\frac{3}{4}$	1	$\frac{3}{4}$	$\frac{5}{8}$
12	$12\frac{3}{4}$	18	16	12	$\frac{3}{4}$	1	$\frac{7}{8}$	$\frac{3}{4}$
*13	14	$19\frac{1}{4}$	$17\frac{1}{4}$	12	$\frac{3}{4}$	1	$\frac{7}{8}$	$\frac{3}{4}$
14	15	$20\frac{1}{4}$	$18\frac{1}{2}$	12	$\frac{7}{8}$	$1\frac{1}{8}$	1	$\frac{7}{8}$
15	16	$21\frac{3}{4}$	$19\frac{1}{2}$	12	$\frac{7}{8}$	$1\frac{1}{8}$	1	$\frac{7}{8}$
16	17	$22\frac{3}{4}$	$20\frac{1}{2}$	12	$\frac{7}{8}$	$1\frac{1}{8}$	1	$\frac{7}{8}$
*17	18	24	$21\frac{3}{4}$	12	$\frac{7}{8}$	$1\frac{1}{8}$	$1\frac{1}{8}$	1
18	19	$25\frac{1}{4}$	23	12	$\frac{7}{8}$	$1\frac{1}{4}$	$1\frac{1}{8}$	1
*19	20	$26\frac{1}{2}$	24	12	$\frac{7}{8}$	$1\frac{1}{4}$	$1\frac{1}{8}$	1
20	21	$27\frac{3}{4}$	$25\frac{1}{4}$	16	$\frac{7}{8}$	$1\frac{1}{4}$	$1\frac{1}{4}$	$1\frac{1}{8}$
21	22	29	$26\frac{1}{2}$	16	$\frac{7}{8}$	$1\frac{3}{8}$	$1\frac{1}{4}$	$1\frac{1}{8}$
*22	23	30	$27\frac{1}{2}$	16	1	$1\frac{3}{8}$	$1\frac{1}{4}$	$1\frac{1}{8}$
*23	24	31	$28\frac{1}{2}$	16	1	$1\frac{3}{8}$	$1\frac{3}{8}$	$1\frac{1}{8}$
24	25	$32\frac{1}{2}$	$29\frac{3}{4}$	16	1	$1\frac{3}{8}$	$1\frac{3}{8}$	$1\frac{1}{4}$

* The Institute recommends that the use of these sizes be avoided.
Thicknesses — The thicknesses given in this Table include a raised face of not more than $\frac{1}{16}$ in high if such is used. **Bolt Holes** — For $\frac{1}{2}$ in and $\frac{5}{8}$ in Bolts the diameter of the holes to be $\frac{1}{16}$ in larger than the diameters of the Bolts, and for larger sizes of Bolts, $\frac{1}{8}$ in. Bolt holes to be drilled off centre lines.

British Standard tables of pipe flanges (for land use)

Table E (superseding Table 2 of Report No. 10-1904). Flanges for pipes, valves, and fittings for working steam pressure above 50 lb and up to 100 lb/in^2

1	1a	2	3	4	5	6(a)	6(b)	6(c)
Nominal Pipe Size	Actual Outside Dia. of Wrought Pipe	Dia. of Flange	Dia. of Bolt Circle	Number of Bolts	Diam. of Bolts	Thickness of Flange		
						Cast Iron	Cast Steel and Br'ze	Iron or Steel (stamped or forged) screwed or riveted on with boss or welded on with fillet
in	in	in	in		in	in	in	in
$\frac{1}{2}$	$2\frac{7}{32}$	$3\frac{3}{4}$	$2\frac{5}{8}$	4	$\frac{1}{2}$	$\frac{1}{2}$	$\frac{3}{8}$	$\frac{1}{4}$
$\frac{3}{4}$	$1\frac{1}{16}$	4	$2\frac{7}{8}$	4	$\frac{1}{2}$	$\frac{1}{2}$	$\frac{3}{8}$	$\frac{1}{4}$
1	$1\frac{11}{32}$	$4\frac{1}{2}$	$3\frac{1}{4}$	4	$\frac{1}{2}$	$\frac{1}{2}$	$\frac{3}{8}$	$\frac{9}{32}$
$1\frac{1}{4}$	$1\frac{11}{16}$	$4\frac{3}{4}$	$3\frac{7}{16}$	4	$\frac{1}{2}$	$\frac{5}{8}$	$\frac{1}{2}$	$\frac{5}{16}$
$1\frac{1}{2}$	$1\frac{29}{32}$	$5\frac{1}{4}$	$3\frac{7}{8}$	4	$\frac{1}{2}$	$\frac{5}{8}$	$\frac{1}{2}$	$\frac{11}{32}$
2	$2\frac{3}{8}$	6	$4\frac{1}{2}$	4	$\frac{5}{8}$	$\frac{3}{4}$	$\frac{9}{16}$	$\frac{3}{8}$
$2\frac{1}{2}$	3	$6\frac{1}{2}$	5	4	$\frac{5}{8}$	$\frac{3}{4}$	$\frac{9}{16}$	$\frac{13}{32}$
3	$3\frac{1}{4}$	$7\frac{1}{4}$	$5\frac{3}{4}$	4	$\frac{5}{8}$	$\frac{3}{4}$	$\frac{9}{16}$	$\frac{7}{16}$
$3\frac{1}{2}$	4	8	$6\frac{1}{2}$	8	$\frac{5}{8}$	$\frac{3}{4}$	$\frac{9}{16}$	$\frac{15}{32}$
4	$4\frac{1}{2}$	$8\frac{1}{2}$	7	8	$\frac{5}{8}$	$\frac{7}{8}$	$\frac{11}{16}$	$\frac{1}{2}$
5	$5\frac{1}{2}$	10	$8\frac{1}{4}$	8	$\frac{5}{8}$	$\frac{7}{8}$	$\frac{11}{16}$	$\frac{9}{16}$
6	$6\frac{1}{2}$	11	$9\frac{1}{4}$	8	$\frac{3}{4}$	$\frac{7}{8}$	$\frac{11}{16}$	$\frac{11}{16}$
7	$7\frac{5}{8}$	12	$10\frac{1}{4}$	8	$\frac{3}{4}$	1	$\frac{3}{4}$	$\frac{3}{4}$
8	$8\frac{5}{8}$	$13\frac{1}{4}$	$11\frac{1}{2}$	8	$\frac{3}{4}$	1	$\frac{3}{4}$	$\frac{3}{4}$
9	$9\frac{5}{8}$	$14\frac{1}{2}$	$12\frac{3}{4}$	12	$\frac{3}{4}$	1	$\frac{13}{16}$	$\frac{13}{16}$
10	$10\frac{3}{4}$	16	14	12	$\frac{3}{4}$	1	$\frac{7}{8}$	$\frac{7}{8}$
12	$12\frac{3}{4}$	18	16	12	$\frac{7}{8}$	$1\frac{1}{8}$	1	1
*13	14	$19\frac{1}{4}$	$17\frac{1}{4}$	12	$\frac{7}{8}$	$1\frac{1}{8}$	1	1
14	15	$20\frac{3}{4}$	$18\frac{1}{2}$	12	$\frac{7}{8}$	$1\frac{1}{4}$	1	$1\frac{1}{8}$
15	16	$21\frac{3}{4}$	$19\frac{1}{2}$	12	$\frac{7}{8}$	$1\frac{1}{4}$	1	$1\frac{1}{4}$
16	17	$22\frac{3}{4}$	$20\frac{1}{2}$	12	$\frac{7}{8}$	$1\frac{1}{4}$	1	$1\frac{1}{4}$
*17	18	24	$21\frac{3}{4}$	12	$\frac{7}{8}$	$1\frac{3}{8}$	$1\frac{1}{8}$	$1\frac{3}{8}$
18	19	$25\frac{1}{4}$	23	16	$\frac{7}{8}$	$1\frac{3}{8}$	$1\frac{1}{8}$	$1\frac{3}{8}$
*19	20	$26\frac{1}{2}$	24	16	$\frac{7}{8}$	$1\frac{3}{8}$	$1\frac{1}{4}$	$1\frac{1}{2}$
20	21	$27\frac{3}{4}$	$25\frac{1}{4}$	16	$\frac{7}{8}$	$1\frac{1}{2}$	$1\frac{1}{4}$	$1\frac{1}{2}$
21	22	29	$26\frac{1}{2}$	16	1	$1\frac{1}{2}$	$1\frac{3}{8}$	$1\frac{5}{8}$
*22	23	30	$27\frac{1}{2}$	16	1	$1\frac{1}{2}$	$1\frac{3}{8}$	$1\frac{3}{4}$
*23	24	31	$28\frac{1}{2}$	16	1	$1\frac{5}{8}$	$1\frac{3}{8}$	$1\frac{3}{4}$
24	25	$32\frac{1}{2}$	$29\frac{3}{4}$	16	$1\frac{1}{8}$	$1\frac{5}{8}$	$1\frac{1}{2}$	$1\frac{7}{8}$

* The Institution recommends that the use of these sizes be avoided.
Thicknesses — The thicknesses given in this Table include a raised face of not more than $\frac{1}{16}$ in high if such is used. **Bolt Holes** — For $\frac{1}{2}$ in and $\frac{5}{8}$ in Bolts the diameter of the holes to be $\frac{1}{16}$ in larger than the diameters of the Bolts, and for larger sizes of Bolts, $\frac{1}{8}$ in. Bolt holes to be drilled off centre lines.

British Standard tables of pipe flanges (for land use)

Table F (superseding Table 2 of Report No. 10-1904). Flanges for pipes, valves, and fittings for working steam pressure above 100 lb and up to 150 lb/in^2

1	1(a)	2	3	4	5	6(a)	6(b)
Nominal Pipe Size	Actual Outside Dia. of Wrought Pipe	Dia. of Flange	Dia. of Bolt Circle	Number of Bolts	Diam. of Bolts	Thickness of Flange — Cast Iron	Thickness of Flange — Cast Steel Bronze, Iron or Steel (stamped or forged) screwed or riveted on with boss or welded on with fillet
in	in	in	in		in	in	in
$\frac{1}{2}$	$\frac{27}{32}$	$3\frac{1}{4}$	$2\frac{5}{8}$	4	$\frac{1}{2}$	$\frac{1}{2}$	$\frac{3}{8}$
$\frac{3}{4}$	$1\frac{1}{16}$	4	$2\frac{7}{8}$	4	$\frac{1}{2}$	$\frac{1}{2}$	$\frac{3}{8}$
1	$1\frac{11}{16}$	$4\frac{1}{4}$	$3\frac{7}{16}$	4	$\frac{5}{8}$	$\frac{1}{2}$	$\frac{3}{8}$
$1\frac{1}{4}$		$5\frac{1}{4}$	$3\frac{7}{8}$	4	$\frac{5}{8}$	$\frac{5}{8}$	$\frac{1}{2}$
$1\frac{1}{2}$	$1\frac{23}{32}$	$5\frac{1}{2}$	$4\frac{1}{8}$	4	$\frac{5}{8}$	$\frac{5}{8}$	$\frac{1}{2}$
2	$2\frac{3}{8}$	$6\frac{1}{2}$	5	4	$\frac{5}{8}$	$\frac{3}{4}$	$\frac{5}{8}$
$2\frac{1}{2}$	3	$7\frac{1}{4}$	$5\frac{3}{4}$	8	$\frac{5}{8}$	$\frac{3}{4}$	$\frac{5}{8}$
3	$3\frac{1}{2}$	8	$6\frac{1}{2}$	8	$\frac{5}{8}$	$\frac{3}{4}$	$\frac{5}{8}$
$3\frac{1}{2}$	4	$8\frac{1}{2}$	7	8	$\frac{5}{8}$	$\frac{7}{8}$	$\frac{3}{4}$
4	$4\frac{1}{2}$	9	$7\frac{1}{2}$	8	$\frac{5}{8}$	$\frac{7}{8}$	$\frac{3}{4}$
5	$5\frac{1}{2}$	11	$9\frac{1}{4}$	8	$\frac{3}{4}$	1	$\frac{7}{8}$
6	$6\frac{1}{2}$	12	$10\frac{1}{4}$	12	$\frac{3}{4}$	1	$\frac{7}{8}$
7	$7\frac{5}{8}$	$13\frac{1}{2}$	$11\frac{1}{2}$	12	$\frac{3}{4}$	1	$\frac{7}{8}$
8	$8\frac{5}{8}$	$14\frac{1}{2}$	$12\frac{3}{4}$	12	$\frac{3}{4}$	$1\frac{1}{8}$	1
9	$9\frac{5}{8}$	16	14	12	$\frac{7}{8}$	$1\frac{1}{8}$	$1\frac{1}{8}$
10	$10\frac{3}{4}$	17	15	12	$\frac{7}{8}$	$1\frac{1}{8}$	$1\frac{1}{8}$
12	$12\frac{1}{4}$	$19\frac{1}{4}$	$17\frac{1}{4}$	16	$\frac{7}{8}$	$1\frac{1}{4}$	$1\frac{1}{4}$
*13	14	$20\frac{1}{2}$	$18\frac{1}{2}$	16	1	$1\frac{1}{4}$	$1\frac{3}{8}$
14	15	$21\frac{1}{4}$	$19\frac{1}{2}$	16	1	$1\frac{3}{8}$	$1\frac{3}{8}$
15	16	$22\frac{1}{4}$	$20\frac{1}{2}$	16	1	$1\frac{3}{8}$	$1\frac{3}{8}$
16	17	24	$21\frac{1}{4}$	20	1	$1\frac{3}{8}$	$1\frac{5}{8}$
*17	18	$25\frac{1}{4}$	23	20	1	$1\frac{1}{2}$	$1\frac{1}{4}$
18	19	$26\frac{1}{2}$	24	20	$1\frac{1}{8}$	$1\frac{1}{2}$	$1\frac{1}{4}$
*19	20	$27\frac{1}{4}$	$25\frac{1}{4}$	20	$1\frac{1}{8}$	$1\frac{1}{2}$	$1\frac{1}{4}$
20	21	29	$26\frac{1}{2}$	24	$1\frac{1}{8}$	$1\frac{5}{8}$	2
21	22	30	$27\frac{1}{2}$	24	$1\frac{1}{8}$	$1\frac{5}{8}$	2
*22	23	31	$28\frac{1}{2}$	24	$1\frac{1}{8}$	$1\frac{5}{8}$	$2\frac{1}{8}$
*23	24	$32\frac{1}{2}$	$29\frac{3}{4}$	24	$1\frac{1}{4}$	$1\frac{3}{4}$	$2\frac{1}{4}$
24	25	$33\frac{1}{2}$	$30\frac{3}{4}$	24	$1\frac{1}{4}$	$1\frac{3}{4}$	$2\frac{1}{4}$

* The Institution recommends that the use of these sizes be avoided.
Thicknesses — The thicknesses given in this Table include a raised face of not more than $\frac{1}{16}$ in high if such be used. **Bolt Holes** — For $\frac{1}{2}$ in and $\frac{5}{8}$ in Bolts the diameters of the holes to be $\frac{1}{16}$ in larger than the diameter of the Bolts, and for larger sizes of Bolts, $\frac{1}{8}$ in. Bolt holes to be drilled off centre lines.

British Standard tables of pipe flanges (for land use)

Table H (superseding Table 2 of Report No. 10-1904). Flanges for pipes, valves, and fittings for working steam pressure above 150 lb and up to 250 lb/in^2

1	1(a)	2	3	4	5	6
Nominal Dia. of Pipe	*Actual Outside Dia. of Wrought Pipe*	*Dia. of Flange*	*Dia. of Bolt Circle*	*Number of Bolts*	*Dia. of Bolts*	*Thickness of Flange* — *Cast Steel and Bronze, Steel (stamped or forged) screwed or riveted on with boss or welded on with fillet*
in	*in*	*in*	*in*		*in*	*in*
$\frac{1}{2}$	$\frac{27}{32}$	$4\frac{1}{2}$	$3\frac{1}{4}$	4	$\frac{5}{8}$	$\frac{1}{2}$
$\frac{3}{4}$	$1\frac{1}{16}$	$4\frac{1}{2}$	$3\frac{1}{4}$	4	$\frac{5}{8}$	$\frac{1}{2}$
1	$1\frac{11}{32}$	$4\frac{3}{4}$	$3\frac{7}{16}$	4	$\frac{5}{8}$	$\frac{9}{16}$
$1\frac{1}{4}$	$1\frac{11}{16}$	$5\frac{1}{4}$	$3\frac{7}{8}$	4	$\frac{5}{8}$	$\frac{11}{16}$
$1\frac{1}{2}$	$1\frac{29}{32}$	$5\frac{1}{2}$	$4\frac{1}{8}$	4	$\frac{5}{8}$	$\frac{11}{16}$
2	$2\frac{3}{8}$	$6\frac{1}{2}$	5	4	$\frac{5}{8}$	$\frac{3}{4}$
$2\frac{1}{2}$	3	$7\frac{1}{4}$	$5\frac{3}{4}$	8	$\frac{5}{8}$	$\frac{3}{4}$
3	$3\frac{1}{2}$	8	$6\frac{1}{2}$	8	$\frac{5}{8}$	$\frac{7}{8}$
$3\frac{1}{2}$	4	$8\frac{1}{2}$	7	8	$\frac{5}{8}$	$\frac{7}{8}$
4	$4\frac{1}{2}$	9	$7\frac{1}{2}$	8	$\frac{5}{8}$	1
5	$5\frac{1}{2}$	11	$9\frac{1}{4}$	8	$\frac{3}{4}$	$1\frac{1}{8}$
6	$6\frac{1}{2}$	12	$10\frac{1}{4}$	12	$\frac{3}{4}$	$1\frac{1}{8}$
7	$7\frac{5}{8}$	$13\frac{1}{4}$	$11\frac{1}{2}$	12	$\frac{3}{4}$	$1\frac{1}{4}$
8	$8\frac{5}{8}$	$14\frac{1}{2}$	$12\frac{3}{4}$	12	$\frac{3}{4}$	$1\frac{1}{4}$
9	$9\frac{5}{8}$	16	14	12	$\frac{7}{8}$	$1\frac{3}{8}$
10	$10\frac{3}{4}$	17	15	12	$\frac{7}{8}$	$1\frac{3}{8}$
12	$12\frac{3}{4}$	$19\frac{1}{4}$	$17\frac{1}{4}$	16	$\frac{7}{8}$	$1\frac{5}{8}$
*13	14	$20\frac{3}{4}$	$18\frac{1}{2}$	16	1	$1\frac{3}{4}$
14	15	$21\frac{3}{4}$	$19\frac{1}{2}$	16	1	$1\frac{7}{8}$
15	16	$22\frac{3}{4}$	$20\frac{1}{2}$	16	1	2
16	17	24	$21\frac{3}{4}$	20	1	$2\frac{1}{8}$
*17	18	$25\frac{1}{4}$	23	20	1	$2\frac{1}{4}$
18	19	$26\frac{1}{2}$	24	20	$1\frac{1}{8}$	$2\frac{3}{8}$
*19	20	$27\frac{3}{4}$	$25\frac{1}{4}$	20	$1\frac{1}{8}$	$2\frac{1}{2}$
20	21	29	$26\frac{1}{2}$	24	$1\frac{1}{8}$	$2\frac{5}{8}$
21	22	30	$27\frac{1}{2}$	24	$1\frac{1}{8}$	$2\frac{3}{4}$
*22	23	31	$28\frac{1}{2}$	24	$1\frac{1}{8}$	$2\frac{3}{4}$
*23	24	$32\frac{1}{2}$	$29\frac{3}{4}$	24	$1\frac{1}{4}$	3
24	25	$33\frac{1}{2}$	$30\frac{3}{4}$	24	$1\frac{1}{4}$	3

* The Institution recommends that the use of these sizes be avoided.
Thicknesses — The thicknesses given in this Table include a raised face of not more than $\frac{1}{16}$ in high if such be used. **Bolt Holes** — For $\frac{1}{2}$ in and $\frac{5}{8}$ in Bolts the diameters of the holes to be $\frac{1}{16}$ in larger than the diameter of the Bolts, and for larger sizes of Bolts, $\frac{1}{8}$ in. Bolt holes to be drilled off centre lines.

Metric pipe flanges to BS 4504

Nominal pressure — 2.5 bar
Thickness of flange depends on type and material

Nominal pipe size	Outside diameter of pipe mm	Diameter of flange mm	Diameter of bolt circle mm	No. of bolts	Size of bolts
10	17.2	75	50	4	M10
15	21.3	80	55	4	M10
20	26.9	90	65	4	M10
25	33.7	100	75	4	M10
32	42.4	120	90	4	M12
40	48.3	130	100	4	M12
50	60.3	140	110	4	M12
65	76.1	160	130	4	M12
80	88.9	190	150	4	M16
100	114.3	210	170	4	M16
125	139.7	240	200	8	M16
150	168.3	265	225	8	M16
200	219.1	320	280	8	M16
250	273	375	335	12	M16
300	323.9	440	395	12	M20
350	355.6	490	445	12	M20
400	406.4	540	495	16	M20
500	508	645	600	20	M20
600	609.6	755	705	20	M24

Nominal pressure — 6 bar
Dimensions as for 2.5 bar for sizes up to 600 NB

Metric pipe flanges to BS 4504
Nominal pressure — 10 bar
Thickness of flange depends on type and material

Nominal pipe size	Outside diameter of pipe mm	Diameter of flange mm	Diameter of bolt circle mm	No. of bolts	Size of bolts
10	17.2	90	60	4	M12
15	21.3	85	65	4	M12
20	26.9	105	75	4	M12
25	33.7	115	85	4	M12
32	42.4	140	100	4	M16
40	48.3	150	110	4	M16
50	60.3	165	125	4	M16
65	76.1	185	145	4	M16
80	88.9	200	160	8	M16
100	114.3	220	180	8	M16
125	139.7	250	210	8	M16
150	168.3	285	240	8	M20
200	219.1	340	295	8	M20
250	273	395	350	12	M20
300	323.9	445	400	12	M20
350	355.6	505	460	16	M20
400	406.4	565	515	16	M24
500	508	670	620	20	M24
600	609.6	780	725	20	M27

Metric pipe flanges to BS 4504
Nominal pressure — 16 bar
Thickness of flange depends on type and material

Nominal pipe size	Outside diameter of pipe mm	Diameter of flange mm	Diameter of bolt circle mm	No. of bolts	Size of bolts
10	17.2	90	60	4	M12
15	21.3	85	65	4	M12
20	26.9	105	75	4	M12
25	33.7	115	85	4	M12
32	42.4	140	100	4	M16
40	48.3	150	110	4	M16
50	60.3	165	125	4	M16
65	76.1	185	145	4	M16
80	88.9	200	160	8	M16
100	114.3	220	180	8	M16
125	139.7	250	210	8	M16
150	168.3	285	240	8	M20
200	219.1	340	295	12	M20
250	273	405	355	12	M24
300	323.9	460	410	12	M24
350	355.6	520	470	16	M24
400	406.4	580	525	16	M27
500	508	715	650	20	M30
600	609.6	840	770	20	M33

Metric pipe flanges to BS 4504

Nominal pressure — 25 bar
Thickness of flange depends on type and material

Nominal pipe size	Outside diameter of pipe mm	Diameter of flange mm	Diameter of bolt circle mm	No. of bolts	Size of bolts
10	17.2	90	60	4	M12
15	21.3	85	65	4	M12
20	26.9	105	75	4	M12
25	33.7	115	85	4	M12
32	42.4	140	100	4	M16
40	48.3	150	110	4	M16
50	60.3	165	125	4	M16
65	76.1	185	145	8	M16
80	88.9	200	160	8	M16
100	114.3	235	190	8	M20
125	139.7	270	220	8	M24
150	168.3	300	250	8	M24
200	219.1	360	310	12	M24
250	273	425	370	12	M27
300	323.9	485	430	16	M27
350	355.6	555	490	16	M30
400	406.4	620	550	16	M33
500	508	730	660	20	M33

Dimensions of tubes

General dimensions of steel tubes to BS 1387:1967
(Subject to standard tolerances and usual working allowances)

Nominal Bore		Outside Diameter				Thickness					
		Light		Heavy & Medium		Light		Medium		Heavy	
in	mm	in	mm	in	mm	in	mm	in	mm	in	mm
$\frac{1}{8}$	6	0.396	10.1	0.411	10.4	0.072	1.8	0.080	2.0	0.104	2.65
$\frac{1}{4}$	8	0.532	13.6	0.547	13.9	0.072	1.8	0.092	2.35	0.116	2.90
$\frac{3}{8}$	10	0.671	17.1	0.685	17.4	0.072	1.8	0.092	2.35	0.116	2.90
$\frac{1}{2}$	15	0.871	21.4	0.856	21.7	0.080	2.0	0.104	2.65	0.128	3.25
$\frac{3}{4}$	20	1.059	26.9	1.072	27.2	0.092	2.35	0.104	2.65	0.128	3.25
1	25	1.328	33.8	1.346	34.2	0.104	2.65	0.128	3.25	0.160	4.05
$1\frac{1}{4}$	32	1.670	42.5	1.687	42.9	0.104	2.65	0.128	3.25	0.160	4.05
$1\frac{1}{2}$	40	1.903	48.4	1.919	48.8	0.116	2.9	0.128	3.25	0.160	4.05
2	50	2.370	60.2	2.394	60.8	0.116	2.9	0.114	3.65	0.176	4.50
$2\frac{1}{2}$	65	2.991	76.0	3.014	76.6	0.128	3.25	0.144	3.65	0.176	4.50
3	80	3.491	88.7	3.524	89.5	0.128	3.25	0.160	4.05	0.192	4.85
4	100	4.481	113.9	4.524	114.9	0.144	3.65	0.176	4.5	0.212	5.40
5	125	—	—	5.534	140.6	—	—	0.192	4.85	0.212	5.40
6	150	—	—	6.539	166.1	—	—	0.192	4.85	0.212	5.40

Dimensions of tubes (continued)

General dimensions of steel tubes to BS 1387:1967
(Subject to standard tolerances and usual working allowances)

Nominal Bore		Weight of Black Tube											
		Light				Medium				Heavy			
		Plain		Screwed		Plain		Screwed		Plain		Screwed	
in	mm	lb/ft	kg/m	lb/ft	kg/m	lb/ft	kg/m	lb/ft	kg/m	lb/ft	kg/m	lb/ft	kg/m
$\frac{1}{8}$	6	0.24	0.36	0.25	0.36	0.27	0.41	0.28	0.41	0.33	0.49	0.33	0.50
$\frac{1}{4}$	8	0.35	0.52	0.35	0.52	0.44	0.65	0.44	0.65	0.52	0.77	0.52	0.77
$\frac{3}{8}$	10	0.45	0.67	0.46	0.68	0.57	0.85	0.58	0.85	0.69	1.02	0.69	1.03
$\frac{1}{2}$	15	0.64	0.95	0.64	0.96	0.82	1.22	0.83	1.23	0.98	1.45	0.98	1.46
$\frac{3}{4}$	20	0.94	1.41	0.95	1.42	1.06	1.58	1.07	1.59	1.27	1.90	1.28	1.91
1	25	1.35	2.01	1.36	2.03	1.64	2.44	1.65	2.46	2.00	2.97	2.01	2.99
$1\frac{1}{4}$	32	1.73	2.58	1.75	2.61	2.11	3.14	2.13	3.17	2.58	3.84	2.60	3.87
$1\frac{1}{2}$	40	2.19	3.25	2.22	3.29	2.43	3.61	2.46	3.65	2.98	4.43	3.01	4.47
2	50	2.76	4.11	2.81	4.18	3.42	5.10	3.47	5.17	4.14	6.17	4.19	6.24
$2\frac{1}{2}$	65	3.90	5.80	3.98	5.92	4.38	6.51	4.46	6.63	5.31	7.90	5.39	8.02
3	80	4.58	6.81	4.69	6.98	5.69	8.47	5.80	8.64	6.76	10.1	6.87	10.3
4	100	6.64	9.89	6.84	10.2	8.14	12.1	8.34	12.4	9.71	14.4	9.41	14.7
5	125	—	—	—	—	10.9	16.2	11.2	16.7	12.0	17.8	12.3	18.3
6	150	—	—	—	—	12.9	19.2	13.3	19.8	14.3	21.2	14.7	21.8

Tube data
Surfaces, areas and contents of tubes

Nominal bore		Surface		Area of inside		Contents	
in	mm	ft²/ft	m²/m	in²	mm²	gal/ft	litre/m
⅛	6	0.11	0.036	0.086	55	0.0037	0.055
¼	8	0.14	0.048	0.163	105	0.0071	0.105
⅜	10	0.18	0.060	0.277	178	0.0120	0.178
½	15	0.22	0.074	0.44	285	0.0196	0.285
¾	20	0.28	0.093	0.75	472	0.0323	0.472
1	25	0.35	0.117	1.17	753	0.0506	0.753
1¼	32	0.44	0.147	1.91	1,447	0.0828	1.45
1½	40	0.50	0.167	2.52	1,872	0.110	1.87
2	50	0.62	0.208	3.98	2,910	0.173	2.91
2½	65	0.78	0.262	6.47	4,610	0.281	4.61
3	80	1.05	0.306	8.90	5,740	0.386	5.74
4	100	1.18	0.393	14.9	9,580	0.645	9.58
5	125	1.44	0.481	22.5	14,500	0.973	14.5
6	150	1.70	0.568	31.7	20,460	1.37	20.5
7	175	1.96	0.60	38.5	25,590	1.67	25.6
8	200	2.23	0.68	50.3	32,690	2.37	32.7
9	225	2.49	0.76	63.6	41,000	2.75	41.0
10	250	2.74	0.84	77.5	50,700	3.35	50.7
11	275	3.01	0.92	91.2	60,700	3.95	60.7
12	300	3.27	1.00	110.7	72,100	4.77	72.1

Suggested maximum working pressures
The pressures given below can be taken as conservative estimates for tubes screwed taper with sockets tapped parallel under normal (non-shock) conditions

	Grade		Nom bore ⅛ to 1 in	1¼ & 1½ in	2 & 2½ in	3 in	4 in	5 in	6 in
Water	light	lb/in²	150	125	100	100	80	—	—
		kN/m²	1000	850	700	700	550	—	—
	medium	lb/in²	300	250	200	200	150	150	125
		kN/m²	2000	1750	1400	1400	1000	1000	850
	heavy	lb/in²	350	300	250	250	200	200	150
		kN/m²	2400	2000	1750	1750	1400	1400	1000
Steam or air	medium	lb/in²	150	125	100	100	80	80	60
		kN/m²	1000	850	700	700	550	550	400
	heavy	lb/in²	175	150	125	125	100	100	80
		kN/m²	1200	1000	850	850	700	700	550

The following allowed for plain end tubes end-to-end welded for steam or compressed air.

medium	lb/in²	250	200	200	150	150	150	125
	kN/m²	1750	1400	1400	1000	1000	1000	850
heavy	lb/in²	300	300	300	200	200	200	75
	kN/m²	2000	2000	2000	1400	1400	1400	1200

Copper tube to BS 2871:1972

Nominal bore mm	Outside dia. mm	Table X Half hard light gauge tube		Table Y Half hard and annealed tube		Table Z Hard drawn thin wall tube	
		Thickness mm	Maximum working pressure N/mm²	Thickness mm	Maximum working pressure N/mm²	Thickness mm	Maximum working pressure N/mm²
6	6	0.6	13.3	0.8	14.4	0.5	11.3
8	8	0.6	9.7	0.8	10.5	0.5	9.8
10	10	0.6	7.7	0.8	8.2	0.5	7.8
12	12	0.6	6.3	0.8	6.7	0.5	6.4
15	15	0.7	5.8	1.0	6.7	0.5	5.0
18	18	0.8	5.6	1.0	5.5	0.6	5.0
22	22	0.9	5.1	1.2	5.7	0.6	4.1
28	28	0.9	4.0	1.2	4.2	0.6	3.2
35	35	1.2	4.2	1.5	4.1	0.7	3.0
42	42	1.2	3.5	1.5	3.4	0.8	2.8
54	54	1.2	2.7	2.0	3.6	0.9	2.5
67	67	1.2	2.0	2.0	2.8	1.0	2.0
76.1	76.2	1.5	2.4	2.0	2.5	1.2	1.9
108	108.1	1.5	1.7	2.5	2.2	1.2	1.7
133	133.4	1.5	1.4	—	—	1.5	1.6
159	159.4	2.0	1.5	—	—	1.5	1.5

Malleable iron pipe fittings

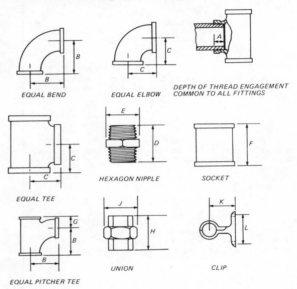

EQUAL BEND

EQUAL ELBOW

DEPTH OF THREAD ENGAGEMENT
COMMON TO ALL FITTINGS

EQUAL TEE

HEXAGON NIPPLE

SOCKET

EQUAL PITCHER TEE

UNION

CLIP

Dimensions of malleable iron pipe fittings

Dimensions in mm

Nominal bore		15	20	25	32	40	50	65	80	100
Depth of thread engagement	A	13	14	16	19	19	24	25	29	35
Bend	B	45	50	63	76	85	102	114	127	165
Elbow	C	28	33	38	45	50	58	69	78	96
Equal Tee	C	28	33	38	45	50	58	69	78	96
Hexagon nipple length	D	44	49	56	64	64	71	80	89	102
across flats	E	23	28	35	44	50	61	77	90	115
Socket length	F	34	39	42	49	54	64	73	81	94
Equal pitcher Tee	B	45	50	63	76	85	102	114	127	165
	G	24	28	33	40	43	53	61	70	87
Union length	H	46	52	57	64	68	75	84	92	106
across flats	J	42	48	57	68	76	92	109	125	155
Pipe clip	K	43	43	51	56	70	76	89	97	118
	L	40	48	54	60	73	86	95	108	143

3 Combustion

Atomic weights of elements occurring in combustion calculations

Element	Symbol	Atomic No.	Atomic weight
Carbon	C	6	12.011
Hydrogen	H	1	1.008
Nitrogen	N	7	14.007
Oxygen	O	8	15.9994
Phosphorus	P	15	30.9738
Sulphur	S	16	32.06

Heat of combustion of important chemicals

Substance	Products of combustion	Chemical equation	Heat of combustion kJ/kg	Btu/lb
Carbon	Carbon dioxide	$C+O_2=CO_2$	33,950	14,590
Carbon	Carbon monoxide	$2C+O_2=2CO$	9,210	3,960
Carbon monoxide	Carbon dioxide	$2CO+O_2=2CO_2$	10,150	4,367
Hydrogen	Water	$2H_2+O_2=2H_2O$	144,200	62,000
Sulphur	Sulphur dioxide	$S+O_2=SO_2$	9,080	3,900
Methane	Carbon dioxide and water	$CH_4+2O_2=CO_2+2H_2O$	55,860	24,017

Ignition temperatures

Wood	300°C	570°F	Petroleum	400°C	750°F
Peat	227°C	440°F	Benzene	415°C	780°F
Bituminous coal	300°C	570°F	Coal-tar oil	580°C	1080°F
Semi anthracite coal	400°C	750°F	Producer gas	750°C	1380°F
Coke	700°C	1290°F	Light hydrocarbons	650°C	1200°F
Hydrogen	500°C	930°F	Heavy hydrocarbons	750°C	1380°F
Carbon monoxide	300°C	570°F	Light gas	600°C	1110°F
Carbon	700°C	1290°F	Naphtha	550°C	1020°F

Composition and calorific value of fuels

Fuel	Composition by weight						Higher calorific value	
	C	H	O+N	S	H_2O	Ash	kJ/kg	Btu/lb
Anthracite	83–87	3.5–4.0	3.0–4.7	0.9	1–3	4–6	32 500–34 000	14 000–14 500
Semi-anthracite	63–76	3.5–4.8	8–10	0.5–1.8	5–15	4–14	26 700–32 500	11 500–14 000
Bituminous coal	46–56	3.5–5.0	9–16	0.2–3.0	18–32	2–10	17 000–23 250	73 00–10 000
Lignite	37	7	13.5	0.5	37	5	16 300	7000
Peat	38–49	3.0–4.5	19–28	0.2–1.0	16–29	1–9	13 800–20 500	5500–8800
Coke	80–90	0.5–1.5	1.5–5.0	0.5–1.5	1–5	5–12	28 000–31 000	12 000–13 500
Charcoal	84	1	—	—	12	3	29 600	12 800
Wood (dry)	35–45	3.0–5.0	34–42	—	7–22	0.3–3.0	14 400–17 400	6200–7500
							kJ/m^3	Btu/ft^3
Town gas	26	56	18	—	—	—	18 600	500
Natural gas	75	25	—	—	—	—	37 200	1000
Propane C_3H_8	82	18	—	—	—	—	93 900	2520
Butane C_4H_{10}	83	17	—	—	—	—	130 000	3490
							kJ/l	Btu/ft^3
Kerosine			—				35 000	154 000
Gas oil	86.2	13.0	—	0.8	—	—	38 000	164 000
Heavy fuel oil	85.0	10.8	—	3.8	—	—	41 200	177 000

Excess of air for good conditions

For anthracite and coke	40%
For semi-anthracite, hand firing	70 to 100%
For semi-anthracite, with stoker	40 to 70%
For semi-anthracite, with travelling grate	30 to 60%
For oil	10 to 20%
For gas	10%

Theoretical values of combustion air and flue gases

Fuel	Theoretical air for combustion Volume at S.T.P.		Theoretical flue gas produced Volume at S.T.P.	
	m^3/kg	ft^3/lb	m^3/kg	ft^3/lb
Anthracite	9.4	150	9.5	152
Semi-anthracite	8.4	135	8.6	137
Bituminous coal	6.9	110	7.0	112
Lignite	5.7	92	5.8	93
Peat	5.7	92	5.9	94
Coke	8.4	134	8.4	135
Charcoal	8.4	134	8.4	135
Wood (dry)	4.4	70	5.0	80
	$\dfrac{m^3}{air}\Big/\dfrac{m^3}{fuel}$	$\dfrac{ft^3}{air}\Big/\dfrac{ft^3}{fuel}$	$\dfrac{m^3}{air}\Big/\dfrac{m^3}{fuel}$	$\dfrac{ft^3}{air}\Big/\dfrac{ft^3}{fuel}$
Town gas	4	4	3.8	3.8
Natural gas	9.5	9.5	8.5	8.5
Propane C_3H_8	24.0	24.0	22	22
Butane C_4H_{10}	31	31	27	27
	$\dfrac{m^3}{air}\Big/\dfrac{litre}{fuel}$	$\dfrac{ft^3}{air}\Big/\dfrac{gal}{fuel}$	$\dfrac{m^3}{air}\Big/\dfrac{litre}{fuel}$	$\dfrac{ft^3}{air}\Big/\dfrac{gal}{fuel}$
Gas oil	9.8	1570	10.4	1670
Heavy fuel oil	10.8	1730	11.6	1860

Heat losses in a boiler

1 Sensible heat carried away by dry flue gases

$$L_1 = W_{cp}\,(t_1-t_n)\qquad \text{kJ per kg of fuel}$$

$$= W_{cp}\,(t_1-t_n)\,\frac{100}{S}\,\text{per cent}$$

2 Heat lost by free moisture in fuel

$$L_2 = w(H-h)\qquad \text{kJ per kg of fuel}$$

$$= w(H-h)\,\frac{100}{S}\,\text{per cent}$$

3 Heat lost by incomplete combustion

$$L_3 = 24{,}000\,\frac{CO}{CO_2+CO}\,C\qquad \text{kJ per kg of fuel}$$

$$= 24{,}000\,\frac{CO}{CO_2+CO}\,C \times \frac{100}{S}\,\text{per cent}$$

4 Heat lost due to Carbon in Ash

$$L_4 = W_c \times 33{,}950 \qquad \text{kJ per kg of fuel}$$

$$= W_c \times 33{,}950 \times \frac{100}{S}$$

5 Heat lost by Radiation and Unaccounted Losses obtained by difference

$$L_s = S - (M + L_1 + L_2 + L_3 + L_4)$$

where W = weight of combustion products, kg per kg fuel
W_c = weight of carbon in ash, kg per kg fuel
w = weight of water in fuel, kg per kg fuel
C_p = specific heat capacity of flue gas, kg per kJ per deg C
   = 1.0
t_i = temperature of flue gas °C
t_A = ambient temperature in boiler room, °C
S = lower calorific valve of fuel, kJ per kg
H = total heat of superheated steam at temperature t_1 and
   atmospheric pressure, kJ per kg

h=sensible heat of water at temperature t_a, kJ per kg
C=weight of carbon in fuel, kg per kg
CO=percentage by volume of carbon monoxide in flue gas
CO_2=percentage by volume of carbon dioxide in flue gas
M=utilized heat in boiler output.

The largest loss is normally the sensible heat in the flue gases. In good practice it is about 20%.

THE RINGELMANN SCALE FOR GRADING DENSITY OF SMOKE

SMOKE NUMBER	0	1	2	3	4	5
LINES mm SPACES mm	ALL WHITE	1 9	2.3 7.7	3.7 6.3	5.5 4.5	ALL BLACK

Observer should stand 30–300 m from stack and hold scale at arm's length. He should then determine the shade in the chart most nearly corresponding to the shade of the smoke. Care should be taken to avoid either bright sunlight or dark buildings in the background.

Sensible heat carried away by flue gases

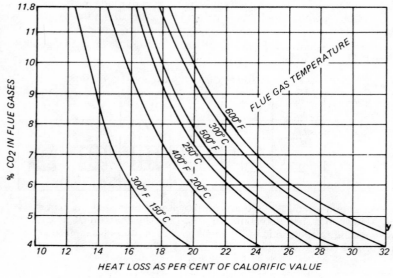

HEAT LOSS IN FLUE GASES FOR NATURAL GAS

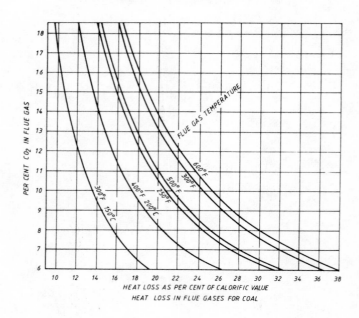

HEAT LOSS IN FLUE GASES FOR COAL

Sensible heat carried away by flue gases

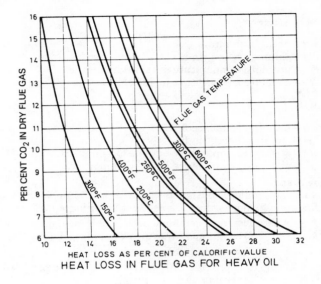

HEAT LOSS IN FLUE GAS FOR HEAVY OIL

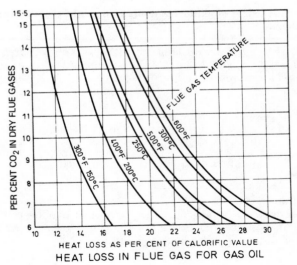

HEAT LOSS IN FLUE GAS FOR GAS OIL

Chimney sizes

Theoretical chimney draught

$$h = 354\,H\left(\frac{1}{T_1} - \frac{1}{T_2}\right)$$

where h=draught in mm water
  H=chimney height in m
  T_1=absolute temperature outside chimney K
  T_2=absolute temperature inside chimney K

$$h = 7.64H\left(\frac{1}{T_1} - \frac{1}{T_2}\right)$$

where h=draught in inches of water
  H=chimney height in ft
  T_1=absolute temperature outside chimney $^\circ$R
  T_2=absolute temperature inside chimney $^\circ$R.

Chimney area

The chimney should be designed to give a maximum velocity of 2 m/s (7 ft/s) for small furnaces, and 10 m/s (30 ft/s) for large furnaces.

$$A = \frac{Q}{V}$$
  where A=cross-sectional area of chimney, m^2
  Q=volume of flue gases at chimney temperature, m^3/s
  V=velocity, m/s

An empirical rule is to provide 1100 mm^2 chimney area per 1 kW boiler rating (1 in^2 per 2000 Btu/hour boiler rating).

Recommended sizes of explosion doors or draught stabilisers for oil firing installations.

Cross-sectional area of chimney in^2	Release opening of stabilizer, approx., in	Cross-sectional area of chimney m^2	Release opening of stabilizer, approx., mm
40–80	6×9	0.025–0.050	150×230
80–200	8×13	0.050–0.125	200×330
200–300	13×18	0.125–0.200	330×450
300–600	16×24	0.200–0.400	400×600
600–1500	24×32	0.400–1.000	600×800

Combustion air

A boiler house must have openings to fresh air to allow combustion air to enter. An empirical rule is to allow 1600 mm^2 free area per 1 kW boiler rating (1.5 in^2 per 2000 Btu/hour boiler rating).

Flue dilution

Flue gases from gas burning appliances can be diluted with fresh air to enable the products of combustion to be discharged at low level or near windows.

Typical arrangements

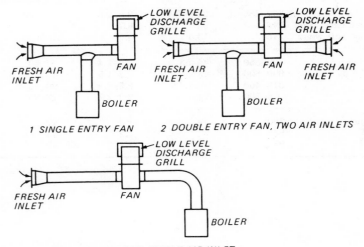

To reduce CO_2 concentration to 1%, fan must handle 100m³ mixed volume per 1m³ natural gas fuel burnt.

In determining fan pressure allowance must be made for pressure due to local wind conditions.

Discharge grille must have free area not less than that of flue.

Fresh air intake must have free area not less than that of flue.

Fresh air intake should be on same face of building as discharge grille in order to balance out wind effect.

Density and specific volume of stored fuels

Fuel	Density		Specific volume	
	kg/m^3	lb/ft^3	m^3 per 1000 kg	ft^3 per ton
Wood	360–385	22.5–2.4	2.5–2.8	90–100
Charcoal, hard wood	149	9.3	6.7	240
Charcoal, soft wood	216	13.5	4.6	165
Anthracite	720–850	45–53	1.2–1.4	42–50
Bituminous coal	690–800	43–50	1.2–1.5	45–52
Peat	310–400	19.5–25	2.5–3.2	90–115
Coke	375–500	23.5–31	2.0–2.7	72–95
Kerosine	790	49	1.3	47
Gas oil	835	52	1.2	43
Fuel oil	930	58	1.1	39

Classification of Oil Fuels
Based on BS 2869

Common Name	Kerosine	Gas oil		Fuel oil or heavy fuel oil		
Class to BS 2869	C1	C2	D	E	F	G
Kinematic viscosity						
cS at 40°C	—	1.0 to 2.0	1.5 to 5.5			
cS at 82.2°C	—			12.5 max.	30 max.	70 max.
Flash point, closed						
Abel, min. °C	—	43	38			
Pensky-Martin, min. °C	—			66	66	66
Sulphur content per cent by mass	0.04	0.2	0.8	3.5	4.0	4.5
Minimum temperature						
for storage °C	ambient	ambient	ambient	10	25	35
for outflow from storage and handling °C	ambient	ambient	ambient	10	30	45
Application	Distillate fuel for free standing flueless domestic appliances	Similar for vapourising and atomising burners on domestic appliances with flues	Distillate fuel for atomising burners for domestic and industrial use	Residual or blended fuels for atomising burners normally requiring preheating before combustion in burner		

Classification of Coal
Based on volatile matter and coking power of clean material

Class	Volatile matter per cent (dry mineral matter free basis)	General description	
101 102	<6.1 6.1– 9.0	Anthracites	
201 202 203 204 206	9.1–13.5 13.6–15.0 15.1–17.0 17.1–19.5 9.1–19.5	Dry steam coals Coking steam coals Heat altered low volatile steam coals	Low volatile steam coals
301 305 306	19.6–32.0 19.6–32.0 19.6–32.0	Prime coking coals Mainly heat altered coals	Medium volatile coals
401 402	32.1–36.0 >36.0	Very strongly coking coals	
501 502	32.1–36.0 >36.0	Strongly coking coals	
601 602	32.1–36.0 >36.0	Medium coking coals	High volatile coals
701 702	32.1–36.0 >36.0	Weakly coking coals	
801 802	32.1–36.0 >36.0	Very weakly coking coals	
901 902	32.1–36.0 >36.0	Non-coking coals	

Flow of oil in pipes

Head loss of various viscosities for laminar flow

Viscosity at temp in pipe cS	4.0	25	45	250	500
i_1	$0.54\times10^{-4}\,\dfrac{f_1}{d_1^4}$	$3.4\times10^{-4}\,\dfrac{f_1}{d_1^4}$	$6.1\times10^{-4}\,\dfrac{f_1}{d_1^4}$	$34\times10^{-4}\,\dfrac{f_1}{d_1^4}$	$67\times10^{-4}\,\dfrac{f_1}{d_1^4}$
i_2	$1.7\times10^{4}\,\dfrac{f_2}{d_2^4}$	$11\times10^{4}\,\dfrac{f_2}{d_2^4}$	$20\times10^{4}\,\dfrac{f_2}{d_2^4}$	$110\times10^{4}\,\dfrac{f_2}{d_2^4}$	$220\times10^{4}\,\dfrac{f_2}{d_2^4}$

$i_1 = i_2$ = head loss in feet of oil per foot of pipe or metres of oil per metre of
   pipe. (Length of pipe to include allowances for bends, valves and
   fittings)
f_1 = flow of oil in gal/hr
f_2 = flow of oil in litre/s
d_1 = internal diameter of pipe in inches
d_2 = internal diameter of pipe in mm.

The above formulae are for laminar flow. Flow is laminar if Reynolds
Number (Re) is less than 1500. Reynolds number can be checked from the
following formulae. As Re is a dimensionless ratio it is the same in all
consistent systems of units. The coefficients in the following formulae
take into account the dimensions of f_1, d_1, f_2, d_2 respectively.

The viscosity to be taken is that at the temperature of the oil in the pipe.

Viscosity at temp in pipe cS	4.0	25	45	250	500
Re	$16\,\dfrac{f_1}{d_1}$	$2.5\,\dfrac{f_1}{d_1}$	$1.0\,\dfrac{f_1}{d_1}$	$0.25\,\dfrac{f_1}{d_1}$	$0.12\,\dfrac{f_1}{d_1}$
	$32\times10^{4}\,\dfrac{f_2}{d_2}$	$4.5\times10^{4}\,\dfrac{f_2}{d_2}$	$2.8\times10^{4}\,\dfrac{f_2}{d_2}$	$0.45\times10^{4}\,\dfrac{f_2}{d_2}$	$0.25\times10^{4}\,\dfrac{f_2}{d_2}$

Heat loss from oil tanks

Position	Oil temperature		Heat loss			
			Unlagged		Lagged	
	°F	°C	$\dfrac{Btu}{ft^2\,hr\,°F}$	$\dfrac{W}{m^2\,K}$	$\dfrac{Btu}{ft^2\,hr\,°F}$	$\dfrac{W}{m^2\,K}$
Sheltered	up to 50	up to 10	1.2	6.8	0.3	1.7
	50–80	10–27	1.3	7.4	0.325	1.8
	80–100	27–38	1.4	8.0	0.35	2.0
Exposed	up to 50	up to 10	1.4	8.0	0.35	2.0
	50–80	10–27	1.5	8.5	0.375	2.1
	80–100	27–38	1.6	9.0	0.4	2.25
In pit			Nil		Nil	

Heat transfer coefficients for coils are:
  Steam to oil: 11.3 W/m² °C   20 Btu/ft² hr °F
  Hot water to oil: 5.7 W/m² °C   10 Btu/ft² hr °F

Heat loss from oil pipes

Nominal bore	Oil temperature		Heat loss		Nominal bore	Oil temperature		Heat loss	
mm	°F	°C	$\dfrac{Btu}{hr\,ft\,°F}$	$\dfrac{W}{mK}$	mm	°F	°C	$\dfrac{Btu}{hr\,ft\,°F}$	$\dfrac{W}{mK}$
15	up to	up to	0.4	0.7	15	80	27	0.5	0.9
20	50	10	0.4	0.7	20	to	to	0.6	1.1
25			0.8	1.4	25	100	38	0.8	1.4
40			1.2	2.1	40			1.1	1.9
50			1.6	2.8	50			1.3	2.2
15	50	10	0.5	0.9					
20	to	to	0.6	1.1					
25	80	27	0.7	1.2					
40			1.0	1.7					
50			1.2	2.1					

Diagrammatic arrangement of oil storage tank

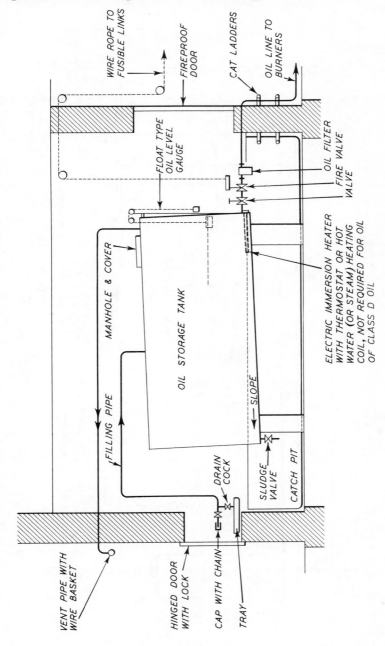

Diagrammatic arrangement of oil storage tank and day oil tank

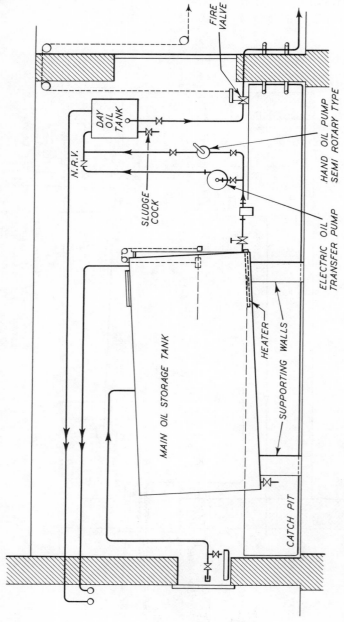

4 Heat and thermal properties of materials

Expansion by heat

Linear expansion is the increase in length
$$L_2 = L_1 (1 + et)$$

Surface expansion is the increase in area
$$A_2 = A_1 (1 + 2et)$$

Volumetric expansion is the increase in volume
$$V_2 = V_1 (1 + 3et)$$

where t = temperature difference   (K)
    L_1 = original length   (m)
    A_1 = original area   (m^2)
    V_1 = original volume   (m^3)
    L_2 = final length   (m)
    A_2 = final area   (m^2)
    V_2 = final volume   (m^3)
    e = coefficient of linear expansion (m/mK)

Sensible heat for heating or cooling

$$H = cM (t_2 - t_1)$$

where H = Heat   (J)
    M = mass   (kg)
    c = specific heat capacity (J/kg K)
    t_1 = initial temperature   (°C)
    t_2 = final temperature   (°C)

Expansion of gases

General gas law

$$PV = wRT$$

where P = pressure

V = volume

w = mass

T = absolute temperature

R = gas constant

$G = wR$ = univeral gas constant which is the same for all gases.

In various units,

G = 1.985 Btu/lb mol °F

   = 1.985 kcal/kg mol K

   = 8.314 kJ/kg mol K

At N.T.P. 1 kg mol occupies 22.4 m^3

            1 lb mol occupies 359 ft^3

Mixtures of gases

$$PV = w\, R_m\, T$$

$$w = w_1 + w_2 + w_3$$

$$R_m = \frac{R_1\, w_1 + R_2\, w_2 + R_3\, w_3}{w_1 + w_2 + w_3} = \text{gas constant of mixture}$$

Methods of heating and expanding gases (not vapours)

Type of expansion	Re-marks	Work done W	Change of internal energy E	Heat absorbed H	Final temp.
Constant pressure	Isobar	$P(V_2-V_1)$	$M C_v (T_2-T_1)$	$M C_p (T_2-T_1)$	$T_1 \dfrac{V_2}{V_1}$
Constant temperature	Isotherm	$P_1 V_1 \log_e \dfrac{V_2}{V_1}$	0	$P_1 V_1 \log_e \dfrac{V_2}{V_1}$	T_1
Constant heat	Adiabatic PV^γ=const.	$\dfrac{P_1 V_1 - P_2 V_2}{\gamma-1}$	$M C_v (T_2-T_1)$	0	$T_1 \left(\dfrac{V_1}{V_2}\right)^{\gamma-1}$
Int. energy & temp. change	Polytrope PV^n=const.	$\dfrac{P_1 V_1 - P_2 V_2}{n-1}$	$M C_v (T_2-T_1)$	$W+E$	$T_1 \left(\dfrac{V_1}{V_2}\right)^{n-1}$

where W = external work done by gas (kJ)
E = increase of internal energy by gas (kJ)
H = total heat absorbed (kJ)
P_1, P_2 = initial, final, pressure (N/m^2)
V_1, V_2 = initial, final, volume (m^3)

T_1, T_2 = initial, final, temperature (°C)
M = mass (kg)
$\gamma = \dfrac{C_p}{C_v}$ dimensionless
n = index of expansion law dimensionless

C_v = specific heat capacity at constant volume (kJ/kg K)
C_p = specific heat capacity of constant pressure (kJ/kg K)

The laws of perfect gases

The Critical Temperature of a substance is that temperature above which it cannot exist as a liquid.

The Critical Pressure is the pressure of a saturated vapour at its critical temperature.

Critical temperatures and pressures of various substances

Substance	Critical temperature °F	°C	Critical pressure absolute lb./sq. in.	atm.	Boiling temp. at atm. pres. °F.	°C.
Air	−220	−140	573	39	—	—
Alcohol (C_2H_6O)	421	216	956	65	172.4	78
Ammonia (NH_3)	266	130	1691	115	−27.4	−33
Benzol (C_6H_6)	554	292	735	50	176	80
Carbon-dioxide (CO_2)	88.2	31	1132	77	−110	−79
Carbon-monoxide (CO)	−222	−141	528	35.9	−310	−190
Ether ($C_4H_{10}O$)	381.2	194	544	37	95	35
Hydrogen (H)	−402	−242	294	20	−423	−253
Nitrogen (N)	−236	−149	514	35	−321	−195
Oxygen (O_2)	−180	−118	735	50	−297	−183
Water (H_2O)	706–716	375–380	3200	217.8	212	100

(From Mark's Mech. Eng. Hand.)

Estimations of temperatures of incandescent bodies

Colours of different temperatures

Faint red	960°F	516°C
Dull red	1290°F	700°C
Brilliant red	1470°F	750°C
Cherry red	1650°F	900°C
Bright cherry red	1830°F	1000°C
Orange	2010°F	1100°C
Bright orange	2190°F	1200°C
White heat	2370°F	1300°C
Bright white heat	2550°F	1400°C
Brilliant white heat	2750°F	1500°C

Heat transfer

Transfer of heat may occur by

1 Conduction
2 Convection
3 Radiation

1 **Conduction** is the transfer of heat through the molecules of a substance.

   (a) Internal Conduction is transmission within a body.

   (b) External Conduction is transmission from one body to another, when the two bodies are in contact.

Thermal Conductivity is the heat flowing through one unit of area and one unit of thickness in one unit of time per degreee temperature difference.

Thermal Conductance is the heat flowing through a structural component of unit area in unit time per degree temperature difference between its faces.

$$H=\frac{AK(t_2-t_1)}{X}=AC(t_2-t_1)$$

$$C=\frac{K}{X}$$

where H = heat flow   W   (Btu/hr)
  A = area m^2 (ft^2)
  K = thermal conductivity   W/mK   (Btu in/hr ft^2 °F)
  C = thermal conductance   W/m^2 K   (Btu/hr ft^2 °F)
  X = thickness   m   (in)
  t_1 = temperature at cooler section °C   (°F)
  t_2 = temperature at hotter section °C   (°F)

Thermal Resistance is the reciprocal of thermal conductance

$$H=\frac{t_2-t_1}{AR}$$ W   (Btu/hr)

$$R=\frac{1}{C}=\frac{X}{K}$$ $\dfrac{m^2\,K}{W}$ $\dfrac{hr\;ft^2\;°F}{Btu}$

2 **Convection** is the transfer of heat by flow of currents within a fluid body. (Liquid or gas flowing over the surface of a hotter or cooler body.)

$$H=aA(t_2-t_1)=\frac{t_2-t_1}{AR_1}\text{ (Btu/hr or watts)}$$

   a = Thermal conductance (Btu/hr sq ft °F or W/m^2 °C)

$$R_1=\frac{1}{aX}=\text{Thermal resistance.}$$

The amount of heat transferred per unit of time is affected by the velocity of moving medium, the area and form of surface and the temp. difference.

3 Radiation is the transfer of heat from one body to another by wave motion.

Stephan-Baltzmann Formula

$$E = C\left(\frac{T}{100}\right)^4$$

E = Heat emission of a body   Btu/hr or Watts
T = Absolute temperature   °R or °K
C = Radiation constant

Quantities of heat transferred between two surfaces:

$$Q_{Rad} = CA\left[\left(\frac{T_1}{100}\right)^4 - \left(\frac{T_2}{100}\right)^4\right]$$

A = Area
$T_1 T_2$ = Absolute temperatures of hot and cold surfaces respectively.

For the absolute black body

C = 5.72   Watts per sq m per (deg C)^4
  = 0.173 Btu per hr per sq ft per (deg F)^4

For other materials see table below.

Radiation constant of building material (C)

	$\dfrac{W}{m^2\,(°C)^4}$	$\dfrac{Btu}{hr\,ft^2\,(°F)^4}$		$\dfrac{W}{m^2\,(°C)^4}$	$\dfrac{Btu}{hr\,ft^2\,(°F)^4}$		$\dfrac{W}{m^2\,(°C)^4}$	$\dfrac{Btu}{hr\,ft^2\,(°F)^4}$
Black body	5.72	0.173	Sand	4.20	0.127	Cast iron, rough		
Cotton	4.23	0.128	Shavings	4.10	0.124	oxidized	5.09	0.154
Glass	5.13	0.155	Silk	4.30	0.130	Copper,		
Wood	4.17	0.126	Water	3.70	0.112	polished	1.19	0.028
Brick	5.16	0.156	Wool	4.30	0.130	Brass, dull	0.152	0.036
Oil paint	4.30	0.130	Wrought iron,			Silver	1.19	0.0046
Paper	4.43	0.134	dull oxidised	5.16	0.156	Zinc, dull	0.152	0.036
Plaster	5.16	0.156	Wrought iron,			Tin	0.26	0.0077
Lamp black	5.16	0.156	polished	1.55	0.047			

Conduction of heat through pipes or partitions

Symbols
t_m = Logarithmic mean temperature difference
t_{a1} = Initial temperature of heating medium
t_{a2} = Final temperature of heating medium
t_1 = Initial temperature of heated fluid
t_2 = Final temperature of heated fluid.

The heat exchange can be classified as follows:

1 **Parallel Flow,** the fluids flow in the same directions over the separating wall.

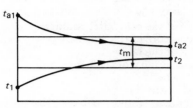

$$t_m = \frac{t_{a1} - t_{a2} + t_2 - t_1}{\log_e \frac{t_{a1} - t_1}{t_{a2} - t_2}} = \frac{\text{Initial temp. dif.} - \text{Final temp. dif.}}{2.3 \log_{10} \frac{\text{Initial temp. dif.}}{\text{Final temp. dif.}}}$$

2 **Counter Flow,** the directions are opposite.

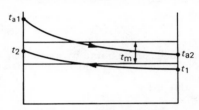

$$t_m = (\text{as before}) = \frac{\text{Initial temp. dif.} - \text{Final temp. dif.}}{2.3 \log_{10} \frac{\text{Initial temp. dif.}}{\text{Final temp. dif.}}}$$

3 **Evaporators or Condensers**
One fluid remains at a constant temperature while changing its state.

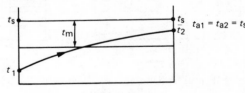

$$t_m = (\text{as before}) = \frac{(t_1 - t_2)}{\log_1 \frac{t_s - t_2}{t_s - t_1}}$$

4 **Mixed Flow**
One of the fluids takes an irregular direction with respect to the other.

$$t_m = \frac{t_{a1} - t_{a2}}{2} - \frac{t_1 - t_2}{2}$$

Heat transfer in the unsteady state

Newton's Law of cooling. In the warming and cooling of bodies, the heat gain or loss respectively, is proportional to the difference between the temperatures of the body and the surroundings.

Let: t_s = Temperature of the cold surroundings
t_1 = Initial temperature of the hot body
t_2 = Temperature of the body
C = Thermal conductivity of the body
P = Density of the body
S = Specific heat of the body
U = Coefficient of heat transfer between the body and the surroundings
R = Radius of a sphere or cylinder, or half thickness of a slab cooled or heated on both faces. Thickness of a slab cooled or heated on one face only
$\theta = (\theta_1 - \theta_2)$ = Cooling time.

Then $\dfrac{t_2 - t_s}{t_1 - t_s} = e^{-K\theta}$

and $\log_e (t_2 - t_s) - \log_e (t_1 - t_s) = -K\theta$.

where K = Constant which can be found by measuring the temperatures of the body at different times θ_1 and θ_2 and which is

$$K = \log_e \frac{t_2 - t_s}{t_1 - t_s} \div (\theta_1 - \theta_2).$$

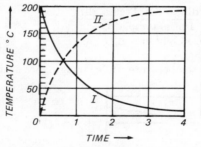 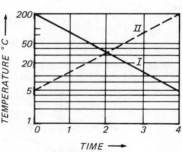

Cooling curve (I) and heating curve (II) showing relation of temperature and time on linear and semi-logarithmic paper.

Graphs showing how the temperature of cooling or heating up bodies can be plotted on semi-logarithmic paper by introducing the following dimensionless ratios

$$Y=\frac{t_s-t_1}{t_s-t_2}, \qquad X=\frac{c\theta}{psR^2}, \qquad m=\frac{c}{UR}$$

The Increased Heat Loss of Buildings during the heating up period causes a greater heat requirement than the steady state. This additional heat loss depends mainly on the type of building, length of heating interruption and heating up time, and type of heating installation. The allowance for covering the increased heat loss during heating up is usually expressed as a percentage of the heat loss in the steady state.

See pages 102 and 103.

The temperatures during warming up of bodies are represented graphically by curves which are symmetrical to cooling down curves.

Logarithmic mean temperature differences

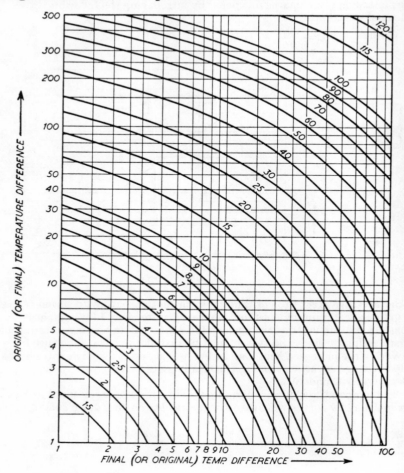

Example of using the chart
Water to water calorifier with counter flow
Primary flow temperature 80°C. Secondary return temperature 10°C
Primary return temperature 70°C. Secondary flow temperature 40°C
Original temperature difference=80–70=10°C
Final temperature difference=70–40=30°C
From chart: Log mean temp. diff.=18°C
The chart can be used equally well for °C or °F.

Transmission of heat

Heat transmission coefficients for metals

			$\dfrac{Watts}{m.^2 deg. C}$	$\dfrac{Btu}{ft^2 hr\ °F}$
Water	Cast iron	Air or Gas	8.0	1.4
Water	Mild steel	Air or Gas	11.0	2.0
Water	Copper	Air or Gas	11.0	2.25
Water	Cast iron	Water	220 to 280	40 to 50
Water	Mild steel	Water	340 to 400	50 to 70
Water	Copper	Water	350 to 450	62 to 80
Air	Cast iron	Air	6.0	1.0
Air	Mild steel	Air	8.0	1.4
Steam	Cast iron	Air	11.0	2.0
Steam	Mild steel	Air	11.0	2.5
Steam	Copper	Air	17.0	3.0
Steam	Cast iron	Water	900	160
Steam	Mild steel	Water	1050	185
Steam	Copper	Water	1170	205

The above values are average coefficients for practically still fluids. The coefficients are dependent on velocities of heating and heated media — on type of heating surface, temperature difference, and other circumstances. For special cases, see literature and manufacturers' data.

Table of $n^{1.3}$ for radiator and pipe coefficients in relation to various temperature differences.

n	$n^{1.3}$	n	$n^{1.3}$	n	$n^{1.3}$	n	$n^{1.3}$	n	$n^{1.3}$	n	$n^{1.3}$
30	83	70	250	110	450	150	674	190	917	230	1176
35	102	75	273	115	477	155	704	195	948	235	1209
40	121	80	298	120	505	160	733	200	980	240	1242
45	141	85	322	125	533	165	763	205	1012	245	1219
50	162	90	347	130	560	170	793	210	1044	250	1310
55	183	95	372	135	589	175	824	215	1075		
60	205	100	398	140	617	180	855	220	1110		
65	226	105	424	145	645	185	887	225	1142		

Heat loss of steel pipes

For various water temperatures and steam pressures

Nominal bore		Heat loss W/m for fluid inside pipe						Heat loss Btu/h ft for fluid inside pipe					
		Water				Steam		Water				Steam	
in	mm	50°C	60°C	75°C	100°C	1 bar	4 bar	120°F	140°F	170°F	212°F	15 psig	60 psig
½	15	30	40	60	90	130	190	30	40	60	95	135	200
¾	20	35	50	70	110	160	220	35	50	75	115	170	230
1	25	40	60	90	130	190	270	40	60	90	135	200	280
1¼	32	50	70	110	160	230	330	50	70	110	165	240	340
1½	40	55	80	120	180	250	370	55	80	130	190	260	380
2	50	65	95	150	220	310	440	65	90	150	230	320	460
2½	65	80	120	170	260	360	530	80	120	180	270	380	550
3	80	100	140	210	300	440	630	100	140	220	310	460	650
4	100	120	170	260	380	550	800	120	170	270	390	570	830
6	150	170	250	370	540	770	1100	170	250	380	560	800	1150

Correction factors for use with above table

Single pipe along skirting or riser	1.0	More than one pipe along ceiling	0.65
More than one pipe along skirting or riser	0.90	Single pipe freely exposed	1.1
Single pipe along ceiling	0.75	More than one pipe freely exposed	1.0

Heat loss of steel pipes

For high temperature difference (MPHW and HPHW)
For various temperature differences between pipe and air

Nominal bore mm	Heat loss for temperature difference (W/m)							
	110°C	125°C	140°C	150°C	165°C	195°C	225°C	280°C
15	130	155	180	205	235	280	375	575
20	160	190	220	255	290	370	465	660
25	200	235	275	305	355	455	565	815
32	240	290	330	375	435	555	700	1000
40	270	320	375	420	485	625	790	1120
50	330	395	465	520	600	770	975	1390
65	390	465	540	615	715	910	1150	1650
80	470	560	650	740	860	1090	1380	1980
100	585	700	820	925	1065	1370	1740	2520
150	815	970	1130	1290	1470	1910	2430	3500
200	1040	1240	1440	1650	1900	2440	3100	4430
250	1250	1510	1750	1995	2300	2980	3780	5600
300	1470	1760	2060	2340	2690	3370	4430	6450

Nominal bore in	Heat loss for temperature difference (Btu/hr/ft)							
	200°F	225°F	250°F	275°F	300°F	350°F	400°F	500°F
$\frac{1}{2}$	140	160	190	215	245	310	390	595
$\frac{3}{4}$	170	200	230	270	305	380	475	680
1	210	245	285	325	370	470	580	840
$1\frac{1}{4}$	265	300	345	400	460	565	715	1035
$1\frac{1}{2}$	290	335	390	450	510	650	815	1160
2	350	410	480	550	630	800	1000	1460
$2\frac{1}{2}$	430	490	560	650	750	880	1190	1700
3	580	655	670	780	900	1130	1410	2040
4	620	730	850	825	1120	1420	1790	2600
6	860	1010	1170	1360	1540	1980	2700	3600
8	1090	1390	1480	1740	2000	2540	3180	4610
10	1320	1535	1810	2100	2425	3100	3900	5700
12	1530	1835	2125	2460	2830	3500	4950	6650

Heat loss of copper pipes

For various temperature differences between pipe and air

Nominal bore		Heat loss for temperature difference (W/m)			Heat loss for temperature difference (Btu/hr ft)		
in	mm	40°C	55°C	72°C	70°F	100°F	130°F
$\frac{1}{2}$	15	21	32	45	22	34	47
$\frac{3}{4}$	22	28	43	60	29	45	53
1	28	34	53	76	36	56	79
$1\frac{1}{4}$	35	41	64	89	43	67	93
$1\frac{1}{2}$	42	47	74	104	49	77	108
2	54	59	93	131	62	97	136
$2\frac{1}{2}$	67	71	111	156	74	116	162
3	76	83	129	181	87	135	189
4	108	107	165	232	111	172	241

Heat loss of insulated copper pipes

For temperature difference 55°C (100°F)
For 25 mm thick insulation with $k = 0.043$ W/m°C (0.3 Btu in/ft^2 hr °F)

Nominal bore		Heat loss		Nominal bore		Heat loss	
in	mm	W/m	Btu/hr ft	in	mm	W/m	Btu/hr ft
$\frac{3}{4}$	22	8	8	2	54	14.5	15
1	28	10	10	$2\frac{1}{2}$	67	16	17
$1\frac{1}{2}$	42	11.5	12	3	76	19	20

Heat loss through lagging

Insulating material	Heat loss through 75 mm thickness per 55 K difference between faces W/m^2
Asbestos	75
Cork	32
Sawdust	54

Loss for bare metal for 55 K difference is approximately 485 W/m^2

Densities

	kg/m^3	lb/ft^3
Metals		
Aluminium	2690	168
Antimony	6690	417
Brass, cast	8100	505
Bronze, gunmetal	8450	529
Copper	8650	551
Gold, pure, cast	19 200	1200
Iron, cast	7480	467
Iron, wrought	7850	486
Lead	11 340	705
Mercury	13 450	840
Nickel	8830	551
Platinum	21 450	1340
Silver	10 500	655
Steel	7900	493
Tin	7280	455
Zinc	7200	444
Solids		
Asbestos	3060	191
Asphalt	1650	103
Brick	1000–2000	62–134
Cement, Portland	3000	187
Cement, Roman	1550	97
Chalk	1500–2800	95–175
Coal	1500–1650	95–103
Coke	1000	62
Concrete, mean	2240	140
Dowtherm	880–1073	55–67
Glass, window	2640	164
Granite	2130	133
Gypsum	2165	135
Ice, at 0°C	910	57
Lime	2740	171

	kg/m^3	lb/ft^3
Limestone	3170	198
Marble	2650	165
Mortar	1400–1750	86–109
Peat	600–1330	37–83
Plaster	1180	73
Porcelain	2300	143
Rubber	920	67
Salt, common	2130	133
Soap	1070	67
Starch	945	59
Sulphur	2020	126
Wax, paraffin	930	58
Wood	700–900	44–56
Liquids		
Acetic acid	1049	66
Alcohol	790	49
Ammonia	610	38
Beer	1030	64
Ether	870	54
Glycerine	1270	79
Oil, mineral	850	53
Oil, vegetable	920	57
Milk	1030	64
Paraffin	810	50
Petrol	700–750	44–47
Turpentine	870	54
Water, distilled	1000	62
Water, sea, 4°C	1030	64

Specific heat capacities of gases

Gas	Formula	Specific heat capacity Btu/lb °F		Specific heat capacity kJ/kg K		$\gamma = C_p/C_v$	Gas constant $=(C_p - C_v)$	
		C_p	C_v	C_p	C_v		ft lb / lb °F	kJ / kg K
Acetylene	C_2H_2	0.350	0.270	1.47	1.13	1.28	59.34	0.34
Air	—	0.251	0.171	1.01	0.716	1.40	53.34	0.29
Ammonia	NH_3	0.523	0.399	2.19	1.67	1.31	96.50	0.52
Blast furnace gas	—	0.245	0.174	1.03	0.729	1.40	55.05	0.297
Carbon dioxide	CO^2	0.210	0.160	0.827	0.632	1.31	38.86	0.189
Carbon monoxide	CO	0.243	0.172	1.02	0.720	1.41	55.14	0.297
Combustion products	—	0.24	—	1.01	—	—	—	—
Ethylene	C_2H_4	0.400	0.330	1.67	1.38	1.20	55.08	0.29
Hydrogen	H_2	3.42	2.44	14.24	10.08	1.40	765.90	4.16
Methane	CH_4	0.593	0.450	2.23	1.71	1.32	111.31	0.60
Nitrogen	N_2	0.247	0.176	1.034	0.737	1.40	54.99	0.297
Oxygen	O^2	0.219	0.157	0.917	0.656	1.40	48.24	0.260
Sulphur dioxide	SO_2	0.154	0.123	0.645	0.515	1.25	24.10	0.130

Density of gases

Gas	Molecular weight	Density at 0°C and atmospheric pressure	
		kg/m^3	lb/ft^3
Acetylene	26	1.170	0.0729
Air	—	1.293	0.0806
Ammonia	17	0.769	0.0480
Blast furnace gas	—	1.250	0.0780
Carbon dioxide	44	1.977	0.1234
Carbon monoxide	28	1.250	0.0780
Combustion products	—	1.11	0.069
Ethylene	28	1.260	0.0786
Hydrogen	2	0.0899	0.0056
Methane	16	0.717	0.0447
Nitrogen	28	1.250	0.0780
Oxygen	32	1.429	0.0892
Sulphur dioxide	64	2.926	0.1828

Specific heat capacities between 0°C and 100°C

Metals	kJ/kg K	Btu/lb °F		kJ/kg K	Btu/lb °F
			Ice	2.11	0.504
Aluminium	0.912	0.218	India rubber	1.1–4.1	0.27–0.98
Antimony	0.214	0.051	Limestone	0.84	0.20
Copper	0.389	0.093			
			Marble	0.88	0.21
Gold	0.130	0.031	Peat	1.88	0.45
Iron	0.460	0.110	Plaster	0.84	0.20
Lead	0.130	0.031			
			Porcelain	1.07	0.255
Mercury	0.138	0.033	Sand	0.82	0.19
Nickel	0.452	0.108	Sulphur	0.72	0.17
Platinum	0.134	0.032	Wood	2.3–2.7	0.55–0.65
Silver	0.234	0.056	**Liquids**		
Tin	0.230	0.055	Acetic acid	2.13	0.51
Zinc	0.393	0.094	Alcohol	2.93	0.70
			Ammonia	0.47	0.11
Metal alloys					
Ball metal	0.360	0.086	Benzol	1.80	0.43
Brass	0.377	0.090	Dowtherm	1.55	0.37
Bronze	0.435	0.104	Ether	2.10	0.50
Nickel steel	0.456	0.109	Ethylene glycol	2.38	0.57
Solder	0.167	0.04	Glycerine	2.41	0.58
			Milk	3.93	0.94
Solids					
Asbestos	0.84	0.20	Naphtholene	1.78	0.43
Ashes	0.84	0.20	Oil, mineral	1.67	0.40
Asphalt	0.80	0.19	Oil, vegetable	1.68	0.40
Brick	0.92	0.22	Paraffin	2.14	0.51
Carbon	0.71	0.17	Petroleum	2.09	0.50
Coke	0.85	0.203	Sulphuric acid	1.38	0.33
Coal	1.31	0.314	Turpentine	1.98	0.47
Concrete	1.13	0.27	Water, fresh	4.19	1.00
Cork	2.03	0.485	Water, sea	3.94	0.94
Glass	0.84	0.20			
Granite	0.75	0.18			
Graphite	0.71	0.17			

Boiling points at atmospheric pressure

	°C	°F		°C	°F
Alcohol	78	172.4	Hydrogen	-253	-423
Ammonia	-33.4	-28.1	Nitrogen	-196	-320
Aniline	184	363	Oxygen	-183	-297
Carbon dioxide	-78.5	-109.3	Sulphur	440	823
Dowtherm	258	496	Toluene	111	230
Ether	35	95	Turpentine	160	320
			Water	100	212
Glycerine	290	554			
Helium	-269	-452			

Latent heats of vaporisation

	kJ/kg	Btu/lb		kJ/kg	Btu/lb
Alcohol	896	385	Hydrogen	461	198
Ammonia	1369	589	Nitrogen	199	86
Anilene	450	193	Oxygen	214	92
Carbon dioxide	574	247	Sulphur	1510	650
Ether	377	162	Toluene	351	151
Helium	21	9	Turpentine	293	126
			Water	2257	970.4

Melting and solidifying points at atmospheric pressure

	°C	°F		°C	°F
Alcohol	-97	-143	Lead	327	621
Aluminium	658	1218	Mercury	-39	-38
Ammonia	-78	-108	Nickel	1455	2646
Aniline	-6	21	Silver	960	1761
Carbon dioxide	-56	-69	Sulphur	106-119	234-247
Copper	1083	1981	Tin	232	449
Dowtherm	12	54	Water	0	32
Glycerine	-16	4	Wax	64	149
Gold	1063	1945	Zinc	419	787
Iron, pure	1530	2786			

Latent heats of melting

	kJ/kg	Btu/lb		kJ/kg	Btu/lb
Aluminium	321	138.2	Lead	22.4	9.65
Ammonia	339	146	Mercury	11.8	5.08
Anilene	113.5	48.8	Nickel	19.4	8.35
Carbon dioxide	184	79	Silver	88.0	37.9
Copper	176	75.6	Sulphur	39.2	16.87
Glycerine	176	75.6	Tin	58.5	25.2
Iron, grey cast	96	41.4	Water	334	144
Iron, white cast	138	59.4	Zinc	118	50.63
Iron slag	209	90.0			

Coefficients of linear expansion Average values between 0°C and 100°C

	$\dfrac{m}{m\,K}\times 10^6$	$\dfrac{in}{in\,°F}\times 10^6$		$\dfrac{m}{m\,K}\times 10^6$	$\dfrac{in}{in\,°F}\times 10^6$
Aluminium	22.2	12.3	Lead	28.0	15.1
Antimony	10.4	5.8	Marble	12	6.5
Brass	18.7	10.4	Masonry	4.5–9.0	2.5–9.0
Brick	5.5	3.1	Mortar	7.3–13.5	4.1–7.5
Bronze	18.0	10.0	Nickel	13.0	7.2
Cement	10.0	6.0	Plaster	25	13.9
Concrete	14.5	8.0	Porcelain	3.0	1.7
Copper	16.5	9.3	Rubber	77	42.8
Glass, hard	5.9	3.3	Silver	19.5	10.7
Glass, plate	9.0	5.0	Solder	24.0	13.4
Gold	14.2	8.2	Steel, nickel	13.0	7.3
Graphite	7.9	4.4	Type metal	19.0	10.8
Iron, pure	12.0	6.7	Wood, oak parallel to grain	4.9	2.7
Iron, cast	10.4	5.9	Wood, oak across grain	5.4	3.0
Iron, forged	11.3	6.3	Zinc	29.7	16.5

Thermal properties of water

Temp. °F	Abs. pressure lb/in²	Density lb/ft³	Specific gravity	Specific volume ft³/lb	Specific heat Btu/ lb °F	Entropy Btu/ lb °F	Absolute viscosity in poises	Total heat Btu/lb
32	0.088	62.42	1.000	0.0160	1.0093	0.0000	0.0179	0
40	0.122	62.42	1.000	0.0160	1.0048	0.01615	0.0155	8
50	0.178	62.42	1.000	0.0160	1.0015	0.03595	0.0131	18
60	0.256	62.38	1.000	0.0160	0.9995	0.05765	0.0113	28
62	0.275	62.35	1.000	0.0160	0.9992	0.05919	0.0110	30
70	0.363	62.30	0.999	0.0160	0.9982	0.0754	0.0098	38
80	0.507	62.22	0.998	0.0160	0.9975	0.0929	0.0086	48
90	0.698	62.11	0.996	0.0161	0.9971	0.1112	0.0076	58
100	0.949	61.99	0.994	0.0161	0.9970	0.1292	0.0068	68
110	1.27	61.86	0.992	0.0161	0.9971	0.1469	0.0062	78
120	1.69	61.71	0.990	0.0162	0.9974	0.1641	0.0056	88
130	2.22	61.55	0.987	0.0162	0.9978	0.1816	0.0051	98
140	2.89	61.38	0.984	0.0163	0.9984	0.1981	0.0047	108
150	3.72	61.20	0.982	0.0163	0.9990	0.2147	0.0043	118
160	4.74	61.00	0.979	0.0164	0.9988	0.2309	0.0040	128
170	5.99	60.80	0.975	0.0164	1.0007	0.2472	0.0037	138
180	7.51	60.58	0.971	0.0165	1.0017	0.2629	0.00345	148
190	9.33	60.36	0.969	0.0166	1.0028	0.2787	0.00323	158
200	11.53	60.12	0.965	0.0166	1.0039	0.2938	0.00302	168
210	14.13	59.92	0.958	0.0167	1.0052	0.3089	0.00287	178
212	14.70	59.88	0.957	0.0167	1.0055	0.3118	0.00285	180
220	17.19	59.66	0.955	0.0168	1.0068	0.3237	0.00272	188.1
230	20.77	59.37	0.950	0.0168	1.0087	0.3385	0.00257	198.2
240	24.97	59.17	0.946	0.0169	1.0104	0.3531	0.00254	208.3
250	29.81	58.84	0.941	0.0170	1.0126	0.3676	0.00230	218.4
260	35.42	58.62	0.940	0.0171	1.0148	0.3818	0.00217	228.6
270	41.85	58.25	0.933	0.0172	1.0174	0.3962	0.00208	238.7
280	49.18	58.04	0.929	0.0172	1.0200	0.4097	0.00200	248.9
290	57.55	57.65	0.923	0.0173	1.0230	0.4236	0.00193	259.2
300	67.00	57.41	0.920	0.0174	1.0260	0.4272	0.00186	262.5
310	77.67	57.00	0.913	0.0175	1.0296	0.4507	0.00179	279.8
320	89.63	56.65	0.906	0.0177	1.0332	0.4643	0.00173	290.2
330	103.00	56.31	0.900	0.0178	1.0368	0.4777	0.00168	300.6
340	118.0	55.95	0.897	0.0179	1.0404	0.4908	0.00163	311.1
350	134.6	55.65	0.890	0.0180	1.0440	0.5040	0.00158	321.7
360	153.0	55.19	0.883	0.0181	1.0486	0.5158	0.00153	332.3
370	173.3	54.78	0.876	0.0182	1.0532	0.5292	0.00149	342.9
380	195.6	54.36	0.870	0.0184	1.0578	0.5420	0.00145	353.5
390	220.2	53.96	0.865	0.0187	1.0624	0.5548	0.00141	364.3
400	247.1	53.62	0.834	0.0186	1.0670	0.5677	0.00137	375.3
450	422	51.3	0.821	0.0195	1.0950	0.6298	—	430.2
500	679	48.8	0.781	0.0205	1.1300	0.6907	—	489.1
550	1043	45.7	0.730	0.0219	1.2000	0.7550	—	553.5
600	1540	41.5	0.666	0.0241	1.3620	0.8199	—	623.2
706.1	3226	19.2	0.307	0.0522	—	1.0785	—	925.0

Thermal properties of water

Temp °C	Abs pressure kN/m²	Density kg/m³	Specific volume m³/kg	Specific heat capacity kJ/kg K	Specific entropy kJ/kg K	Dynamic viscosity centipoise	Specific enthalpy kJ/kg
0	0.6	1000	0.00100	4.217	0	1.78	0
5	0.9	1000	0.00100	4.204	0.075	1.52	21.0
10	1.2	1000	0.00100	4.193	0.150	1.31	41.9
15	1.7	999	0.00100	4.186	0.223	1.14	62.9
20	2.3	990	0.00100	4.182	0.296	1.00	83.8
25	3.2	997	0.00100	4.181	0.367	0.890	104.8
30	4.3	996	0.00100	4.179	0.438	0.798	125.7
35	5.6	994	0.00101	4.178	0.505	0.719	146.7
40	7.7	991	0.00101	4.179	0.581	0.653	167.6
45	9.6	990	0.00101	4.181	0.637	0.596	188.6
50	12.5	988	0.00101	4.182	0.707	0.547	209.6
55	15.7	986	0.00101	4.183	0.767	0.504	230.5
60	20.0	980	0.00102	4.185	0.832	0.467	251.5
65	25.0	979	0.00102	4.188	0.893	0.434	272.4
70	31.3	978	0.00102	4.190	0.966	0.404	293.4
75	38.6	975	0.00103	4.194	0.016	0.378	314.3
80	47.5	971	0.00103	4.197	1.076	0.355	335.3
85	57.8	969	0.00103	4.203	1.134	0.334	356.2
90	70.0	962	0.00104	4.205	1.192	0.314	377.2
95	84.5	962	0.00104	4.213	1.250	0.297	398.1
100	101.33	962	0.00104	4.216	1.307	0.281	419.1
105	121	955	0.00105	4.226	1.382	0.267	440.2
110	143	951	0.00105	4.233	1.418	0.253	461.3
115	169	947	0.00106	4.240	1.473	0.241	482.5
120	199	943	0.00106	4.240	1.527	0.230	503.7
125	228	939	0.00106	4.254	1.565	0.221	524.3
130	270	935	0.00107	4.270	1.635	0.212	546.3
135	313	931	0.00107	4.280	1.687	0.204	567.7
140	361	926	0.00108	4.290	1.739	0.196	588.7
145	416	922	0.00108	4.300	1.790	0.190	610.0
150	477	918	0.00109	4.310	1.842	0.185	631.8
155	543	912	0.00110	4.335	1.892	0.180	653.8
160	618	907	0.00110	4.350	1.942	0.174	674.5
165	701	902	0.00111	4.364	1.992	0.169	697.3
170	792	897	0.00111	4.380	2.041	0.163	718.1
175	890	893	0.00112	4.389	2.090	0.158	739.8
180	1000	887	0.00113	4.420	2.138	0.153	763.1
185	1120	882	0.00113	4.444	2.187	0.149	785.3
190	1260	876	0.00114	4.460	2.236	0.145	807.5
195	1400	870	0.00115	4.404	2.282	0.141	829.9
200	1550	863	0.00116	4.497	2.329	0.138	851.7
225	2550	834	0.00120	4.648	2.569	0.121	966.8
250	3990	800	0.00125	4.867	2.797	0.110	1087
275	5950	756	0.00132	5.202	3.022	0.0972	1211
300	8600	714	0.00140	5.769	3.256	0.0897	1345
325	12 130	654	0.00153	6.861	3.501	0.0790	1494
350	16 540	575	0.00174	10.10	3.781	0.0648	1672
360	18 680	526	0.00190	14.60	3.921	0.0582	1764

Properties of water

Density: At 4°C 1 litre=1 kg
At 62°F 1 gal=10 lb

Freezing temperature	0°C	32°F
Boiling temperature	100°C	212°F
Latent heat of melting	334 kJ/kg	144 Btu/lb
Latent heat of evaporation	2,270 kJ/kg	977 Btu/lb
Critical temperature	380–386°C	706–716°F
Critical pressure	23,520 kN/m^2	3,200 lb/in^2

Specific heat capacity

water	4.187 kJ/kg K	1.00 Btu/lb °F
ice	2.108 kJ/kg K	0.504 Btu/lb °F
water vapour	1.996 kJ/kg K	0.477 Btu/lb °F

Thermal expansion

From 4°C to 100°C water expands by $\frac{1}{24}$ of its original volume.

Bulk modulus of elasticity   2,068,500 kN/m^2
300,000 lb/in^2

5 Properties of steam and air

Properties of steam and other vapours

A **vapour** is any substance in the gaseous state which does not even approximately follow the general gas laws.

Highly superheated vapours are gases, if the superheat is sufficiently great, and they then approximately follow the general gas law.

Conditions of vapours

1 **Dry Saturated vapour** is free from unvaporized liquid particles.

2 **Wet Saturated vapour** carries liquid globules in suspension.

3 **Superheated vapour** is vapour the temperature of which is higher than that of the boiling point corresponding to the pressure.

Dryness fraction or quality of saturated vapour (X) is the percentage of dry vapour present in the given amount of the wet saturated vapour.

$$X = \frac{W_s}{W_s + W_w} \times 100\%$$

W_s = Weight of dry steam in steam considered
W_w = Weight of water in steam

The heat of the liquid 'h' is the heat in Joules per kg required to raise the temperature of the liquid from $0\,°C$ to the temperature at which the liquid begins to boil at the given pressure.

$$h = ct$$

c = Mean specific heat capacity of water
t = Temperature of formation of steam at pressure considered $°C$

The latent heat of evaporation 'L' is the heat required to change a liquid at a given temperature and pressure into a vapour at the same temperature and pressure. It is divided into two parts

1 External latent heat of vapour = External work heat
2 Internal latent heat of vapour = Heat due to change of state

The total heat of a vapour (or enthalpy) is the amount of heat which must be supplied to 1 kg of the liquid which is at $0\,°C$ to convert it at constant pressure into vapour at the temperature and pressure considered.

Total heat of dry saturated vapour
$$H = h + L \text{ (Joules per kg)}$$
h = Heat of liquid at the temperature of the wet vapour, Joules per kg
L = Latent heat, Joules per kg

Total heat of wet saturated vapour
$$H_w = h + xL \text{ (Joules per kg)}$$
$\quad x$ = Dryness factor

Total heat of superheated vapour
$$H_s = h + L + c(t_s - t). \text{ (Joules per kg)}$$
c = Mean specific heat capacity of superheated vapour at the pressure and
degree of superheat considered
t_s = Temperature of superheat °C
t_1 = Temperature of formation of steam °C

Specific volumes of wet vapour
$$V_w = (1 - x) V + x V_D$$
$$\dot{V}_w = x V_D, \quad x = \frac{V_w}{V_D}, \text{ when } x = \text{very small}$$
V_w = Specific volume of the wet vapour, m³ per kg
V_D = Specific volume of dry saturated vapour of the same pressure, m³ per kg
(Can be found from the Vapour Tables).

Specific volume of superheated vapour
Approximate method by using Charles' Law
$$V = \frac{V_s T_s}{T_1}.$$

Entropy of steam

1 Entropy of water
Change of Entropy $= \log_e \dfrac{T_1}{T}$

T_1, T = Absolute temperature.

Entropy of water above freezing-point $= \phi_w = \log_e \dfrac{T_1}{273}$

2 Entropy of evaporation
Change of Entropy during evaporation $= \dfrac{dL}{T}$

Entropy of 1 kg of wet steam above freezing point
$$\phi_s = \phi_w + \frac{xL_1}{T_1}$$

3 Entropy of superheated steam
Change of entropy per kg of steam during superheating $= C_p \log_e \dfrac{T}{T_1}$

Total entropy of 1 kg of superheated steam above freezing point

$$=\phi_w+\frac{L_1}{T_1}+C_p \log_e \frac{T_s}{T_1}.$$

$L_1=$Latent heat of evaporation at T_1 °C absolute
$T_1=$Absolute temperature of evaporation
$T_s=$Absolute temperature of superheat.

Temperature — entropy diagram for steam

Shows the relationship between Pressure, Temperature, Dryness Fraction and Entropy.

When two of these factors are given the two others can be found on the chart.

The ordinates represent the Absolute Temperature and the Entropy.

The chart consists of the following lines:
1   Isothermal lines
2   Pressure lines
3   Lines of dryness fraction
4   Water line between water and steam
5   Dry steam lines
6   Constant volume lines

The total heat is given by the area, enclosed by absolute zero base water line and horizontal and vertical line from the respective points.

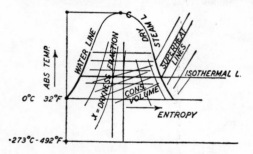

An adiabatic expansion is a vertical line (expansion at constant entropy, no transfer of heat).

$C=$Critical temperature of steam
= 706°F to 716°F
= 375°C to 380°C

Critical pressure: 3200 lb/in^2=217.8 atm=23,500 kN/m^2

Mollier or total heat — entropy chart

Contains the same lines as the temperature-entropy diagram, but with ordinates representing the total heat and entropy of steam. This diagram is used to find the drop in the total heat of steam during an adiabatic expansion.

Total heat of superheated steam (Btu per lb)

Abs. Pres. lb/in²	Sat. temp. °F	Degrees of Superheat °F						
		0	40	80	120	160	200	280
20	228	1157.1	1177.2	1197.2	1216.9	1236.6	1256.1	1294.9
30	250.3	1165.5	1185.9	1206.1	1226.1	1245.9	1265.6	1304.7
40	267.2	1171.6	1192.3	1212.9	1233.0	1253.0	1272.8	1312.2
50	280.9	1176.3	1197.3	1218.1	1238.5	1258.6	1278.5	1317.9
60	292.6	1180.1	1201.4	1222.2	1242.8	1263.1	1283.2	1322.9
70	302.8	1183.3	1204.7	1225.8	1246.6	1266.9	1287.2	1327.1
80	311.9	1186.1	1207.9	1229.1	1250.0	1270.5	1290.9	1330.8
90	320.2	1188.5	1210.5	1232.1	1253.0	1273.7	1294.0	1334.2
100	327.9	1190.7	1212.9	1234.6	1255.7	1276.5	1297.0	1337.3
120	341.3	1194.3	1216.9	1239.0	1260.4	1281.3	1302.0	1342.6
140	353.0	1197.2	1220.2	1242.5	1264.2	1285.5	1306.3	1347.1
160	363.6	1199.7	1222.9	1245.6	1267.6	1289.1	1310.0	1351.1
180	373.1	1201.7	1225.5	1248.3	1270.7	1292.2	1313.2	1354.6
200	381.8	1203.5	1227.6	1250.7	1273.1	1295.0	1316.2	1358.0
250	401.0	1207.0	1231.7	1255.7	1278.9	1301.2	1322.6	1364.9
300	417.4	1209.4	1235.0	1259.5	1283.2	1305.8	1327.6	1370.3
400	444.7	1212.1	1239.6	1265.4	1289.9	1313.3	1335.8	1379.6
500	467.1	1213.2	1242.2	1269.1	1294.7	1318.8	1341.9	1386.6

Entropy of superheated steam (Btu per °F per lb)

Abs. Pres. lb/in²	Sat. temp. °F	Degrees of Superheat °F						
		0	40	80	120	160	200	280
20	228	1.7333	1.7617	1.7883	1.8134	1.8372	1.8596	1.9017
30	250.3	1.7017	1.7298	1.7560	1.7807	1.8041	1.8261	1.8472
40	267.2	1.6793	1.7071	1.7331	1.7575	1.7806	1.8025	1.8233
50	280.9	1.6619	1.6895	1.7153	1.7397	1.7626	1.7843	1.8049
60	292.6	1.6477	1.6752	1.7010	1.7253	1.7480	1.7694	1.7899
70	302.8	1.6357	1.6632	1.6889	1.7130	1.7357	1.7570	1.7774
80	311.9	1.6254	1.6527	1.6784	1.7024	1.7251	1.7463	1.7665
90	320.2	1.6161	1.6436	1.6692	1.6931	1.7157	1.7367	1.7569
100	327.9	1.6079	1.6353	1.6608	1.6847	1.7073	1.7283	1.7484
120	341.3	1.5935	1.6210	1.6467	1.6705	1.6928	1.7138	1.7337
140	353.0	1.5813	1.6088	1.6345	1.6583	1.6805	1.7014	1.7212
160	363.6	1.5706	1.5983	1.6240	1.6479	1.6701	1.6909	1.7107
180	373.1	1.5610	1.5890	1.6148	1.6386	1.6607	1.6815	1.7013
200	381.8	1.5525	1.5806	1.6063	1.6301	1.6523	1.6730	1.6929
250	401.0	1.5342	1.5628	1.5886	1.6125	1.6347	1.6554	1.6751
300	417.4	1.5190	1.5479	1.5740	1.5980	1.6203	1.6410	1.6607
400	444.7	1.4941	1.5240	1.5506	1.5749	1.5973	1.6181	1.6379
500	467.1	1.4740	1.5049	1.5322	1.5568	1.5795	1.6004	1.6201

Properties of saturated steam

(Based on Callendar's Values)

Abs. Pres.	Temp.	Specific Volume	Density	Heat of			Entropy
				Liquid	Evap	Sat. Vap.	
p	t	v	w	h	L	H	S
$lb\ in^2$	$°F$	ft^3/lb	lb/ft^3	Btu/lb	Btu/lb	Btu/lb	$Btu/lb\ °F$
0.5	79.5	640.5	0.00156	47.4	1045	1092	2.0299
1	101.7	333.1	0.0030	69.5	1033	1102	1.9724
2	126.1	173.5	0.0058	93.9	1020	1114	1.9159
3	141.5	118.6	0.0085	109.3	1012	1121	1.8833
4	153.0	90.5	0.0111	120.8	1005	1126	1.8600
5	162.3	73.4	0.0136	130.1	1000	1130	1.8422
6	170.1	61.9	0.0162	137.9	995	1133	1.8277
7	176.9	53.6	0.0187	144.8	991	1136	1.8156
8	182.9	47.3	0.0212	150.8	988	1139	1.8049
9	188.3	42.4	0.0236	156.3	985	1141	1.7956
10	193.2	38.4	0.0261	161.1	982	1143	1.7874
12	202.0	32.4	0.0309	169.9	977	1147	1.7731
14	209.6	28.0	0.0357	177.6	972	1150	1.7611
14.7	212.0	26.8	0.0373	180.0	970	1151	1.7573
16	216.3	24.7	0.0404	184.4	968	1152.5	1.7506
18	222.4	22.2	0.0451	190.5	964	1155	1.7414
20	228.0	20.1	0.0498	196.1	961	1157	1.7333
22	233.1	18.37	0.0545	201.3	958	1159	1.7258
24	237.8	16.93	0.0591	206.1	955	1161	1.7189
26	242.2	15.71	0.0636	210.5	952	1162.5	1.7126
28	246.4	14.66	0.0682	214.8	949	1164	1.7069
30	250.3	13.72	0.0728	218.8	947	1165.5	1.7017
35	259.3	11.86	0.0843	228	941	1169	1.6898
40	267.2	10.48	0.0953	236	936	1172	1.6793
45	274.4	9.37	0.1067	243	931	1174	1.6701
50	281.0	8.50	0.1175	250	926	1176	1.6619
55	287.0	7.74	0.1292	256	922	1178	1.6547
60	292.6	7.16	0.1397	262	919	1180	1.6479
65	297.9	6.64	0.1506	267	914	1182	1.6415
70	303.0	6.20	0.1613	272	911	1183	1.6357
75	307.5	5.81	0.1721	277	907	1185	1.6304
80	312.0	5.47	0.1828	282	904	1186	1.6254
85	316.2	5.16	0.1938	286	901	1187	1.6206
90	320.2	4.89	0.2045	290	898	1189	1.6161
95	324.1	4.65	0.2150	295	895	1190	1.6120
100	327.9	4.43	0.2257	298	893	1191	1.6079
105	331.4	4.23	0.2364	302	890	1192	1.6041
110	334.8	4.04	0.2475	306	887	1193	1.6004
115	338.1	3.88	0.2577	309	884	1194	1.5969

Properties of saturated steam

Abs. Pres.	Temp.	Specific Volume	Density	Heat of			Entropy
				Liquid	Evap	Sat. Vap.	
p	t	v	w	h	L	H	S
lb in²	°F	ft³/lb	lb/ft³	Btu/lb	Btu/lb	Btu/lb	Btu/lb °F
120	341.3	3.73	0.2681	312	882	1194	1.5935
125	344.4	3.59	0.2786	316	879	1195	1.5903
130	347.3	3.46	0.2890	319	877	1196	1.5872
135	350.2	3.33	0.3003	322	875	1197	1.5842
140	353.0	3.22	0.3106	325	872	1197	1.5813
145	355.8	3.12	0.3205	328	870	1198	1.5785
150	358.4	3.02	0.3311	331	868	1199	1.5758
160	363.6	2.84	0.3521	336	864	1200	1.5706
170	368.4	2.68	0.3731	341	860	1201	1.5657
180	373.1	2.54	0.3937	346	856	1202	1.5610
190	377.5	2.41	0.4149	351	852	1203	1.5567
200	382	2.29	0.4347	356	848	1203	1.5525
220	390	2.09	0.4785	364	841	1205	1.5448
240	387	1.93	0.5181	372	834	1206	1.5376
260	404.5	1.78	0.5618	380	827	1207.5	1.5310
280	411.1	1.66	0.6024	387	821	1208.5	1.5241
300	417.4	1.55	0.6452	394	815	1209.4	1.5190
350	431.8	1.34	0.7463	410	801	1211.1	1.5058
400	444.7	1.17	0.8547	425	787.5	1212.1	1.4941
450	456.4	1.04	0.9615	437.8	775	1212.8	1.4836
500	467.1	0.94	1.0638	450.1	763.1	1213.2	1.4740

Specific enthalpy of superheated steam (kJ/kg)

Absolute pressure kN/m²	Sat. temp. °C	Steam temperature °C						
		120	150	180	200	230	250	280
150	111.4	2711	2772	2832	2872	2932	2972	3033
200	120.2	—	2769	2830	2870	2931	2971	3031
250	127.4	—	2765	2827	2868	2929	2969	3030
350	138.9	—	2756	2821	2863	2925	2966	3028
400	143.6	—	2752	2818	2860	2923	2964	3026
500	151.8	—	—	2811	2855	2919	2961	3023
600	158.8	—	—	2805	2850	2915	2958	3021
700	165.0	—	—	2798	2844	2911	2954	3018
800	170.4	—	—	2791	2839	2907	2950	3015
900	175.4	—	—	2784	2833	2902	2947	3012
1000	179.9	—	—	2777	2827	2898	2943	3009
1100	184.1	—	—	—	2821	2893	2939	3006
1200	188.0	—	—	—	2814	2889	2935	3003
1400	195.0	—	—	—	2801	2879	2928	2997
1600	201.4	—	—	—	—	2869	2919	2991
2000	212.4	—	—	—	—	2848	2902	2978
2500	223.9	—	—	—	—	2820	2880	2960
3500	242.5	—	—	—	—	—	2828	2922

Specific entropy of superheated steam (kJ/kg K)

Absolute pressure kN/m²	Sat. temp. °C	Steam temperature °C						
		120	150	180	200	230	250	280
150	111.4	7.269	7.419	7.557	7.644	7.767	7.845	7.957
200	120.2	—	7.279	7.420	7.507	7.631	7.710	7.822
250	127.4	—	7.169	7.311	7.400	7.525	7.604	7.717
350	138.9	—	6.998	7.146	7.237	7.364	7.444	7.558
400	143.6	—	6.929	7.079	7.171	7.299	7.380	7.495
500	151.8	—	—	6.965	7.059	7.190	7.272	7.388
600	158.8	—	—	6.869	6.966	7.100	7.183	7.300
700	165.0	—	—	6.786	6.886	7.022	7.107	7.225
800	170.4	—	—	6.712	6.815	6.954	7.040	7.156
900	175.4	—	—	6.645	6.751	6.893	6.980	7.101
1000	179.9	—	—	6.584	6.692	6.838	6.926	7.049
1100	184.1	—	—	—	6.638	6.787	6.876	7.001
1200	188.0	—	—	—	6.587	6.739	6.831	6.956
1400	195.0	—	—	—	6.494	6.653	6.748	6.877
1600	201.4	—	—	—	—	6.577	6.674	6.806
2000	212.4	—	—	—	—	6.440	6.546	6.685
2500	223.9	—	—	—	—	6.292	6.407	6.558
3500	242.5	—	—	—	—	—	6.173	6.349

Properties of saturated steam

| Absolute pressure kN/m² | Temp. °C | Specific volume m³/kg | Density kg/m³ | Specific enthalpy of | | | Specific entropy of steam kJ/kg K |
				Liquid kJ/kg	Evapora-tion kJ/kg	Steam kJ/kg	
0.8	3.8	160	0.00626	15.8	2493	2509	9.058
2.0	17.5	67.0	0.0149	73.5	2460	2534	8.725
5.0	32.9	28.2	0.0354	137.8	2424	2562	8.396
10.0	45.8	14.7	0.0682	191.8	2393	2585	8.151
20.0	60.1	7.65	0.131	251.5	2358	2610	7.909
28	67.5	5.58	0.179	282.7	2340	2623	7.793
35	72.7	4.53	0.221	304.3	2327	2632	7.717
45	78.7	3.58	0.279	329.6	2312	2642	7.631
55	83.7	2.96	0.338	350.6	2299	2650	7.562
65	88.0	2.53	0.395	368.6	2288	2657	7.506
75	91.8	2.22	0.450	384.5	2279	2663	7.457
85	95.2	1.97	0.507	398.6	2270	2668	7.415
95	98.2	1.78	0.563	411.5	2262	2673	7.377
100	99.6	1.69	0.590	417.5	2258	2675	7.360
101.33	100	1.67	0.598	419.1	2257	2676	7.355
110	102.3	1.55	0.646	428.8	2251	2680	7.328
130	107.1	1.33	0.755	449.2	2238	2687	7.271
150	111.4	1.16	0.863	467.1	2226	2693	7.223
170	115.2	1.03	0.970	483.2	2216	2699	7.181
190	118.6	0.929	1.08	497.8	2206	2704	7.144
220	123.3	0.810	1.23	517.6	2193	2711	7.095
260	128.7	0.693	1.44	540.9	2177	2718	7.039
280	131.2	0.646	1.55	551.4	2170	2722	7.014
320	135.8	0.570	1.75	570.9	2157	2728	6.969
360	139.9	0.510	1.96	588.5	2144	2733	6.930
400	143.6	0.462	2.16	604.7	2133	2738	6.894
440	147.1	0.423	2.36	619.6	2122	2742	6.862
480	150.3	0.389	2.57	633.5	2112	2746	6.833
500	151.8	0.375	2.67	640.1	2107	2748	6.819
550	155.5	0.342	2.92	655.8	2096	2752	6.787
600	158.8	0.315	3.175	670.4	2085	2756	6.758
650	162.0	0.292	3.425	684.1	2075	2759	6.730
700	165.0	0.273	3.66	697.1	2065	2762	6.705
750	167.8	0.255	3.915	709.3	2056	2765	6.682
800	170.4	0.240	4.16	720.9	2047	2768	6.660
850	172.9	0.229	4.41	732.0	2038	2770	6.639
900	175.4	0.215	4.65	742.6	2030	2772	6.619
950	177.7	0.204	4.90	752.8	2021	2774	6.601
1000	179.9	0.194	5.15	762.6	2014	2776	6.583

Properties of saturated steam (cont.)

Absolute pressure kN/m²	Temp. °C	Specific volume m³/kg	Density kg/m³	Specific enthalpy of			Specific entropy of steam kJ/kg K
				Liquid kJ/kg	Evaporation kJ/kg	Steam kJ/kg	
1050	182.0	0.186	5.39	772	2006	2778	6.566
1150	186.0	0.170	5.89	790	1991	2781	6.534
1250	189.8	0.157	6.38	807	1977	2784	6.505
1300	191.6	0.151	6.62	815	1971	2785	6.491
1500	198.3	0.132	7.59	845	1945	2790	6.441
1600	201.4	0.124	8.03	859	1933	2792	6.418
1800	207.1	0.110	9.07	885	1910	2795	6.375
2000	212.4	0.0995	10.01	909	1889	2797	6.337
2100	214.9	0.0949	10.54	920	1878	2798	6.319
2300	219.6	0.0868	11.52	942	1858	2800	6.285
2400	221.8	0.0832	12.02	952	1849	2800	6.269
2600	226.0	0.0769	13.01	972	1830	2801	6.239
2700	228.1	0.0740	13.52	981	1821	2802	6.224
2900	232.0	0.0689	14.52	1000	1803	2802	6.197
3000	233.8	0.0666	15.00	1008	1794	2802	6.184
3200	237.4	0.0624	16.02	1025	1779	2802	6.158
3400	240.9	0.0587	17.04	1042	1760	2802	6.134
3600	244.2	0.0554	18.06	1058	1744	2802	6.112
3800	247.3	0.0524	19.08	1073	1728	2801	6.090
4000	250.3	0.0497	21.0	1087	1713	2800	6.069

Taken by permission of Cambridge University Press from *Thermodynamic Tables in S.I. (metric) Units* by Haywood.

Properties of air

Symbols

V	volume of air-vapour mixture	m^3
m	mass of air-vapour mixture	kg
p_a	partial pressure of dry air	N/m^2
p_{wa}	actual partial pressure of water vapour	N/m^2
p_{ws}	saturation pressure of water vapour	N/m^2
p_t	total pressure of mixture	N/m^2
t	dry bulb temperature	$°C$
T	absolute dry bulb temperature$=273+t$	K
ϕ	relative humidity	per cent
X	specific humidity of air vapour mixture	g/kg
X_s	specific humidity of saturated air	g/kg
ρ_a	density of dry air	kg/m^3
ρ_w	density of water vapour	kg/m^3
ρ	density of air vapour mixture	kg/m^3
R	gas constant	J/kg K
	$=286$ for air	
	$=455$ for water vapour	

Atmospheric air is a mixture of dry air and water vapour. It can be treated as an ideal gas without great discrepancies and the gas laws can be applied to it.

General Gas Law
$$pV=mRT$$
$$\rho =\frac{m}{V}=\frac{p}{RT}$$

Density of Dry Air
$$\rho_a=0.00350 \frac{p_a}{T}$$

Density of Water Vapour
$$\rho_w=0.00220 \frac{p_w}{T}$$

Density of Air-water Vapour Mixture
$$\rho=0.00350 \frac{p_t}{T}-0.00133 \frac{p_{ws}\phi}{100T}$$

Air-water vapour mixture is always lighter than dry air.

Humidity is the term applied to the quantity of water vapour present in the air.

Absolute Humidity is the actual mass of water vapour present, expressed in grams water vapour per kilogram mixture.

Specific Humidity is the actual mass of water vapour present, expressed in grams water vapour per kilogram dry air.

$$X = \frac{622 \, \phi \rho_{ws}}{(\rho - \rho_{ws}) \, 100} \text{ g/kg}$$

Specific Humidity of Saturated Air

$$X_s = \frac{622 \, \rho_{ws}}{\rho - \rho_{ws}} \text{ g/kg}$$

Relative Humidity is

either   ratio of actual partial pressure of water vapour to vapour pressure at saturation at actual dry bulb temperature.

or   ratio of actual vapour density to vapour density at saturation at actual dry bulb temperature.

or   ratio of actual mass of water vapour in given air volume to mass of water vapour required to saturate this volume.

It is usually expressed in %

$$\phi = \frac{p_{wa}}{p_{ws}} \times 100 = \frac{\rho_w}{\rho_{ws}} \times 100 = \frac{X}{X_s} \times 100\%$$

Saturated Air holds the maximum mass of water vapour at the given temperature. Any lowering of the air temperature will cause condensation of water vapour.

Dry Bulb Temperature is the air temperature as indicated by a thermometer which is not affected by the moisture of the air.

Wet Bulb Temperature is the temperature of adiabatic saturation. It is the temperature indicated by a moistened thermometer bulb exposed to a current of air.

Dew Point Temperature is the temperature to which air with a given moisture content must be cooled to produce saturation of the air and the commencement of condensation of the vapour in the air.

Specific Enthalpy of dry air

$H = 1.01\ t$ kJ/kg

Specific Enthalpy of air-water vapour mixture is composed of the sensible heat of the air and the latent heat of vapourisation of the water vapour present in the air and the sensible heat of the vapour.

$H = 1.01\ t + X(2463 + 1.88\ t)$ kJ/kg

1.01 is the specific heat capacity of dry air.
2463 is the latent heat of vapourisation of water at $0\,°C$.
1.88 is the specific heat capacity of water vapour at constant pressure.

Thermal expansion of air

Dry air expands or contracts uniformly $\dfrac{1}{886}$ of its volume per $°C$ under constant pressure.

Humidity Chart for Air (Psychrometric Chart)
See Chart No. 5. The chart shows the relationship between
1   Dry bulb temperature.
2   Wet bulb temperature.
3   Dew point.
4   Relative humidity.
5   Specific humidity.
6   Vapour pressure.
7   Specific enthalpy.

When any two of these are given the other five can be read from the chart. The chart contains the following lines
  (i)   Lines of constant temperature.
 (ii)   Lines of constant specific enthalpy, which are also lines of constant wet bulb temperature.
(iii)   Lines of constant relative humidity.
(iv)   Lines of constant dewpoint, which are also lines of constant moisture content.

Specific Heat Capacity of dry air

$s = 1.01$ kJ/kg K
  $= 1.23$ kJ/m^3 K at standard density

Air condition

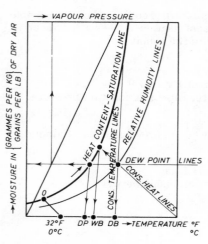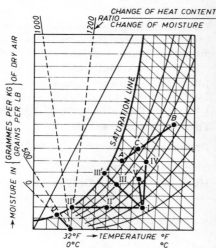

D.P.=Dew point temperature.
W.B.=Wet bulb temperature.
D.B.=Dry bulb temperature.

Change of condition of air	Indicated in above sketch	Remarks
Cooling with constant moisture	From I to II	Dew point temperature in intersection II[1], with saturation line
Adiabatic change	From I to III, saturation at III[1]	No heat is added or extracted
Temperature constant	From I to IV	

Mixing of air, air volume V_A of condition A is to be mixed with air volume V_B of condition B. Condition of mixture is C

$$\frac{\text{Distance AC}}{\text{Distance BC}} = \frac{\text{Air volume } V_B}{\text{Air volume } V_A}.$$

Relative humidity in per cent

For various room temperatures and various differences between wet- and dry-bulb temperatures

Dry bulb temp °C	Difference between dry bulb and wet bulb (°C)											
	0	1	2	3	4	5	6	7	8	9	10	11
10	100	88	77	66	55	44	34	25	15	6	0	0
11	100	89	78	67	56	46	36	27	18	9	2	0
12	100	89	78	68	58	48	39	29	21	12	3	0
13	100	90	79	69	60	50	41	32	34	15	6	1
14	100	90	80	70	61	52	43	34	26	17	8	2
15	100	90	81	71	62	53	44	36	28	20	11	5
16	100	90	81	71	63	54	46	37	30	22	14	8
17	100	91	82	72	64	56	48	39	32	25	17	11
18	100	91	82	73	65	57	49	41	34	27	20	13
19	100	91	83	74	66	59	51	43	36	29	23	16
20	100	91	83	74	67	59	52	44	38	31	25	18
21	100	92	83	75	68	61	53	46	40	33	27	20
22	100	92	83	75	68	61	54	47	41	34	28	22
23	100	92	84	76	69	62	55	48	42	36	30	24
24	100	92	84	76	70	63	56	49	43	37	31	26
25	100	92	85	77	71	64	57	51	45	39	33	28
26	100	92	85	77	71	64	58	52	46	40	34	29
27	100	93	85	78	72	65	59	53	47	42	36	31
28	100	93	85	78	72	66	59	54	48	43	37	32
29	100	93	86	79	73	67	60	55	49	44	39	34
30	100	93	86	79	73	67	61	56	50	45	40	35
31	100	93	86	80	74	68	62	57	51	46	41	36
32	100	93	86	80	74	68	63	57	52	47	42	37
33	100	93	87	81	75	69	64	58	53	48	43	38
34	100	93	87	81	75	69	64	59	53	49	44	39
35	100	94	87	82	76	70	65	60	54	50	45	40
36	100	94	87	82	76	70	65	60	55	50	46	41
37	100	94	88	82	76	71	66	61	56	51	47	42
38	100	94	88	82	76	71	66	61	56	52	47	43

Relative humidity in per cent

For various room temperatures and various differences between wet- and dry-bulb temperatures.

Dry-bulb temp. (°F)	Difference between dry-bulb and wet-bulb temperature (°F)										
	0	2	4	6	8	10	12	14	16	18	20
50	100	87	74	62	50	39	28	17	7	0	0
52	100	88	75	63	52	41	30	20	10	0	0
54	100	88	76	65	54	43	33	23	14	5	0
56	100	88	77	66	55	45	35	26	17	8	0
58	100	88	77	67	57	47	38	28	20	11	3
60	100	89	78	68	58	49	40	31	22	14	6
62	100	89	79	69	60	50	41	33	25	17	9
64	100	90	79	70	61	52	43	35	27	20	12
66	100	90	80	71	62	53	45	37	29	22	15
68	100	90	81	72	63	55	47	39	31	24	17
70	100	90	81	72	64	56	48	40	33	26	20
72	100	91	82	73	65	57	49	42	35	28	22
74	100	91	82	74	66	58	51	44	37	30	24
76	100	91	83	74	67	59	52	45	38	32	26
78	100	91	83	75	67	60	53	46	40	34	28
80	100	91	83	76	68	61	54	47	41	35	29
82	100	92	84	76	69	62	55	49	43	37	31
84	100	92	84	77	70	63	56	50	44	38	32
86	100	92	85	77	70	63	57	51	45	39	34
88	100	92	85	78	71	64	58	52	46	41	35
90	100	92	85	78	71	65	59	53	47	42	37
92	100	92	85	78	72	65	59	54	48	43	38
94	100	93	86	79	72	66	60	54	49	44	39
96	100	93	86	79	73	67	61	55	50	45	40
98	100	93	86	79	73	67	61	56	51	46	41
100	100	93	86	80	74	68	62	57	52	47	42

Mixture of air and saturated water vapour

Temp. °C	Pressure of sat. vapour kN/m^3	Mass of sat. vapour		Vol. of vapour		Specific entropy of sat. vapour kJ/kg
		per m^3 of mixture g/m^3	per kg of dry air g/kg	of dry air m^3/kg	of mixture m^3/kg	
−15	0.160	1.6	1.0	0.731	0.732	−12.6
−10	0.266	2.3	1.6	0.745	0.746	−6.1
−5	0.399	3.4	2.5	0.759	0.761	+1.09
0	0.612	4.9	3.8	0.773	0.775	9.4
1	0.652	5.2	4.1	0.776	0.778	11.3
2	0.705	5.6	4.4	0.779	0.781	12.9
3	0.758	6.0	4.7	0.782	0.784	14.7
4	0.811	6.4	5.0	0.784	0.787	16.6
5	0.865	6.8	5.4	0.787	0.790	18.5
6	0.931	7.3	5.8	0.791	0.793	20.5
7	0.998	7.7	6.2	0.793	0.796	22.6
8	1.06	8.3	6.7	0.796	0.800	24.7
9	1.14	8.8	7.1	0.799	0.802	26.9
10	1.22	9.4	7.6	0.801	0.805	29.2
11	1.30	10	8.2	0.805	0.808	31.5
12	1.40	11	8.8	0.807	0.812	34.1
13	1.49	11	9.4	0.810	0.814	36.6
14	1.60	12	10.0	0.813	0.818	39.2
15	1.70	13	10.6	0.816	0.821	41.8
16	1.81	14	11.4	0.818	0.824	44.8
17	1.93	14	12.1	0.822	0.828	47.7
18	2.06	15	12.9	0.824	0.831	50.7
19	2.19	16	13.8	0.827	0.833	54.0
20	2.33	17	14.7	0.830	0.837	57.8
21	2.49	18	15.6	0.833	0.840	61.1
22	2.63	19	16.6	0.835	0.844	64.1
23	2.81	20	17.7	0.838	0.847	67.8
24	2.98	22	18.8	0.841	0.850	72.0
25	3.17	23	20.0	0.844	0.854	75.8
26	3.35	24	21.4	0.847	0.858	80.4
27	3.55	26	22.6	0.850	0.861	84.6
28	3.78	27	24.0	0.853	0.865	89.2
29	3.99	29	25.6	0.855	0.869	94.3
30	4.23	30	27.2	0.858	0.873	99.6
35	5.61	39	36.6	0.873	0.892	129
40	7.35	51	48.8	0.887	0.912	166
45	9.56	65	65.0	0.901	0.935	213
50	12.3	82	86.2	0.915	0.959	273
55	15.7	104	114	0.929	0.987	352
60	19.9	130	152	0.943	1.020	456
65	24.9	161	204	0.958	1.057	599

Mixture of air and saturated water vapour

Temp °F	Press of sat vapour in Hg	Weight of sat vapour		Volume in ft³		Enthalpy of mixture Btu/lb
		Grains per ft³	per lb of dry air. Grains per lb	of 1 lb of dry air	of 1 lb of dry air & vapour to saturate	
0	0.0375	0.472	5.47	11.58	11.59	0.852
10	0.00628	0.772	9.16	11.83	11.58	3.831
20	0.01027	1.238	15.01	12.09	12.13	7.137
30	0.1646	1.943	24.11	12.34	12.41	10.933
32	0.1806	2.124	26.47	12.39	12.47	11.83
33	0.1880	2.206	27.57	12.41	12.49	12.18
34	0.1957	2.292	28.70	12.44	12.52	12.60
35	0.2036	2.380	29.88	12.47	12.55	13.02
36	0.2119	2.471	31.09	12.49	12.58	13.44
37	0.2204	2.566	32.35	12.52	12.61	13.87
38	0.2292	2.663	33.66	12.54	12.64	14.31
39	0.2384	2.764	35.01	12.57	12.67	14.76
40	0.2478	2.868	36.41	12.59	12.70	15.21
41	0.2576	2.976	37.87	12.62	12.73	15.67
42	0.2678	3.087	39.38	12.64	12.76	16.14
43	0.2783	3.201	40.93	12.67	12.79	16.62
44	0.2897	3.319	42.55	12.69	12.82	17.10
45	0.3003	3.442	44.21	12.72	12.85	17.59
46	0.3120	3.568	45.94	12.74	12.88	18.09
47	0.3240	3.698	47.73	12.77	12.91	18.60
48	0.3364	3.832	49.58	12.79	12.94	19.12
49	0.3492	3.970	51.49	12.82	12.97	19.65
50	0.3624	4.113	53.47	12.84	13.00	20.19
51	0.3761	4.260	55.52	12.87	13.03	20.74
52	0.3903	4.411	57.64	12.89	13.07	21.30
53	0.4049	4.568	59.83	12.92	13.10	21.87
54	0.4200	4.729	62.09	12.95	13.13	22.45
55	0.4356	4.895	64.43	12.97	13.16	23.04
56	0.4517	5.066	66.85	13.00	13.20	23.64
57	0.4684	5.242	69.35	13.02	13.23	24.25
58	0.4855	5.424	71.93	13.05	13.26	24.88
59	0.5032	5.611	74.60	13.07	13.30	25.52
60	0.5214	5.804	77.30	13.10	13.33	26.18

Mixture of air and saturated water vapour (cont.)

Temp °F	Pressure of sat vapour in Hg	Weight of sat vapour per lb of dry air Grains per ft³	Grains per lb	Volume in ft³ of 1 lb of dry air	of 1 lb of dry air & vapour to saturate	Enthalpy of mixture Btu/lb
61	0.5403	6.003	80.2	13.12	13.36	26.84
62	0.5597	6.208	83.2	13.15	13.40	27.52
63	0.5798	6.418	86.2	13.17	13.43	28.22
64	0.6005	6.633	89.3	13.20	13.47	28.93
65	0.6218	6.855	92.6	13.22	13.50	29.65
66	0.6438	7.084	95.9	13.25	13.54	30.39
67	0.6664	7.320	99.4	13.27	13.58	31.15
68	0.6898	7.563	103.0	13.30	13.61	31.92
69	0.7139	7.813	106.6	13.32	13.65	32.71
70	0.7386	8.069	110.5	13.35	13.69	33.51
71	0.7642	8.332	114.4	13.38	13.73	34.33
72	0.7906	8.603	118.4	13.40	13.76	35.17
73	0.8177	8.882	122.6	13.43	13.80	36.03
74	0.8456	9.168	126.9	13.45	13.84	36.91
75	0.8744	9.46	131.4	13.48	13.88	37.81
76	0.9040	9.76	135.9	13.50	13.92	38.73
77	0.9345	10.07	140.7	13.53	13.96	39.67
78	0.9658	10.39	145.6	13.55	14.00	40.64
79	0.9981	10.72	150.6	13.58	14.05	41.63
80	1.0314	11.06	155.8	13.60	14.09	42.64
85	1.212	12.89	184.4	13.73	14.31	48.04
90	1.421	14.96	217.6	13.86	14.55	54.13
95	1.659	17.32	256.3	13.98	14.80	61.01
100	1.931	19.98	301.3	14.11	15.08	68.79
105	2.241	22.99	354	14.24	15.39	77.63
110	2.594	26.38	415	14.36	15.73	87.69
115	2.993	31.8	486	14.49	16.10	99.10
120	3.444	34.44	569	14.62	16.52	112.37
125	3.952	39.19	667	14.75	16.99	127.54
130	4.523	44.49	780	14.88	17.53	145.06
135	5.163	50.38	913	15.00	18.13	165.34
140	5.878	56.91	1,072	15.13	18.84	189.22
150	7.566	72.10	1,485	15.39	20.60	250.30

Man and air

(a) **Respiration.** An adult at rest breathes 16 respirations per minute, about 50 m^3/hr (about 17.5 ft^3hr). When working the rate is 3 to 6 times more.

Average composition of exhaled air

Oxygen   16.5%
Carbon dioxide   4.0%
Nitrogen and argon 79.5%

Quantity of carbon dioxide exhaled in 24 hrs is about 1 kg (2.2 lb).

(b) **Equilibrium of Heat.** Heat is generated within the human body by combustion of food. Heat is lost from the human body by

1 Conduction and convection   about 25%
2 Radiation   about 43%
3 Evaporation of moisture   about 30%
4 Exhaled air   about 2%

Evaporation prevails at high ambient temperatures. Conduction and convection prevail at low ambient temperatures.

Heat is liberated at a rate such that the internal body temperature is maintained at 37°C (98.6 °F).

Proportion of sensible and latent heat dissipated by man at fairly hard work

Dry bulb temp									
	°C	13	15	18	21	24	27	30	32
	°F	55	60	65	70	75	80	85	90
Sensible heat	%	75	68	60	51	42	31	20	10
Latent heat	%	25	32	40	49	58	69	80	90

(c) **Heat Loss of Human Body.** The total heat loss of an adult (sensible and latent) is approximately 117 W at room temperatures between 18°C and 30°C (about 400 Btu/hr).

Thermal indices are combinations of air temperature, radiant temperature, air movement and humidity to give a measure of a person's feeling of warmth.

(i) *Equivalent temperature* combines the effects of air temperature, radiation and air movement. Numerically it is the temperature of a uniform enclosure in which a sizeable black body maintained at 24 °C in still air would lose heat at the same rate as in the environment under consideration. It is measured by a Eupatheoscope.

(ii) *Effective temperature* is an arbitrary index on the basis of subjective assessments of the degree of comfort felt by people in various environments. It takes into account air temperature, air movement and humidity. Numerically it is the temperature of still, saturated air which would produce an identical degree of comfort.

(iii) *Globe temperature* combines the effects of air temperature, radiation and air movement. Numerically it is the reading of a thermometer with its bulb at the centre of a blackened globe 150 mm dia. It is similar to the equivalent temperature but easier to measure.

(iv) *Resultant temperature* is similar to globe temperature but the globe used is 100 mm dia. This makes it rather less sensitive to radiation.

(v) *Environmental temperature* combines air temperature and radiation. Numerically it is given by the formula

$$t_{ei} = \frac{2}{3} t_r + \frac{1}{3} t_a$$

where t_{ei} = environmental temperature   °C
       t_r = mean radiant temperature of surroundings   °C
       t_a = air temperature   °C

It is not very different from the other scales when air velocity is low and air and radiant temperatures are not widely different, and is easier to use in calculations.

Atmospheric data. Composition of air

Dry air is a mechanical mixture of gases.

	Dry air per cent		Atmospheric at sea level
	By volume	By weight	By volume
Oxygen	21.00	23.2	20.75
Nitrogen	78.03	75.5	77.08
Carbon dioxide	0.03	0.046	0.03
Hydrogen	0.01	0.007	0.01
Rare gases	0.93	1.247	0.93
Water vapour	—	—	1.20

The composition of air is unchanged to a height of approximately 10 000 metres. The average air temperature diminishes at the rate of about 0.6 °C for each 100 m of vertical height.

Altitude-density tables for air

Altitude m	Barometer mm Hg	Altitude m	Barometer mm Hg	Altitude m	Barometer mm Hg
0	749	600	695	1,350	632
75	743	750	681	1,500	620
150	735	900	668	1,800	598
250	726	1,000	658	2,100	577
300	723	1,200	643	2,400	555
450	709				

Altitude ft	Barometer in Hg	Altitude ft	Barometer in Hg	Altitude ft	Barometer in Hg
0	29.92	2,000	27.72	4,500	25.20
250	29.64	2,500	27.20	5,000	24.72
500	29.36	3,000	26.68	6,000	23.79
750	29.08	3,500	26.18	7,000	22.90
1,000	28.80	4,000	25.58	8,000	22.04
1,500	28.31				

Normal Temperature and Pressure (NTP) is 0 °C and 101.325 kN/m^2. Standard Temperature and Pressure (STP) used for determination of fan capacities is 20 °C and 101.6 kN/m^2 or 60 °F and 30 in Hg. (These two sets of conditions do not convert directly, but the density of dry air is 1.22 kg/m^3=0.0764 lb/ft^3 at both conditions.)

6 Heat losses

Heat input has to balance heat loss by
1. conduction and convection through walls, windows, etc.
2. infiltration of cold air.

1 Heat loss through walls, windows, doors, ceilings, floors, etc.

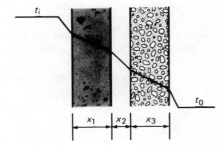

$$H = AU(t_i - t_o)$$

$$U = \frac{1}{\dfrac{1}{f_1} + \dfrac{x_1}{k_1} + \dfrac{x_2}{k_2} + \dfrac{x_3}{k_3} + \dfrac{1}{f_o}}$$

where

H = heat transmitted (W)
A = area of exposed surface (m^2)
U = overall coefficient of heat transmission (W/m^2 K)
t_i = inside air temperature (°C)
t_o = outside air temperature (°C)
x = thickness of material (m)
k = thermal conductivity of material (W/m K)
f_i = surface conductance for inside wall (W/m^2 K)
f_o = surface conductance for outside wall (W/m^2 K)

$$C = \frac{k}{x} = \text{conductance} = \text{heat flow through unit area in unit time (W/m}^2\text{ K)}$$

$$R = \frac{x}{k} = \frac{1}{c} = \text{thermal resistivity}$$

2   Heat loss by infiltration

$$H = sdnV (t_i - t_o)$$

where

H = heat loss	(kW)
s = specific heat capacity of air	(kJ/kg K)
d = density of air	(kg/m^3)
n = number of air changes	(1/s)
V = volume of room	(m^3)
t_1 = inside air temperature	(°C)
t_o = outside air temperature	(°C)

Safety additions to heat loss calculations

1   For aspect North East, 10%.
      West, 5%

2   For exposure 5%–10% for surfaces exposed to wind

3   For intermittent heating
      Buildings heated during day only, 10–15%
      Buildings not in use daily, 25–30%
      Buildings with long periods between use (e.g. churches), up to 50%

4   For height

Height of room	m	5	6	7	8	9	10	11	12 and more
Addition	%	2.5	5	7.5	10	12.5	15	17.5	20

Air movement. Air movement makes any conditions of temperature and humidity feel colder; it lowers the effective temperature. An air velocity of 0.12 m/s may be considered as practically still air. A slight air movement is desirable for comfort to remove layers of humid and warm air from the surface of the human body. A higher air velocity is required in air at high temperature and high relative humidity than in air at low temperature and low relative humidity.

Entering air temperature in plenum heating systems must not be too much above or below the room temperature.

For heating
   normally   air entering temperature 26–32°C
   with good mixing   air entering temperature 38–49°C

For cooling
   inlets near occupied zones   5–9°C below room temperature
   high velocity jets, diffusion nozzles   17°C below room temperature

Allowance for warming up
(a) rooms heated daily (not at night)

$$H = \frac{0.063\,(n-1)\,H_o}{Z}\ \text{W}$$

(b) rooms not heated daily

$$H = \frac{0.1\,(Z+8)\,H_t}{Z}\ \text{W}$$

where H=heat required for warming up   (W)
        H_o=heat loss through outside surface   (W)
        H_t=total heat loss   (W)
        n=interruption of heating   (hr)
        Z=warming up time   (hr)

Air temperatures at various levels
Increase of temperature from 1.5 m to 6 m is at the rate of 7% of temperature at 1.5 m per m. No further increase after 6 m.

$$t' = t + 0.07\,(h-1.5)\,t$$

    t'=temperature at given level above floor   (°C)
    t=temperature of 1.5 m above floor   (°C)
    h=height of given level above floor   (m)

Temperature of unheated spaces

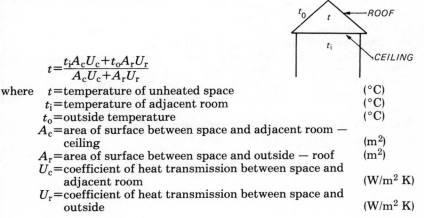

$$t = \frac{t_i A_c U_c + t_o A_r U_r}{A_c U_c + A_r U_r}$$

where t=temperature of unheated space   (°C)
        t_i=temperature of adjacent room   (°C)
        t_o=outside temperature   (°C)
        A_c=area of surface between space and adjacent room —
            ceiling   (m²)
        A_r=area of surface between space and outside — roof   (m²)
        U_c=coefficient of heat transmission between space and
            adjacent room   (W/m² K)
        U_r=coefficient of heat transmission between space and
            outside   (W/m² K)

Combined coefficient for ceiling and roof

$$U_E = \frac{U_R U_c}{U_R + \dfrac{U_c}{r}}$$

where U_E=combined coefficient of heat transmission
from inside to outside, based on ceiling
area   (W/m^2 K)
U_R=coefficient of heat transmission of roof   (W/m^2 K)
U_c=coefficient of heat transmission of ceiling (W/m^2 K)
r=ratio of roof area to ceiling area   (dimensionless)

Design winter indoor temperatures (°C)

Heated rooms					
Bars	18	Gyms	15	Stores	15
Bathrooms	22	Halls,		Swimming baths	27
Bedrooms	18	assembly	18	Waiting rooms	18
Changing rooms	22	entrance	16	Wards	18
Churches	18	Hotel rooms	21	Warehouses	16
Cloakrooms	16	Laboratories	20		
Classrooms	20	Lecture rooms	20	*Unheated rooms*	
Corridors	16	Libraries	20	Attics	0
Dining rooms	20	Living rooms	21	Attics under	
Dressing rooms	21	Museums	20	insulated roof	4
Exhibition halls	18	Offices	20	Cellars	0
Factories		Operating theatres	24	Foyers with doors	
sedentary work	18	Prisons	18	frequently opened	0
light work	16	Recreation rooms	18	with doors not	
heavy work	13	Restaurants	18	frequently opened	4
		Shops	18	Internal rooms	2

Design winter outdoor temperatures

For England −4°C to 0°C.

Design infiltration rates

	Air changes per hour		Air changes per hour
Bars	1	Laboratories	1
Bathrooms	2	Lecture rooms	$1\frac{1}{2}$
Bedrooms	1	Libraries	$\frac{1}{2}$
Changing rooms	$\frac{1}{2}$	Living rooms	$1\frac{1}{2}$
Churches	$\frac{1}{2}$	Museums	1
Cloakrooms	1	Offices	1
Classrooms	2	Operating theatres	$\frac{3}{4}$
Corridors	$1\frac{1}{2}$	Prisons	2
Dining rooms	1	Recreation rooms	1
Dressing rooms	1	Restaurants	1
Exhibition halls	$\frac{1}{2}$	Shops	1
Factories	$1-1\frac{1}{2}$	Stores	$\frac{1}{2}$
Gyms	1	Swimming baths	$\frac{1}{2}$
Halls, assembly	$\frac{1}{2}$	Waiting rooms	1
entrance	2	Wards	2
Hotel rooms	1	Warehouses	$\frac{1}{2}$

Heat loss calculations for high buildings

Floor	Addition to infiltration rate	Designation of U-valve
Ground, 1st	nil	Normal
2nd to 4th	25%	Normal
5th to 11th	50%	Normal
Above 11th	100%	Severe

Infiltration heat loss

Heat loss for 1 air change per hour $= 0.34$ W/m^3 K (0.018 Btu/hr ft^3 °F).

Heat loss calculation

Contract temperatures and their equivalents
Inside temperatures obtained with a certain system with outside temperatures other than for which the system is designed. (Empirical formula by J. Roger Preston.)

$$t_4 = (t_1^{12} - t_2^{12} + t_3^{12})^{\frac{1}{12}}$$

where
  t_1 = Contract inside temperature (K)
  t_2 = Contract outside temperature (K)
  t_3 = Existing outside temperature (K)
  t_4 = Estimated inside temperature (K)

(Formula remains unchanged if all temperatures are in °F absolute.)

Table for 30°F contract outside and 60°F contract inside

Existing Outside temp. °F	20	22	24	26	28	**30**	32	34	36	38	40
Inside temp. °F	55	56	57	58	59	**60**	61	62	63	64	65

Table for 0°C contract outside and 20°C contract inside

Existing Outside temp. °C	−5	−4	−3	−2	−1	**0**	+1	2	3	4	5
Inside temp. °C	17.8	18.3	18.8	19.0	19.6	**20**	20.5	21.0	21.4	21.7	22.5

Thermal conductivities

Material	Conductivity k		Resistivity 1/k	
	$\dfrac{Btu\ in}{ft^2\ hr\ °F}$	W/m K	$\dfrac{ft^2\ hr\ °F}{Btu\ in}$	m K/W
Air	0.18	0.026	5.56	38.6
Aluminium	1050	150		
Asbetolux	0.8	0.12	1.25	8.67
Asbestos:				
flues and pipes	1.9	0.27	0.53	3.68
insulating board	1.0	0.14	1.0	6.93
lightweight slab	0.37	0.053	2.70	18.7
Asphalt: light	4.0	0.58	0.25	1.73
heavy	8.5	1.23	0.12	0.83
Brass	550	150		
Bricks: common	9.9	1.43	0.10	0.69
engineering	5.5	0.79	0.18	1.25
Brine	3.3	0.48	0.30	2.10
Building board	0.55	0.079	1.82	12.62
paper	0.45	0.065	2.22	15.39
Caposite	0.36	0.052	2.78	19.28
Cardboard	1.0 to 2.0	0.144 to 0.288	1.0 to 0.5	6.9 to 3.5
Celotex	0.33	0.048	3.0	21.0
Concrete: 1:2:4	10.0	1.4	0.10	0.69
lightweight	2.8	0.40	0.36	2.5
Copper	2100	300		
Cork	0.30	0.043	3.33	23.1
Densotape	1.7	0.25	0.58	4.0
Diatomaceous earth	0.60	0.087	1.66	11.5
Econite	0.68	0.098	1.47	10.19
Felt	0.27	0.039	3.70	25.7
Fibreglass	0.25	0.036	4.0	27.7
Firebrick	9.0	1.30	0.11	0.76
Fosalsil	1.0	0.14	0.10	0.69
Glass	7.3	1.05	0.14	0.97
Glasswool	0.28	0.04	3.6	24.8
Gold	2150	310		

Thermal conductivities *(continued)*

Material	Conductivity k		Resistivity $1/k$	
	$\dfrac{Btu\ in}{ft^2\ hr\ °F}$	W/m K	$\dfrac{ft^2\ hr\ °F}{Btu\ in}$	m K/W
Granwood floor blocks	2.20	0.32	0.45	3.1
Gyproc plasterboard	1.1	0.16	0.91	6.3
Gypsum plasterboard	1.1	0.16	0.91	6.3
Hardboard	0.65	0.094	1.54	10.68
Holoplast: 25 mm panel	0.95	0.14	1.05	7.3
Ice	16.0	2.31	0.0625	0.43
Insulating board	0.41	0.059	2.45	16.99
Iron: cast	450	65	0.0022	0.154
wrought	400	58	0.0025	0.0172
Jute	0.25	0.036	4.0	27.7
Kapok	0.25	0.036	4.0	27.7
Lead	240	35	0.0042	0.029
Linoleum: cork	0.5	0.072	2.0	13.9
p.v.c.	1.5	0.22	0.67	4.65
rubber	2.1	0.30	0.48	3.33
Marinite	0.74	0.11	1.35	9.36
Mercury	48	7	0.021	0.143
Mica sheet	4.5	0.65	0.22	1.53
Mineral wool	0.39	0.056	3.33	23.1
Nickel	400	58	0.0025	0.0172
On ozote	0.20	0.029	5.0	34.7
Paper	0.90	0.13	0.11	7.69
Perspex	1.45	0.21	0.69	4.8
Plaster	3.3	0.48	0.30	2.1
Platinum	480	69	0.0021	0.0145
Polystyrene: cellular	0.23	0.033	4.3	29.8
Polyurethane: cellular	0.29	0.042	3.45	23.9
Polyzote	0.22	0.032	4.55	31.5
Porcelain	7.2	1.04	0.14	0.96

Thermal conductivities *(continued)*

Material	Conductivity k		Resistivity 1/k	
	$\dfrac{Btu\ in}{ft^2\ hr\ °F}$	W/m K	$\dfrac{ft^2\ hr\ °F}{Btu\ in}$	m K/W
Refractory brick alumina	2.2	0.32	0.45	3.1
diatomaceous	0.9	0.13	1.11	7.70
silica	10.0	1.44	0.10	0.69
vermiculite insulating	1.35	0.19	0.74	5.13
Refractory concrete:				
diatomaceous	1.8	0.26	0.56	3.9
aluminous cement	3.2	0.46	0.31	2.15
Rubber: natural	1.1	0.16	0.91	6.3
silicone	1.6	0.23	0.63	4.4
Sand	2.9	0.42	0.35	2.4
Scale, boiler	16.0	2.3	0.0625	0.43
Silver	2900	420		
Sisalkraft building paper	0.46	0.066	2.17	15.0
Slate	14.0	2.0	0.071	0.5
Snow	1.5	0.22	0.67	4.65
Steel, soft	320	46		
Steel wool	0.75	0.108	1.33	9.22
Stillite	0.25	0.036	4.0	27.7
Stone: granite	20.3	2.9	0.05	0.35
limestone	10.6	1.5	0.09	0.62
marble	17.4	2.5	0.06	0.42
sandstone	13.0	1.9	0.08	0.55
Sundeala: insulating board	0.36	0.052	2.78	19.3
medium hardboard	0.51	0.074	2.0	13.9
Tentest	0.35	0.05	2.86	19.8
Thermalite	1.4	0.20	0.71	4.9
Tiles: asphalt and asbestos	3.8	0.55	0.26	1.8
burnt clay	5.8	0.84	0.17	1.2
concrete	8.0	1.2	0.13	0.90
cork	0.58	0.084	1.72	11.9
plaster	2.6	0.37	0.38	2.63

Thermal conductivities *(continued)*

Material	Conductivity k		Resistivity $1/k$	
	$\dfrac{Btu\ in}{ft^2\ hr\ °F}$	$W/m\ K$	$\dfrac{ft^2\ hr\ °F}{Btu\ in}$	$m\ K/W$
Timber: balsa	0.33	0.048	3.0	20.8
beech	1.16	0.17	0.86	5.97
cypress	0.67	0.097	1.49	10.3
deal	0.87	0.13	1.15	7.97
fir	0.76	0.11	1.3	9.1
oak	1.11	0.16	0.90	6.24
plywood	0.96	0.14	1.04	7.21
teak	0.96	0.14	1.04	7.21
Treetex	0.39	0.056	2.56	17.8
Water	4.15	0.60	0.24	1.7
Weyboard	0.63	0.091	1.60	11.1
Weyroc	1.0	0.14	1.0	6.9
Woodwool	0.28	0.040	3.58	24.8
Wool	0.30	0.043	3.33	23.1
Zinc	440	64		
Sawdust	0.49	0.071	2.04	14.1
Cotton waste	0.41	0.059	2.4	16.9

Thermal transmittance coefficients for building elements

Orientation / Exposure legend:

Orientation	Exposure
S	Sheltered
W SW SE	Normal
NW	Severe
N NE E	—

		Sheltered		Normal		Severe		Normal		Severe		Severe	
		Btu/ft² hr °F	W/m² K	Btu/ft² hr °F	W/m² K	Btu/ft² hr °F	W/m² K	Btu/ft² hr °F	W/m² K	Btu/ft² hr °F	W/m² K	Btu/ft² hr °F	W/m² K
Walls													
Solid brick Unplastered	100 mm	0.50	2.9	0.55	3.1	0.59	3.4	0.64	3.6	0.69	3.9	0.75	4.3
	225 mm	0.39	2.2	0.42	2.4	0.44	2.5	0.47	2.7	0.50	2.9	0.53	3.0
	340 mm	0.32	1.8	0.34	1.9	0.35	2.0	0.37	2.1	0.39	2.2	0.41	2.3
Solid brick Plastered	100 mm	0.46	2.6	0.49	2.8	0.53	3.0	0.57	3.2	0.61	3.5	0.65	3.7
	225 mm	0.36	2.1	0.38	2.2	0.41	2.3	0.43	2.4	0.45	2.6	0.48	2.7
	340 mm	0.30	1.7	0.32	1.8	0.33	1.9	0.35	2.0	0.36	2.1	0.38	2.2
	455 mm	0.26	1.5	0.27	1.5	0.28	1.6	0.29	1.6	0.30	1.7	0.31	1.8
	560 mm	0.23	1.3	0.23	1.3	0.24	1.4	0.25	1.4	0.26	1.5	0.26	1.5
Cavity brick Unventilated	270 mm	0.27	1.5	0.28	1.6	0.29	1.6	0.30	1.7	0.31	1.8	0.32	1.8
	390 mm	0.23	1.3	0.24	1.4	0.25	1.4	0.26	1.5	0.27	1.5	0.27	1.5
	500 mm	0.21	1.2	0.21	1.2	0.22	1.2	0.22	1.2	0.23	1.3	0.24	1.4
Cavity brick Ventilated	270 mm	0.30	1.7	0.31	1.8	0.33	1.9	0.34	1.9	0.36	2.0	0.37	2.1
	390 mm	0.26	1.5	0.27	1.5	0.28	1.6	0.29	1.6	0.30	1.7	0.31	1.8
	500 mm	0.22	1.2	0.23	1.3	0.24	1.4	0.25	1.4	0.25	1.4	0.26	1.5
Concrete	100 mm	0.55	3.1	0.60	3.4	0.66	3.8	0.71	4.0	0.78	4.4	0.85	4.8
	150 mm	0.49	2.8	0.53	3.0	0.58	3.3	0.63	3.6	0.68	3.9	0.73	4.1
	200 mm	0.45	2.5	0.48	2.7	0.52	3.0	0.56	3.2	0.60	3.4	0.64	3.6
	250 mm	0.41	2.3	0.44	2.5	0.47	2.7	0.50	2.8	0.53	3.0	0.57	3.2
Wood Tongued and grooved	25 mm	0.41	2.3	0.44	2.5	0.47	2.7	0.50	2.8	0.53	3.0	0.56	3.2
	38 mm	0.34	1.9	0.36	2.0	0.38	2.2	0.40	2.3	0.42	2.4	0.44	2.5

Exposure

Orientation	S · W SW SE · NW · N NE E — Sheltered		Normal		Severe		Sheltered		Normal		Severe	
	Btu/ft² hr °F	W/m² K	Btu/ft² hr °F	W/m² K	Btu/ft² hr °F	W/m² K	Btu/ft² hr °F	W/m² K	Btu/ft² hr °F	W/m² K	Btu/ft² hr °F	W/m² K
Walls												
Asbestos sheeting 6 mm	0.64	3.1	0.72	4.1	0.80	4.6	0.89	5.1	1.00	5.7	1.12	6.4
Corrugated iron 1.6 mm	0.79	4.5	0.91	5.2	1.04	5.9	1.20	6.8	1.40	8.0	1.67	9.5
Stone 300 mm	0.41	2.3	0.44	2.5	0.47	2.7	0.50	2.8	0.53	3.0	0.56	3.2
450 mm	0.34	1.9	0.36	2.0	0.38	2.2	0.40	2.3	0.42	2.4	0.44	2.5
600 mm	0.29	1.6	0.31	1.8	0.32	1.8	0.33	1.9	0.35	2.0	0.36	2.0
Cavity, inner leaf 100 mm thermalite, outer leaf 100 mm brick, 50 mm cavity	0.18	1.0	0.18	1.0	0.19	1.1	0.19	1.1	0.19	1.1	0.21	1.2
Cavity, inner leaf thermalite 100 mm, outer leaf brick 100 mm, air gap 50 mm, lined internally plasterboard	0.16	0.92	0.17	0.95	0.17	0.97	0.17	0.99	0.18	1.0	0.18	1.0
Windows												
Single glazed	0.70	4.0	0.79	4.5	0.88	5.0	1.00	5.7	1.14	6.5	1.30	7.4
Double glazed 20 mm air gap	0.41	2.3	0.44	2.5	0.47	2.7	0.50	2.8	0.53	3.0	0.56	3.2
12 mm air gap	0.44	2.4	0.47	2.6	0.51	2.9	0.54	2.9	0.58	3.1	0.62	3.3
6 mm air gap	0.47	2.7	0.51	2.9	0.54	3.1	0.58	3.3	0.63	3.6	0.67	3.8
3 mm air gap	0.52	2.9	0.57	3.2	0.61	3.5	0.68	3.9	0.73	4.1	0.79	4.5
Triple glazed 20 mm air gap	0.29	1.6	0.31	1.8	0.32	1.8	0.33	1.9	0.35	2.0	0.36	2.0
12 mm air gap	0.32	1.7	0.34	1.8	0.35	2.0	0.37	2.0	0.39	2.1	0.41	2.2
6 mm air gap	0.35	2.0	0.37	2.1	0.39	2.2	0.41	2.3	0.43	2.4	0.46	2.6
3 mm air gap	0.41	2.3	0.44	2.5	0.47	2.7	0.50	2.8	0.54	3.1	0.57	3.2

	Exposure					
	Sheltered		Normal		Severe	
	$\frac{Btu}{ft^2\,hr\,°F}$	$W/m^2\,K$	$\frac{Btu}{ft^2\,hr\,°F}$	$W/m^2\,K$	$\frac{Btu}{ft^2\,hr\,°F}$	$W/m^2\,K$
Flat roofs						
Asphalt on 150 mm concrete	0.58	3.3	0.64	3.6	0.70	4.0
Asphalt on 150 mm concrete with plaster underneath	0.51	2.9	0.55	3.1	0.61	3.5
Asphalt on 150 mm hollow tiles	0.45	2.5	0.48	2.7	0.52	3.0
Asphalt on 150 mm hollow tiles with lightweight screed and plaster underneath	0.30	1.7	0.32	1.8	0.33	1.9
Asphalt with screed on 50 mm woodwool slabs on timber joists and plaster ceiling	0.16	0.9	0.18	1.0	0.21	1.2
Asphalt with screed on 50 mm woodwool slabs on steel framing	0.24	1.4	0.26	1.5	0.28	1.6
Pitched roofs						
Corrugated aluminium sheeting	0.90	5.1	1.15	6.6	1.45	8.3
Corrugated steel sheeting	0.90	5.1	1.15	6.6	1.45	8.3
Tiles on battens and roofing felt with rafters and plasterboard ceiling	0.32	1.8	0.35	2.0	0.39	2.2
Tiles on battens and roofing felt with rafters and plasterboard ceiling with boarding on rafters	0.26	1.5	0.30	1.7	0.33	1.9
Tiles on battens and rafters with plasterboard ceiling	0.44	2.5	0.49	2.8	0.53	3.0
Tiles on battens and rafters with plasterboard ceiling and boarding on rafters	0.32	1.8	0.35	2.0	0.39	2.2
Tiles on battens and roofing felt with rafters and no ceiling below	0.69	3.9	0.76	4.3	0.83	4.7
Tiles on battens and boarding with rafters and no ceiling below	0.53	3.0	0.58	3.3	0.63	3.6
Tiles on battens only with rafters and no ceiling below	1.00	5.7	1.11	6.3	1.23	7.0
Roof glazing						
Skylight	1.00	5.7	1.20	6.8	1.40	8.0
Laylight with lantern over	0.57	3.2	0.60	3.4	0.63	3.6

Thermal transmittance coefficients for building elements

	$\dfrac{Btu}{ft^2\,hr\,°F}$	$W/m^2\,K$
Floors		
Solid floors in contact with earth:		
Up to 4 m square	0.25	1.4
4 to 8m square	0.15	0.75
10 m wide more than 12 m long	0.09	0.50
30 m wide more than 40 m long	0.035	0.20
Suspended floors above ground:		
Up to 4 m square	0.14	0.80
4 to 8 m square	0.20	1.2
10 m wide more than 12 m long	0.40	2.2
30 m wide more than 40 m long	0.80	4.5

Internal resistance R_{S1}

	$\dfrac{ft^2\,hr\,°F}{Btu}$	$\dfrac{m^2\,K}{W}$
Walls	0.70	0.123
Floors	0.85	0.150
Ceilings and roofs	0.60	0.106

External resistance R_{S2}

Orientation	*Exposure*					
	Sheltered		*Normal*		*Severe*	
	$\dfrac{ft^2\,hr\,°F}{Btu}$	$\dfrac{m^2\,K}{W}$	$\dfrac{ft^2\,hr\,°F}{Btu}$	$\dfrac{m^2\,K}{W}$	$\dfrac{ft^2\,hr\,°F}{Btu}$	$\dfrac{m^2\,K}{W}$
S	0.73	0.128	0.57	0.100	0.43	0.076
W, SW, SE	0.57	0.100	0.43	0.076	0.30	0.053
NW	0.43	0.076	0.30	0.053	0.18	0.032
N, NE, E	0.43	0.076	0.30	0.053	0.07	0.012
Horizontal (roof)	0.40	0.070	0.25	0.044	0.10	0.018

Note: The data for surface resistances are applicable to plain surfaces but not to bright metallic surfaces.

The resistance of a corrugated surface is less than that of a plain one, generally by about 20%.

Thermal resistivity of air spaces

Material bounding space	resistivity (x/k) in m^2 K/W for thickness of air space in mm									
	15	20	25	35	50	65	75	90	100	115
Glass	0.141	0.145	0.148	0.155	0.165	0.172	0.176	0.183	0.186	0.188
Brick	0.150	0.153	0.158	0.165	0.175	0.185	0.190	0.197	0.200	0.203

Material bounding space	resistivity (x/k) in $\dfrac{ft^2\ hr\ °F}{Btu}$ for thickness of air space in in.									
	$\frac{1}{2}$	$\frac{3}{4}$	1	$1\frac{1}{2}$	2	$2\frac{1}{2}$	3	$3\frac{1}{2}$	4	$4\frac{1}{2}$	5
Glass	0.79	0.82	0.85	0.89	0.94	0.97	1.00	1.04	1.06	1.07	1.08
Brick	0.84	0.87	0.90	0.95	1.04	1.04	1.08	1.11	1.14	1.16	1.17

Condensation on glass windows

The chart gives the maximum permissible heat transfer coefficient of the glass necessary to prevent condensation at various indoor and outdoor temperatures and humidity.

Example
Inside temp.	15°C
Inside rel. humidity	30%
Outside temps.	−5°C

From chart, maximum permissible thermal transmittance coefficient is 7.0 W/m^2 K.

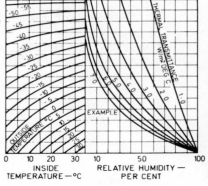

Fuel consumption

1 Direct method

$$F = \frac{Hn \, (t_i - t_2) \, 100}{EC \, (t_i - t_o)}$$

where

F=fuel consumption during time n (kg)
H=heat loss for temperature difference $(t_i - t_o)$ (kW)
n=time over which fuel consumption is required   (s)
E=efficiency of utilization of fuel   (%)
C=calorific value of fuel   (kJ/kg)
t_i=inside temperature   (°C)
t_a=average outside temperature during period considered   (°C)
t_o=outside design temperature   (°C)

$$E = E_1 \, E_2 \, E_3 \, E_4$$

where

E_1=boiler efficiency   (60–75%)
E_2=efficiency of pipework (loss of heat from pipes)   (80–90%)
E_3=efficiency of heaters   (90–100%)
E_4=efficiency of control (loss due to over heating)   (80–95%)
E=efficiency of utilization of fuel   (35–65%)

2 Degree day method

Degree days give the extent and length of time that the outdoor temperature is below 15.5°C.

number of degree days =   number of days ×
in a stated period   (15.5°C − average outdoor temperature °C)

$$F = \frac{hD \, 100}{EC}$$

$$h = \frac{24 \times 3600 \times H}{(15.5 - t_o)}$$

where

F=fuel consumption over period considered   (kg)
h=heat loss per degree day   (kJ/degree
                                    day)
E=efficiency of utilization of fuel, as above   (%)
C=calorific value of fuel   (kJ/kg)
H=heat loss for design conditions   (kW)
t_o=outside design temperature   (°C)
D=actual number of degree days in period considered   (number)

Degree days for United Kingdom

Base temperature 15.5°C

Region	Month												
	Jan.	Feb.	Mar.	Apr.	May	Jun.	Jul.	Aug.	Sep.	Oct.	Nov.	Dec.	Total
Thames Valley	346	304	282	197	113	47	24	27	56	132	256	333	2118
South Eastern	370	329	310	224	145	74	44	48	84	163	280	356	2427
Southern	339	307	294	214	141	68	41	42	76	145	258	328	2253
South Western	293	272	267	197	131	58	32	30	55	114	215	276	1940
Severn Valley	344	311	292	209	129	56	31	34	69	143	259	328	2205
Midland	371	335	318	233	152	76	46	51	92	172	290	358	2494
West Pennines	359	323	304	222	139	66	41	43	79	155	280	346	2357
North Western	366	333	319	239	163	82	55	56	94	169	296	357	2531
Borders	376	343	332	259	193	176	73	72	108	184	300	361	2718
North Eastern	374	334	317	234	154	76	48	50	87	171	295	360	2500
East Pennines	362	323	304	217	139	66	40	42	77	157	281	350	2358
East Anglia	378	334	315	232	143	71	46	43	74	154	283	360	2433
West Scotland	368	335	316	235	163	83	61	63	106	179	303	354	2565
East Scotland	379	343	326	252	189	100	69	71	106	185	308	368	2696
North East Scotland	396	359	345	270	206	111	85	86	124	199	322	381	2884
Wales	323	301	292	228	156	80	49	43	72	136	239	301	2220
Northern Ireland	359	325	311	237	167	86	61	63	100	170	288	343	2510

7 Cooling loads

Cooling load for air conditioning consists of:
   conduction and convection through walls, windows, etc.
   absorption of solar radiation on walls, windows, etc.
   heat emission of occupants.
   infiltration of warm outdoor air.
   heat emission of lights and other electrical or mechanical appliances.

1 Heat gain through walls, windows, doors, etc.

$$H = AU (t_o - t_i)$$

where
H = Heat gained   (W)
A = area of exposed surface   (m^2)
U = coefficient of heat transmission   (W/m^2 K)
t_0 = outside air temperature   (°C)
T_i = indoor air temperature   (°C)

Coefficients of heat transmission are the same as for heat losses in winter.

2 Solar radiation

$$H = AF\alpha J$$

where
H = heat gained   (W)
A = area of exposed surface   (m^2)
F = radiation factor = proportion of absorbed radiation which is transmitted to interior
α = absorption coefficients = proportion of incident radiation which is absorbed
J = intensity of solar radiation striking the surface   (W/m^2)

3 Heat emission of occupants

Heat and moisture given off by human body; tabulated data.

4   Heat gain by infiltration

$$H = nVd \, (h_o - h_i)$$

where
H = heat gain	(kW)
n = number of air changes	(s^{-1})
V = volume of room	(m^3)
d = density of air	(kg/m^3)
h_o = enthalpy of outdoor air with water vapour	(kJ/kg)
h_i = enthalpy of indoor air with water vapour	(kJ/kg)

5   Heat emission of appliances

All power consumed is assumed to be dissipated as heat.

heat emission in kW = appliance input rating in kW

Design summer indoor conditions

Optimum temperature   20°C to 22°C
Optimum relative humidity 40% to 65%

Desirable indoor conditions in summer for exposures less than 3 hours

Outside dry bulb temp.	Inside air conditions with dewpoint constant at 14°C		
	Dry bulb	Wet bulb	Relative humidity
°C	°C	°C	%
35	27	18.5	44
32	26	18.0	46
29	25	17.8	52
27	24	17.5	51
24	23	17.2	57
21	22	17.0	57

Relation of effective temperature, to dry and wet bulb temperatures and humidity, with summer and winter comfort zones

Charts for velocities up to 0.1m/s i.e. practically still air.
For an air velocity of 0.4m/s the effective temperature decreases by 1°C.

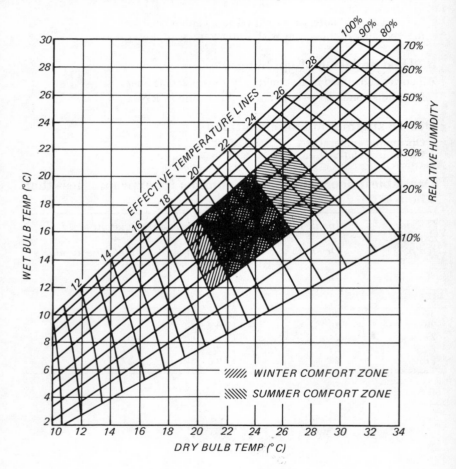

Radiation factor (F)

Proportion of radiation absorbed by wall transmitted to interior.

$\dfrac{U\text{-}value\ of\ wall}{W/m^2 K}$	F
1.0	0.04
1.5	0.06
2.0	0.08
2.5	0.10
3.0	0.12
3.5	0.14
4.0	0.16
4.5	0.18
5.0	0.20

For glass, proportion of incident radiation transmitted directly and proportion absorbed and transmitted = 0.84

Absorption coefficient (α)

Proportion of radiation falling on wall absorbed by it.

Type of surface	α
Very light surface, white stone, light cement	0.4
Medium dark surface, unpainted wood, brown stone, brick, red tile	0.7
Very dark surface, slate roofing, very dark paints	0.9

Time lag in transmission of solar radiation through walls

Type of wall	Time lag hours
150 mm concrete	3
100 mm lightweight blocks	$2\frac{1}{2}$
560 mm brick	10
75 mm concrete with 25 mm thermal insulation board	2
50 mm timber	$1\frac{1}{2}$

Transmission of radiation through shaded windows

Type of shading	Proportion transmitted
Canvas awning, plain	0.28
Canvas awning, aluminium bands	0.22
Inside shade, fully drawn	0.45
Inside shade, half drawn	0.68
Inside Venetian blind, slats at 45°, aluminium	0.58
Outside Venetian blind, slats at 45°, aluminium	0.22

Intensity of solar radiation

For latitude 45°

Solar time	Intensity of solar radiation for orientation (W/m^2)							
	NE	E	SE	S	SW	W	NW	Horizontal
5	79	75	28					6
6	281	312	164					82
7	470	612	394					284
8	441	691	539	69				492
9	290	612	577	205				663
10	104	455	539	309				791
11		237	438	382	101			864
12			287	404	287			890
13			101	382	438	237		864
14				309	539	455	104	791
15				205	577	612	290	663
16				69	539	691	441	492
17					394	612	470	284
18					164	312	281	82

Heat emitted by human body

Still air

Air temperature	(°C)	10	12	14	16	18	20	22	24	26	28	30	32
Sensible heat	(W)	136	126	115	106	98	92	85	77	69	58	47	33
Latent heat	(W)	21	21	21	21	23	27	33	41	49	60	69	81
Total	(W)	157	147	136	127	121	119	118	118	118	118	116	114
Moisture	(g/hr)	31	31	31	31	34	40	48	60	73	88	102	120

Air velocity 1 M/S

Air temperature	(°C)	10	12	14	16	18	20	22	24	26	28	30	32
Sensible heat	(W)	152	142	131	122	112	104	97	88	81	69	55	38
Latent heat	(W)	19	19	19	19	19	20	25	32	38	49	61	77
Total	(W)	171	161	150	143	131	124	122	120	119	118	116	115
Moisture	(g/hr)	28	28	28	28	28	29	36	47	57	73	89	114

8 Heating systems

Hot water heating

Hot water carries heat through pipes from the boiler to room or space heaters.

Classification by pressure

Type	Abbreviation	Flow temp. °C	Temp. drop °C
Low pressure hot water heating	LPHW		
(a) pumped circulation		50–90	10–15
(b) gravity circulation		90	20
Medium pressure hot water	MPHW	90–120	15–35
High pressure hot water	MPHW	120–200	27–85

Classification by pipe system
One-pipe or two-pipe system ⎱
Up-feed or down-feed system ⎰ See typical schemes on page 127.

Design procedure for hot water heating system
1 Heat losses of rooms to be heated.
2 Boiler output.
3 Selection of room heating units.
4 Type, size and duty of circulating pump.
5 Pipe scheme and pipe sizes.
6 Type and size of expansion tank.

1 Heat losses
Calculated with data in section 6.

2 Boiler

$$B = H(1+X)$$

where

B = boiler rating   (kW)
H = total heat loss of plant   (kW)
X = margin for heating up   (0.10 to 0.15)

Boilers with correct rating to be selected from manufacturers' catalogues.

HOT WATER PIPE SYSTEMS
1 PUMPED SYSTEMS
(a) OPEN EXPANSION TANK

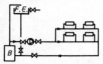

(i) One-pipe system

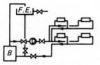

(ii) Two-pipe system

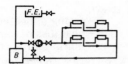

(iii) Reverse return
total length of flow is the same through all radiators

(b) CLOSED EXPANSION TANK

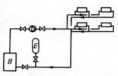

Two-pipe system taken as example
other systems also possible with expansion
tank in same relative position

(c) COMBINED HEATING AND HOT WATER SYSTEM

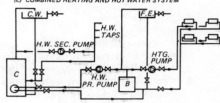

2 GRAVITY SYSTEMS

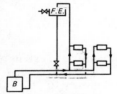

(i) Two-pipe upfeed system

(ii) Two-pipe drop system

(iii) One-pipe drop system

(iv) Two-pipe drop system with boiler
and radiators at same level

(v) One-pipe ring main system

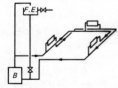

(vi) Two-pipe reverse return ring main
system

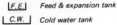 F.E. Feed & expansion tank

C.W. Cold water tank

 Hot water calorifier

⋈ Valve   ⊘ Pump

Ⓔ Closed expansion vessel   B Boiler

⊏⊐ Radiator

3 Room heaters

$$R = H\,(1+X)$$

where

R = rating of heaters in room   (W)
H = heat loss of room   (W)
X = margin for heating up   (0.10 to 0.15)

Heaters with correct rating to be selected from manufacturers' catalogues.

4 Pump size

$$Q = \frac{H}{(h_1 - h_2)\,d}$$

where

Q = volume of water   (m³/s)
H = total heat loss of plant   (kW)
h_1 = enthalpy of flow water   (kJ/kg)
h_2 = enthalpy of return water   (kJ/kg)
d = density of water at pump   (kg/m³)

For LPHW this reduces to

$$Q = \frac{H}{4.185\,(t_1 - t_2)}$$

where

t_1 = flow temperature   (°C)
t_2 = return temperature   (°C)

Pump head is chosen to give reasonable pipe sizes according to extent of system.

For LPHW 10 to 60 kN/m² with pipe friction resistance 80 to 250 N/m² per m run.

For HPHW 60 to 250 kN/m² with pipe friction resistance 100 to 300 N/m² per m run.

Gravity systems

$$p = hg\,(\varrho_2 - \varrho_1)$$

where

p = circulating pressure available   (N/m²)
h = height between centre of boiler and centre of radiator   (m)
ρ_1 = density of water at flow temperature   (kg/m³)
ρ_2 = density of water at return temperature   (kg/m³)
g = acceleration of gravity = 9.81   (m/sᵉ)

5   Pipe sizes

$$p_7 = p_1 + p_2$$
$$p_1 = il$$

$$p_2 = \Sigma F \frac{V^2}{2}$$

alternatively,

$$p_2 = \Sigma l_E$$

where

p_7 =	total pressure loss in system	(N/m^2)
p_1 =	pressure loss in pipes due to friction	(N/m^2)
p_2 =	pressure loss in fittings	(N/m^2)
i =	pipe friction resistance per length	(N/m^2 per m run)
l =	length of pipe	(m)
F =	coefficient of resistance	
V =	velocity of water	(m/s)
ϱ =	density of water	(kg/m^3)
l_E =	equivalent length of fitting	(m)

i can be obtained from Chart 1.

Typical values of p_2/p_1

Heating installations in buildings	0.40 to 0.50
District heating mains	0.10 to 0.30
Heating mains within boiler rooms	0.70 to 0.90

6   Expansion tank

(a)   Open tank (For LPHW only)

Expansion of water from 7°C to 100°C=approx. 4%.

Requisite volume of expansion tank=$0.08X$ water contents of system.
Water content for typical system is approximately 1 litre for every 1 m^2 of radiator surface.

(b)   Closed tank

$$V_t = V_e \frac{p_w}{p_w - p_i} \qquad\qquad V_e = V_w \frac{\varrho_1 - \varrho_2}{\varrho_2}$$

where

V_t =	volume of tank	(m^3)
V_e =	volume by which water content expands	(m^3)
V_w =	volume of water in system	(m^3)
p_w =	pressure of tank at working temperature	(kN/m^2)
p_i =	pressure of tank when filled cold	(kN/m^2)
ϱ_1 =	density of water at filling temperature	(kg/m^3)
ϱ_2 =	density of water at working temperature	(kg/m^3)

p_w to be selected so that working pressure at highest point of system corresponds to a boiling point approximately 10 K above working temperature

p_w = working pressure at highest point + static pressure difference between highest point and tank±pump pressure (+ or − according to position of pump).

Either p_i or V_t can be chosen independently to determine value of the other.

Approximate size of expansion tank for LPHW

Boiler rating	Tank size		Ball valve size	Cold feed size	Open vent size	Overflow size
kw	litre	BS Ref.	mm n.b.	mm n.b.	mm n.b.	mm n.b.
12	54	SCM 90	15	20	25	25
25	54	SCM 90	15	20	25	32
30	68	SCM 110	15	20	25	32
45	68	SCM 110	15	20	25	32
55	86	SCM 135	15	20	25	32
75	114	SCM 180	15	25	32	32
150	191	SCM 270	15	25	32	32
225	227	SCM 320	20	32	40	40
275	264	SCM 360	20	32	40	40
375	327	SCM 450/1	20	40	50	40
400	336	SCM 450/2	20	40	50	50
550	423	SCM 570	25	40	50	50
800	709	SCM 910	25	50	65	50
900	841	SCM 1130	25	50	65	65
1200	1227	SCM 1600	25	50	65	65

Safety valves

Safety valve setting=pressure on outlet side of pump $+70$ kN/m^2.
For gravity systems, safety valve setting=pressure in system $+15$ kN/m^2.
To prevent leakage due to shocks in system, it is recommended that the setting should be not less than 240 kN/m^2.
Valves should have clearances to allow a lift of $\frac{1}{5}\times$diameter.

Safety valve sizes for water boilers

Boiler rating	Minimum clear bore of safety valves and vents
kW	mm
275	1×20
350	1×25
440	1×32
530	1×40
880	2×40
1,500	80 to 150

Recommended flow temperatures for LPHW systems

Outside temperature	°C	0	2	4	7	10
Boiler flow temperature	°C	80	70	56	45	37

Resistance of fittings for LPHW pipe systems

Values of F for different fittings

Radiators	3.0	Tee, straight way	1.0
Boilers	2.5	branch	1.5
Abrupt velocity change	1.0	counter current	3.0
Cross-over	0.5		

Fitting		Nominal bore mm					
		15	20	25	32	40	50
Radiator valve:	angle	7	4	4	4	—	—
	straight	4	2	2	2	—	—
Gate valve:	screwed	1.5	0.5	0.5	0.5	0.5	0.5
	flanged	0	0	0	0	0	0
Elbow		2	2	1.5	1.5	1.0	1.0
Bend		1.5	1.5	1.0	1.0	0.5	0.5

Frictional resistance of fittings for various velocities and values of F

Resistance in kN/m^2

Velocity m/s	Value of F						
	1	2	3	4	5	10	15
0.24	0.029	0.057	0.086	0.115	0.144	0.285	0.43
0.50	0.125	0.25	0.375	0.50	0.62	1.25	1.87
0.75	0.28	0.56	0.84	1.12	1.40	2.80	4.20
1.0	0.50	1.00	1.50	2.00	2.50	5.00	7.50
1.2	0.72	1.44	2.15	2.85	3.60	7.20	10.80
1.5	1.12	2.25	3.35	4.50	5.60	11.20	16.8
1.7	1.44	2.90	4.30	5.80	7.20	14.4	21.6
2.0	2.00	4.00	6.00	8.00	1.00	19.9	29.9
2.4	2.85	5.70	8.60	11.50	1.44	28.7	43.1
2.8	3.90	7.80	11.70	15.60	1.95	39.1	58.6
3.0	4.50	9.00	13.50	17.90	2.24	44.9	67.3

Loss of Head in inches w.g.

Velocity ft/s	Value of F						
	1	2	3	4	5	10	15
1	0.18	0.36	0.54	0.72	0.90	1.80	2.70
1.5	0.22	0.45	0.67	0.90	1.12	2.25	3.37
2	0.72	1.5	2.2	3.0	3.6	7.20	10.8
3	1.6	3.3	4.9	6.6	8.2	16.3	24.4
4	3.0	5.8	8.7	11.6	14.5	28.9	43.4
5	4.5	9.0	13.6	18.0	22.6	45.2	67.8
6	6.5	13.0	19.6	26.0	32.6	65.2	97.8
7	8.9	17.7	26.6	35.4	44.3	88.6	133.0
8	11.6	23.2	34.7	46.4	57.9	116.0	174.0
9	14.7	29.3	44.0	58.6	73.3	147.0	220.0
10	18.0	36.2	54.3	72.4	90.5	181.0	272.0

Resistance of valves and fittings to flow of fluids in terms of equivalent length of straight pipe

Description of fitting		Nominal diameter										
	in mm	½ 15	¾ 20	1 25	1¼ 32	1½ 40	2 50	2½ 65	3 80	4 100	5 125	6 150
Globe Valve	E.L. ft m	13 4	16 5	26 8	35 11	40 12	55 17	65 20	80 24.5			
Angle Valve	E.L. ft m	8 2.5	11 3.5	15 4.5	18 5.5	20 6	27 8.3	32 10	40 12			
Gate Valve	E.L. ft m	0.3 0.09	0.5 0.15	0.5 0.15	0.5 0.15	1 0.3	1 0.3	1.5 0.45	2 0.6	2.5 0.75	3 0.9	3 0.9
Elbow	E.L. ft m	1 0.3	2 0.6	2 0.6	3 0.9	4 1.2	5 1.5	6 1.8	8 2.5	11 3.5	13 4	17 5.2
Long Sweep Elbow	E.L. ft m	1 0.3	1.5 0.45	2 0.6	2.5 0.75	3 0.9	3 1.0	5 1.2	4 1.5	6 1.8	8 2.5	10 3.0
Run of Tee	E.L. ft m	1 0.3	1.5 0.45	2.5 0.75	2.5 0.8	3 0.9	3 1.0	4 1.2	5 1.5	6 1.8	8 2.5	10 3.0
Run of Tee, reduced to ½	E.L. ft m	1 0.3	2 0.5	2 0.7	3 0.9	4 1.2	5 1.5	6 1.8	8 2.5	11 3.5	13 4	17 5.2
Branch of Tee	E.L. ft m	3.5 1.1	5 1.5	6 1.8	8 2.5	10 3.0	13 4	15 4.5	18 5.5	24 7.3	30 9	35 11
Sudden Enlargement $\frac{d}{D}=\frac{1}{4}$	E.L. ft m	1 0.3	2 0.5	2 0.7	3 0.9	4 1.2	5 1.5	6 1.8	8 2.5	11 3.5	13 4	17 5.2
$\frac{d}{D}=\frac{1}{2}$	E.L. ft m	1 0.3	1.5 0.45	2 0.6	2.5 0.75	3 0.9	3.5 1.1	4 1.2	5 1.5	7 2.1	9 2.7	11 3.5
$\frac{d}{D}=\frac{3}{4}$	E.L. ft m	0.3 0.09	0.5 0.15	0.5 0.15	1 0.25	1 0.3	1 0.35	1.5 0.45	2 0.6	2.3 0.75	3 0.9	3 1.0
Sudden Contraction $\frac{d}{D}=\frac{1}{4}$	E.L. ft m	0.8 0.25	1.0 0.3	1.2 0.35	1.5 0.45	2.0 0.6	2.5 0.75	3 0.9	4 1.2	5 1.5	6 1.8	8 2.5
$\frac{d}{D}=\frac{1}{2}$	E.L. ft m	0.5 0.15	0.8 0.25	1.0 0.3	1.2 0.35	1.5 0.45	2 0.6	2 0.6	3 0.9	4 1.2	5 1.5	6 1.8
$\frac{d}{D}=\frac{3}{4}$	E.L. ft m	0.4 0.12	0.5 0.15	0.6 0.18	1.0 0.3	1.0 0.3	1.5 0.4	1.5 0.5	2.0 0.6	2.5 0.8	3 0.9	3.5 1.1
Ordinary Entrance	E.L. ft m	1 0.3	1 0.3	1.5 0.45	2 0.6	2.5 0.75	3 0.9	3.5 11	4.5 1.4	6 1.8	8 2.5	10 3.0

Circulating pressures for gravity heating
Pressure in N/m² per m circulating height

Return temp. (°C)	Flow temp. (°C)							
	95	90	85	80	75	70	65	60
50	257	223	190	159	129	101	74	39
55	332	200	168	136	106	97	50	24
60	209	176	143	112	82	53	26	—
65	183	150	117	87	56	27	—	—
70	156	123	90	59	28	—	—	—
75	127	94	61	30	—	—	—	—
80	98	64	31	—	—	—	—	—
85	66	32	—	—	—	—	—	—

Head in inches water gauge per foot circulating height

Return temp. (°F)	Flow temp. (°F)						
	200	190	180	170	160	150	140
120	0.324	0.277	0.230	0.187	0.145	0.104	0.068
130	0.293	0.244	0.198	0.153	0.111	0.070	0.035
140	0.258	0.210	0.163	0.118	0.077	0.036	—
150	0.221	0.172	0.126	0.081	0.040	—	—
160	0.181	0.133	0.086	0.040	—	—	—
170	0.140	0.090	0.044	—	—	—	—
180	0.096	0.046	—	—	—	—	—
190	0.048	—	—	—	—	—	—

Boiler and radiators at same level
Circulating pressure in N/m² for 90°C flow temperature 70°C return, return downcomers bare.

Horizontal extent of plant (m)	Horizontal distance of downcomer from main riser (m)						
	5	5–10	10–15	15–20	20–30	30–40	40–50
Up to 10	69	177	—	—	—	—	—
10–15	69	108	147	196	245	—	—
25–50	49	78	108	137	177	235	294

Head in inches water gauge for 195°F flow temperature, 160°F return, return downcomers bare.

Horizontal extent of plant (ft)	Horizontal distance of downcomer from main riser (ft)						
	16	16–32	32–48	48–64	64–96	96–125	125–160
Up to 32	0.275	0.710	—	—	—	—	—
32–82	0.275	0.430	0.600	0.800	1.00	—	—
82–164	0.200	0.310	0.430	0.550	0.710	0.950	1.180

Panel heating

Invisible panel heating installations are heating systems using as heating surfaces pipe coils embedded in the concrete structure. The coils are generally constructed from black, mild steel tubes to BS 1387:1967 15 or 20 mm nom bore. Coils embedded in concrete or plaster to be tested to a hydraulic pressure of 3400 kN/m^2 for half an hour.

Heating coils in form of hair pins are generally used, maximum length of 15 mm nom bore coils approximately 55 m long.

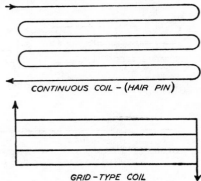

CONTINUOUS COIL – (HAIR PIN)

Grid coils have less resistance, are more rigid, but there is a danger of short circuiting, therefore they are seldom used.

GRID–TYPE COIL

Advantages of panel heating systems

Saving of floor space.

No visible heaters and tubing, no dust collection.

No staining of walls, cleanliness and low maintenance.

More even temperature distribution, no excessive temperature at ceiling height.

Lower air temperature, therefore lower heat loss and saving of fuel.

Disadvantages

More expensive first cost than radiator and convector heating.

Special building structure sometimes required.

Time lag for heating up.

Invisible heating panels can be arranged as

   A   Ceiling panels

   B   Floor panels

   C   Wall panels

The advantages of one type over another are small; advantages and disadvantages can be summarised as shown on page 137.

Panel heating

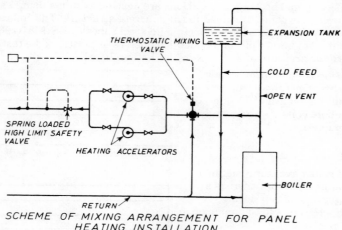

SCHEME OF MIXING ARRANGEMENT FOR PANEL
HEATING INSTALLATION

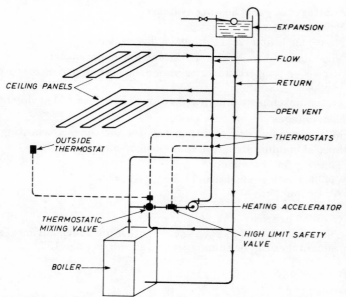

PIPE SCHEME OF PANEL HEATING INSTALLATION

Ceiling panels

Advantages
Never obstructed by furniture.   Comfortable conditions.
Higher permissible surface temperature than for floor panels, therefore smaller heating surface and lower cost.

Disadvantages
Not suitable for low rooms.   Feet shaded under desk in schools.
Not advisable for rooms with very Special ceiling structure required.
cold floors.

Applications
Hospitals, schools, flats, offices.

Data
Coils: 15 mm tubes at 150 mm centres.

Flow temp. 54°C (130°F)   Output to below 205 W/m^2 (65 Btu/
Return temp. 46°C (115°F)   hr ft^2)
Temp. drop 8°C (15°F)   Loss to above 32 W/m^2 (10 Btu/hr
Panel surface temp. 43°C (110°F) ft^2)
Emission by radiation 70%
Emission by convection 30%

Floor panels

Advantages
Heat transfer partly by convection, comfort for feet.
No special building structure required, coils embedded in floor slab or screed.

Disadvantages
Permissible surface temperature is low, therefore larger heating surfaces are required than for ceiling panels, and the first costs are higher.
Risk of panels being covered by furniture.

Applications
Schools, nurseries (especially where children play on floor), single-floor buildings, churches, factories.

Data
Coils: 15 mm or 20 mm tubes at approximately 230 mm centres.

Flow temp. 32°C (90°F)   Output 125 W/m^2 (40 Btu/hr ft^2)
Return temp. 24°C (75°F)   Loss to below 19 W/m^2 (6 Btu/hr ft^2)
Temp. drop 8°C (15°F)   Emission by radiation 55%
Panel surface temp. 24°C max   Emission by convection 45%
(75°F)

Wall panels

Advantages
No special wall structure is required, panels are embedded in plaster. Wall panels are useful under windows as an addition to floor panels to cover the heat loss of windows.

Disadvantages
Difficulty in arranging pipe connections.
Danger of covering wall panels by furniture.

Applications:
Halls, staircases.

Data:
Coils: 15 mm tubes at 150 mm centres.

Flow temp. 32° to 38°C (90° to 100°F)

Return temp. 24° to 32°C (75° to 90°F)

Temp. drop 8°C (15°F)

Panel surface temp. 26° to 29°C 78° to 85°F)

Output 142 W/m^2 (45 Btu/hr ft^2)

Loss to outside 19 W/m^2 (6 Btu/hr ft^2)

Emission by radiation 65%

Emission by convection 35%

Plaster for invisible heating panels

Heating coils embedded in concrete, wired to cork slabs or to suspended ceilings require careful treatment as to floating and finishing.

The suspended ceilings are covered with expanded metal lathing and pricked up with lime, sand and cement. When the pricking-up coat is stiff enough it should be well scratched with a wire comb ready to receive the floating coat.

Where time does not permit the rendering coat with cement to become thoroughly dry the metal lathing can be covered with gauged coarse stuff (lime and sand).

Sometimes heating panels are covered with lathwork and can be treated as previously mentioned if time is short.

A good mixture for lath or expanded metal is 4 parts of sand, 1 part of lime, and 1 part of cement; all floating coats should be lime 1, sand 3, with the usual hair added to this mix. About 30 per cent of plaster of Paris is added, floating the area to be covered to the ordinary thickness of the other part of the plastering surface, usually about 16 mm thick.

The finishing coat should be applied within 24 hours and composed of setting stuff, 3 parts of washed sand and 2 parts of lime putty. Two parts of this mixture is gauged on the board to 1 part of plaster.

This is applied to the floating coat as evenly as possible, following on with a covering of hessian scrim about 760 mm wide, pressing it well into the plaster, making a surface if possible without the addition of any extra application of plaster.

The canvas should overlap the panel about 150 mm with the ends of the canvas unthreaded or opened out.

Panel heaters

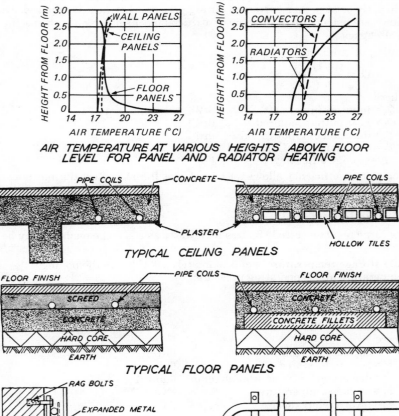

AIR TEMPERATURE AT VARIOUS HEIGHTS ABOVE FLOOR LEVEL FOR PANEL AND RADIATOR HEATING

TYPICAL CEILING PANELS

TYPICAL FLOOR PANELS

TYPICAL WALL PANEL

Off peak (storage) heating

Electricity is used during off peak periods to heat thermal stores from which the heat is then extracted during periods when heat is required. The stores are usually made of stone or artificial blocks having a high specific heat capacity.

Rating of unit

$$Q_1 = \frac{100\,Q_2 T_2}{\eta\,T_1}$$

where

Q_1 = input rating of unit   (kW)
Q_2 = heat output required   (kW)
T_1 = duration of input to unit   (hr)
T_2 = duration of heating period   (hr)
η = storage efficiency   (%)

The storage efficiency allows for loss of heat from the store during the charging period. It is 90–95%.

Electrode systems

For large plants electrode boilers with water as a storage medium may be used.

Safe storage temperature is approximately 10°C below the boiling temperature at the operating pressure.

Capacity of storage vessel

$$V = \frac{1000\,H}{4.2\,\varrho\,(t_1 - t_2)}$$

where

V = capacity of vessel   (litre)
H = heat to be stored   (kJ)
ϱ = density of water at storage temp.   (kg/m^3)
t_1 = storage temperature   (°C)
t_2 = return temperature   (°C)

Boiler rating

$$Q = \frac{H}{3600\,T}$$

where

Q = boiler rating   (kW)
H = heat to be stored   (kJ)
T = duration of boiler operation   (hr)

High temperature H.W. heating

Heat in kJ given up by 1 kg of water for various temperature drops

Return temp. (°C)	Flow temperature (°C)																					
	210	200	195	190	185	180	175	170	165	160	155	150	145	140	135	130	125	120	115	110	105	100
75	569	538	516	493	471	449	427	405	383	351	340	318	297	275	254	232	220	190	170	147	126	105
80	547	516	494	471	449	427	405	383	361	339	318	296	275	253	232	210	198	168	145	125	104	83
85	527	496	474	451	429	407	385	363	341	319	300	278	255	233	212	190	178	148	127	105	84	63
90	506	475	453	430	408	396	374	342	320	298	277	255	234	212	191	169	158	127	106	85	63	42
95	495	454	432	409	387	365	342	321	299	277	256	234	213	191	170	148	136	106	85	63	42	21
100	464	433	411	388	366	344	322	300	278	256	235	213	192	170	149	127	115	85	64	42	21	
105	443	412	390	367	345	323	301	279	257	235	214	192	171	149	128	106	94	64	43	21		
110	422	391	369	346	324	302	280	258	236	214	193	171	150	128	107	85	73	43	22			
115	400	369	347	324	302	280	258	236	214	192	171	150	128	107	85	63	51	21				
120	379	348	327	303	281	259	237	215	193	171	150	128	107	85	64	42	31					
125	349	317	296	273	251	229	207	185	163	141	120	98	77	55	33	12						
130	337	306	284	259	239	217	195	173	151	129	108	86	65	43	22							
135	315	284	262	239	217	195	173	151	129	108	86	65	43	22								
140	294	263	241	218	196	174	152	130	108	86	65	43	22									
145	272	241	219	196	174	151	130	108	86	64	43	21										
150	251	220	198	176	153	131	109	87	65	43	22											
155	229	198	177	155	133	111	89	67	45	22												
160	208	177	155	133	110	88	66	44	22													
165	186	155	133	110	88	66	44	22														
170	124	133	111	88	66	44	22															
175	142	111	89	67	45	23																
180	122	89	67	45	22																	
185	98	67	45	22																		
190	76	45	23																			
195	53	22																				
200	31																					

Example: Flow temperature = 180°C
Return temperature = 130°C
Heat given up by 1 kg of water 217 kJ

High temperature H.W. heating

Return temp. (°F)	Flow temperature (°F)																			
	400	390	380	370	360	350	340	330	320	310	300	290	280	270	260	250	240	230	220	210
170	237.3	226.3	215.5	204.9	194.3	183.7	173.1	162.6	152.1	141.8	131.5	121.2	110.9	100.7	90.5	80.4	70.3	60.2	50.1	40
180	227.3	216.3	205.5	194.9	184.3	173.7	163.1	152.6	142.2	131.8	121.5	111.2	100.9	90.7	80.5	70.4	60.3	50.2	40.1	30
190	217.3	206.3	195.5	184.9	174.3	163.7	153.1	142.6	132.1	121.8	111.5	101.2	90.9	80.7	70.5	60.4	50.3	40.2	30.1	20
200	207.3	196.3	185.5	174.9	164.3	153.7	143.1	132.6	122.1	111.8	101.5	91.2	80.9	70.7	60.5	50.4	40.3	30.2	20.1	10
210	197.3	186.3	175.5	164.9	154.3	143.7	133.1	122.6	112.2	101.8	91.5	81.2	70.9	60.7	50.5	40.4	30.3	20.2	10.1	
220	187.3	176.2	165.4	154.8	144.2	133.6	123.0	112.5	102.1	91.7	81.4	71.1	60.8	50.7	40.5	30.3	20.2	10.1		
230	177.1	166.1	155.3	144.7	134.1	123.6	112.9	102.4	92.0	81.6	71.3	61.2	50.8	40.6	30.5	20.3	10.1			
240	167.0	156.0	145.2	134.6	124.0	113.4	102.8	92.3	81.9	71.5	61.2	50.9	40.6	30.4	20.4	10.1				
250	156.3	145.9	135.1	124.5	113.9	103.3	92.7	82.2	71.8	61.4	51.2	40.8	30.5	20.3	10.1					
260	146.7	135.7	124.9	114.3	103.3	93.1	83.0	72.0	61.6	51.2	40.9	30.6	20.5	10.2						
270	136.6	125.6	114.8	104.2	93.6	83.0	72.4	61.9	51.5	41.1	30.8	20.5	10.2							
280	126.4	115.4	104.6	94.0	83.4	72.8	62.2	51.9	41.3	30.9	20.6	10.3								
290	116.1	105.1	94.3	83.7	73.1	62.5	51.9	41.4	31.1	20.7	10.3									
300	105.8	94.3	84.0	73.4	62.8	52.2	41.6	31.0	20.7	10.4										
310	95.5	84.5	73.7	63.1	52.5	41.9	31.3	20.8	10.4											
320	85.0	74.5	63.2	52.5	41.9	31.3	21.0	10.5												
330	74.7	63.7	52.9	41.9	31.3	21.2	10.6													
340	64.1	53.1	42.3	31.8	21.2	10.6														
350	53.6	42.6	31.8	21.2	10.6															
360	42.0	31.0	21.4	10.6																
370	32.4	21.0	10.6																	
380	21.8	10.8																		
390	11.0																			

Example: Flow temperature = 350°F
Return temperature = 240°F
Heat given up by 1 lb of water is 113.4 Btu per lb

Heat in Btu given up by 1 lb of water for various temperature drops

Heat pumps

The heat pump is a common refrigeration unit arranged in such a way that it can be used for both cooling and heating, or for heating only. The initial cost of the installation is high, and savings and advantages are achieved mainly when heating and cooling are required in winter and summer respectively.

Operation of the heat pump:
Referring to the scheme drawing below, the heat pump consists of the following parts:

Compressor, with driving motor, for raising the pressure and temperature of the refrigerant vapour.

Condenser, for extracting heat from the refrigerant.

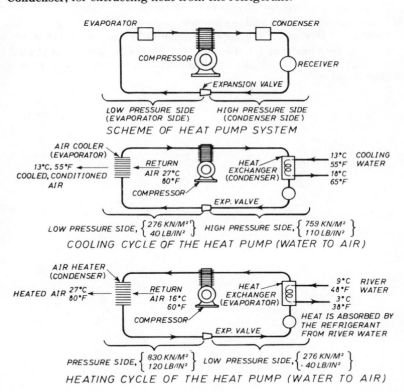

SCHEME OF HEAT PUMP SYSTEM

COOLING CYCLE OF THE HEAT PUMP (WATER TO AIR)

HEATING CYCLE OF THE HEAT PUMP (WATER TO AIR)

Receiver (storage tank) to hold the liquid refrigerant in the high pressure side before it passes the expansion valve.

Expansion valve, for causing expansion of the refrigerant and for lowering the pressure from the high pressure to the low pressure side of the system.

Evaporator, in which heat is absorbed by the refrigerant from some source. Water, earth or air can be used as the source of heat.

A commercial refrigeration unit and a heat pump consist of the same units and the same plant can be used either for cooling or heating.

The changing of the system from cooling to heating can be carried out by either of the following methods

(a) Leave the flow of the refrigerant unchanged and change the circuit of the heat source and the medium to be heated.

(b) Leave the heat source and the medium to be heated unchanged and reverse the flow of the refrigerant by a suitable pipe and valve scheme.

Schemes for a heat pump indicating suitable temperatures when used for cooling and heating are shown, the data being chosen for the purpose of illustration only.

9 Steam systems

Steam heating

Steam carries heat through pipes from the boiler to room or space heaters.

This is now seldom used as a method of space heating. This section is included for reference when old systems have to be examined or altered, and for design of systems in industrial premises where steam is available and steam-to-water calorifiers cannot be justified. Steam is also used for process heating in industry and the data in this section can also be used for pipe sizing.

Classification of steam heating systems

1 By pressure
    (a) High pressure steam heating system
    (b) Low pressure steam heating system
        Up to about 3 lb/in^2 or 20 kN/m^2
    (c) Vacuum system
2 By method of returning condensate
    (a) Gravity system
    (b) Mechanical system
3 By pipe scheme
    (a) One-pipe or two-pipe system
    (b) Up-feed or down-feed system

(See illustrations on page 146.)

Steam heating systems

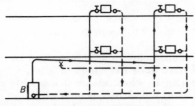

UP FEED TWO PIPE GRAVITY AIR
VENT SYSTEM-WET RETURN

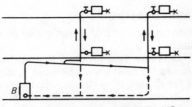

UP FEED ONE PIPE GRAVITY AIR
VENT SYSTEM-WET RETURN

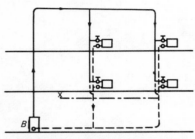

DOWN FEED TWO PIPE GRAVITY AIR
VENT SYSTEM-WET RETURN

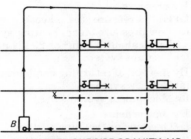

DOWN FEED ONE PIPE GRAVITY AIR
VENT SYSTEM-WET RETURN

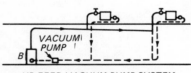

UP FEED VACUUM PUMP SYSTEM

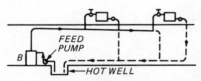

ATMOSTPHERIC SYSTEM HOT WELL OPEN
TO ATMOSTPHERE

KEY

B	BOILER
🔥	RADIATOR
——	STEAM MAIN
- - -	CONDENSATE MAIN
-·-·-	VENT PIPE
🔧	RADIATOR VALVE
—o—	STEAM TRAP
→×	VENT

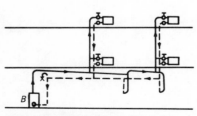

UP FEED TWO PIPE GRAVITY SYSTEM–
DRY RETURN

Vacuum differential heating system

In vacuum steam heating systems, a partial vacuum is maintained in the return line by means of a vacuum pump. The vacuum maintained is approx. 3 to 10 in mercury=approx. 75 to 250 mm mercury.

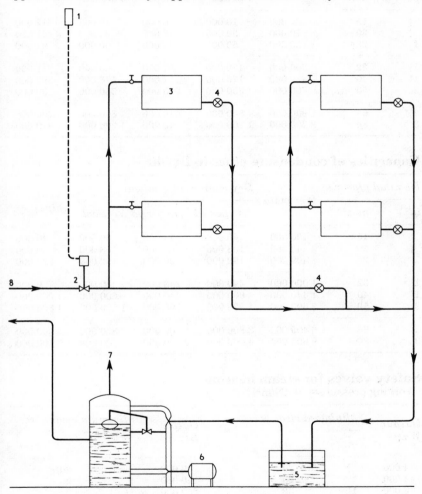

1 OUTSIDE THERMOSTAT
2 CONTROL VALVE
3 RADIATORS
4 STEAM TRAPS

5 CONDENSE RECEIVER
6 VACUUM PUMP
7 VENT
8 STEAM SUPPLY

Capacities of condensate pipes in watts

| Nominal pipe size | | Wet main | Dry main with gradient | | | Vent pipes |
in	mm		1 in 200	1 in 600	Vertical	
$\frac{1}{2}$	15	30 000	10 000	6 000	10 000	12 000
$\frac{3}{4}$	20	70 000	30 000	18 000	30 000	47 000
1	25	120 000	50 000	34 000	50 000	94 000
$1\frac{1}{4}$	32	300 000	120 000	80 000	120 000	211 000
$1\frac{1}{2}$	40	420 000	176 000	117 000	176 000	293 000
2	50	760 000	350 000	225 000	350 000	530 000
$2\frac{1}{2}$	65	1 900 000	800 000	510 000	800 000	1 200 000
3	80	2 700 000	1 200 000	740 000	1 200 000	1 870 000

Capacities of condensate pipes in Btu/hr

| Nominal pipe size | | Wet main | Dry main with gradient | | | Vent pipes |
in	mm		$\frac{1}{16}$ in per yd	$\frac{1}{16}$ in per yd	Vertical	
$\frac{1}{2}$	15	100 000	40 000	24 000	40 000	40 000
$\frac{3}{4}$	20	240 000	108 000	68 000	108 000	160 000
1	25	400 000	192 000	120 000	192 000	320 000
$1\frac{1}{4}$	32	1 000 000	440 000	280 000	440 000	720 000
$1\frac{1}{2}$	40	1 440 000	600 000	400 000	600 000	1 000 000
2	50	2 600 000	1 120 000	700 000	1 120 000	1 800 000
$2\frac{1}{2}$	65	6 400 000	2 800 000	1 760 000	2 800 000	4 000 000
3	80	9 600 000	4 000 000	2 520 000	4 000 000	6 400 000

Safety valves for steam heating
(Working pressure = 70 kN/m^2)

| Output Watts | Minimum clear bore | | Output Btu/hr | Minimum clear bore | |
	in	mm		in	mm
24 000	$\frac{1}{4}$	20	80 000	$\frac{1}{4}$	20
44 000	1	25	150 000	1	25
73 000	$1\frac{1}{4}$	32	250 000	$1\frac{1}{4}$	32
100 000	$1\frac{1}{2}$	40	350 000	$1\frac{1}{2}$	40
230 000	2	50	800 000	2	50
275 000	$2\frac{1}{2}$	65	950 000	$2\frac{1}{2}$	65
440 000	Two 2	Two 50	1 500 000	Two 2	Two 50

Suction lift of boiler feed pumps for various water temperatures

Temp of feed water °F	Max suction lift (ft)	Minimum pressure head (ft)	Temp of feed water (°C)	Max suction lift (m)	Minimum pressure head (m)
130	10		55	3	
150	2		65	2	
170	7		77	0.6	
175	0	0	80	0	0
190		5	87.5		1.5
200		10	95		3.5
210		15	99		4.5
212		17	100		5.0

Quantities of flash steam

Condensate Absolute pressure (kN/m²)	Condensate Temperature (°C)	Percentage of condensate flashed off at reduction of pressure to kN/m² absolute					
		400	260	170	101.33	65	35
1500	198.3	11.3	14.0	16.4	18.9	20.4	23.2
1150	186.0	8.7	11.5	13.9	16.5	18.4	20.9
800	170.4	5.5	8.2	10.8	13.4	15.4	17.9
650	162.0	3.7	6.5	9.1	11.8	13.7	16.3
500	151.8	1.6	4.6	7.1	9.8	11.8	14.4
400	143.6	—	3.0	5.5	8.3	10.3	12.9
260	128.7	—	—	2.6	5.4	7.5	10.2
170	115.2	—	—	—	2.8	5.0	7.7
101.33	100	—	—	—	—	2.2	4.9

Condensate Gauge pressure lb/in²)	Condensate Temperature (°F)	Percentage of condensate flashed off at reduction of pressure to lb/in² gauge or in Hg vacuum					
		40	20	10	0	10 in	20 in
200	388	11.5	14.3	16.2	18.8	20.5	23.2
150	366	9.0	11.8	13.0	16.4	18.2	20.9
100	338	5.8	8.6	10.6	13.3	15.1	17.9
80	324	4.2	7.1	9.1	11.9	13.7	16.5
60	308	2.3	5.2	7.3	10.0	11.8	14.7
40	287	—	3.0	5.0	7.8	9.7	12.6
20	259	—	—	2.1	5.0	6.8	9.8
10	240	—	—	—	2.9	4.8	7.8
0	212	—	—	—	—	1.9	5.0

Scheme of flash steam recovery

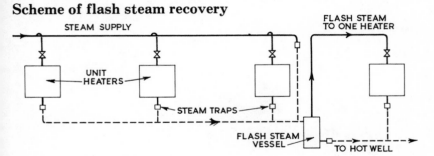

Sizing steam mains

The *Available Pressure Drop* is the difference between the initial or boiler pressure and the required final pressure at the end of the line.

$$p = p_j - p_k$$

The available pressure drop is used to overcome friction in pipes and pressure losses in fittings.

$$p_t = p_1 + p_2$$

For *low pressure steam*

$$p_1 = p_a l$$

$$p_2 = \Sigma F \frac{v^2 \varrho}{2}$$

Alternatively

$$p_2 = p_a l_e$$

and

$$p_t = p_a (l + l_e)$$

p_a can be read from Chart 2 for given steam flow and pipe size.
For *high pressure steam* Chart 3 can be used. In this the auxiliary value b_x is used in place of the pressure drop per unit length.

$$b_x = b_j - b_k$$
$$b_j = p_j^{1.9375}$$
$$b_k = p_k^{1.9375}$$

In the above formula

p_t = total pressure drop in system	(N/m^2)
p_j = initial or boiler pressure	(N/m^2)
p_k = final pressure	(N/m^2)
p_1 = pressure loss in pipes due to friction	(N/m^2)
p_2 = pressure loss in fittings	(N/m^2)
p_a = pipe friction resistance per length	(N/m^2)
F = coefficient of resistance	
v = steam velocity	(m/s)
ϱ = density of steam	(kg/m^3)
l = length of pipe	(m)
l_e = equivalent length of fitting	(m)

Ratio $\dfrac{p_2}{p_1}$ is generally about 0.33.

Total pressure drop is generally about 6 per cent of initial pressure per 100 m of pipe system.

Typical steam velocities

Exhaust steam	20–30 m/s	(70–100 ft/s)
Saturated steam	30–40 m/s	(100–130 ft/s)
Superheated steam	40–60 m/s	(130–200 ft/s)

Table for pipe sizing

For use with Chart 3

$b=p^{1.9375}$

p	b	p	b	p	b	p	b	p	b
14	167	38	1150	74	4180	160	18 620	420	121 300
15	190	39	1210	76	4400	165	19 860	440	132 100
16	215	40	1270	78	4630	170	20 990	460	144 500
17	240	41	1330	80	4870	180	22 130	480	157 800
18	270	42	1400	82	5110	190	25 820	500	169 800
19	300	43	1470	84	5350	200	28 840	520	182 800
20	330	44	1540	86	5390	210	31 620	540	196 800
21	365	45	1610	88	5850	220	34 670	560	211 300
22	400	46	1680	90	6110	230	37 930	580	224 900
23	435	47	1750	92	6380	240	41 020	600	241 000
24	470	48	1820	94	6660	250	44 460	620	258 200
25	510	49	1890	96	6940	260	47 750	640	275 400
26	550	50	1960	98	7220	270	51 400	660	289 700
27	590	52	2120	100	7500	280	54 950	680	307 600
28	635	54	2280	105	8250	290	59 160	700	325 100
29	680	56	2440	110	9020	300	63 100	750	371 500
30	720	58	2610	115	9830	310	67 450	800	421 700
31	775	60	2790	120	10 680	320	71 780	850	461 300
32	825	62	2970	125	11 500	330	74 130	900	526 000
33	875	64	3150	130	12 470	340	80 540	950	588 800
34	925	66	3350	135	13 420	350	84 920	1000	648 600
35	980	68	3550	140	14 390	360	90 160		
36	1035	70	3750	145	15 400	380	99 540		
37	1090	72	3960	150	16 450	400	110 200		

Values of F for fittings

Fitting	Nom bore					
	$\frac{1}{2}$ in 15 mm	$\frac{3}{4}$ in 20 mm	1 in 25 mm	$1\frac{1}{4}$ in 32 mm	$1\frac{1}{2}$ in 40 mm	2 in 50 mm
Radiator	1.5	1.5	1.5	1.5	1.5	1.5
Abrupt velocity change	1.0	1.0	1.0	1.0	1.0	1.0
Cross over	0.5	0.5	0.5	0.5	0.5	0.5
Angle valve	9	9	9	9		
Globe valve	15	17	19	30		
Angle cock	7	4	4	4		
Straight cock	4	2	2	2		
Gate valve	1.5	0.5	0.5	0.5	0.5	0.5
Damper	3.5	2	2	1.5	1.5	1
Elbow	2	2	1.5	1.5	1	1
Long sweep elbow	1.5	1.5	1	1	0.5	0.5
Short radius bend	2	2	2	2	2	2
Long radius bend	1	1	1	1	1	1
Tee straight	1	1	1	1	1	1
branch	1.5	1.5	1.5	1.5	1.5	1.5
counter current	3.0	3.0	3.0	3.0	3.0	3.0
double branch	1.5	1.5	1.5	1.5	1.5	1.5

Resistance of fittings for various velocities and values of F
Resistance in N/m²

Steam velocity m/s	Value of F						
	1	2	3	4	5	10	15
4	5.2	10.4	15.6	20.8	26.0	52	78
6	11.7	23.4	35.1	46.8	58.5	117	176
9	26.3	52.6	78.9	105.2	131.5	263	395
12	46.8	93.6	140.4	177.2	234.0	468	702
15	73.1	146.2	219.3	292.4	365.5	731	1097
18	105.3	210.6	315.9	421.2	526.5	1053	1580
21	143.4	286.8	430.2	573.6	717.0	1434	2151
24	187.2	374.4	561.6	748.8	936.0	1872	2808
27	236.9	473.8	710.7	947.6	1185	2369	3554
30	292.5	585.0	877.5	1170	1463	2925	4388

Resistance in lb/in²

Steam velocity ft/s	Value of F						
	1	2	3	4	5	10	15
14	0.000874	0.00175	0.00262	0.00350	0.00437	0.00874	0.0131
20	0.00178	0.00357	0.00535	0.00714	0.00892	0.0178	0.0268
30	0.00401	0.00803	0.0120	0.0160	0.0201	0.0401	0.0602
40	0.00714	0.0143	0.0214	0.0286	0.0357	0.0714	0.107
50	0.0112	0.0223	0.0335	0.0446	0.0558	0.112	0.167
60	0.0161	0.0321	0.0482	0.0642	0.0803	0.161	0.241
70	0.0219	0.0437	0.0696	0.0874	0.109	0.219	0.328
80	0.0285	0.0571	0.0856	0.1142	0.143	0.285	0.428
90	0.0361	0.0723	0.108	0.1446	0.181	0.361	0.542
100	0.0446	0.0892	0.134	0.1784	0.223	0.446	0.669

High pressure steam pipes

Resistance of valves and fittings to flow of steam
Expressed as an equivalent length of straight pipe

| Nom bore of pipe | | Bends of standard radius | | | | Barrel of tee | | | | Branch of tee | | Valves | | | | | | Lyre expansion bends | |
| | | 90° | | 45° | | Plain | | Reduced 25% | | | | Through | | Angle | | Globe | | | |
in	mm	ft	m	ft	m	ft	m	ft	m	ft	m	ft	m	ft	m	ft	m	ft	m
1	25	0.5	0.15	0.4	0.12	0.5	0.15	0.7	0.21	2.2	0.67	0.4	0.12	1.5	0.46	3.3	1.0	2.2	0.67
1¼	32	0.7	0.21	0.5	0.15	0.7	0.21	0.9	0.27	2.9	0.89	0.5	0.15	2.0	0.61	4.3	1.3	2.9	0.88
1½	40	0.9	0.27	0.7	0.21	0.9	0.27	1.1	0.33	3.6	1.1	0.7	0.21	2.4	0.73	5.4	1.6	3.6	1.1
2	50	1.3	0.40	1.0	0.30	1.3	0.40	1.6	0.49	5.1	1.6	1.3	0.40	3.4	1.0	7.6	2.3	5.1	1.6
2½	65	1.6	0.49	1.2	0.37	1.6	0.49	2.1	0.64	6.6	2.0	1.6	0.49	4.5	1.4	10.0	3.0	6.6	2.0
3	80	2.1	0.64	1.6	0.49	2.1	0.64	2.6	0.80	8.3	2.5	2.1	0.64	5.6	1.7	12.0	3.7	8.3	2.5
4	100	2.9	0.88	2.2	0.67	2.9	0.88	3.7	1.1	12.0	3.7	2.2	0.67	7.9	2.4	18.0	5.5	12.0	3.7
5	125	3.8	1.2	2.9	0.88	3.8	1.2	4.8	1.5	15.0	4.6	2.9	0.89	10.0	3.0	23.0	7.0	15.0	4.6
6	150	4.7	1.4	3.6	1.1	4.7	1.4	6.0	1.8	19.0	5.8	3.6	1.1	13.0	4.0	29.0	8.8	19.0	5.8
7	175	5.7	1.7	4.3	1.3	5.7	1.7	7.2	2.2	23.0	7.0	4.3	1.3	15.0	4.6	34.0	10	23.0	7.0
8	200	6.7	2.0	5.0	1.5	7.6	2.0	8.5	2.6	27.0	8.2	5.0	1.5	18.0	5.5	40.0	12	27.0	8.2
9	225	7.7	2.3	5.8	1.8	7.7	2.3	9.8	3.0	31.0	10	5.8	1.7	21.0	6.4	46.0	14	31.0	9.5
10	250	8.7	2.7	6.6	2.0	8.7	2.7	11.0	3.4	35.0	11	6.6	1.8	24.0	7.3	53.0	16	35.0	11

10 Domestic services

Domestic hot water supply

Classification
Direct System. Secondary water is heated by direct mixing with boiler water in a hot water cylinder.
Indirect system. Secondary water is heated by indirect heating by primary water from boiler in an indirect cylinder or calorifier.

Design procedure for domestic hot water
1 Determination of demand (quantity and temperature).
2 Selection of type, capacity and heating surface of calorifier.
3 Selection of boiler.
4 Pipe scheme and pipe sizes

1 Demand
Hot water is normally stored and supplied at 60°C. For canteens and large kitchens it may be required at 65°C. Where lower temperatures are necessary for safety (e.g. nursery schools, centres for handicapped) if may be stored and supplied at a lower temperature (usually 40°–50°C) or stored and supplied at a higher temperature and reduced by mixing with cold water in a blender at the point of draw off.

Quantity is determined either according to number of occupants or according to number of fittings.

2 Calorifier

$$H = \frac{4.2 \, V \, (\theta_2 - \theta_1)}{3600 \, t}$$

where

H = heating capacity	(kW)
V = volume stored	(litre)
θ_1 = temperature of cold feed water	(°C)
θ_2 = temperature of hot water	(°C)
t = time in which contents are to be raised from θ_1 to θ_2	(hr)

For instantaneous heating (non-storage calorifier or direct heater).
$$H = 4.2 \, v \, (\theta_2 - \theta_1)$$
where
v = demand in litre/s.

Storage systems are usually designed for $t=1$ hr or 2 hr. A shorter warming up time enables the volume of the calorifier to be reduced but may require a higher rate of heating.

Heating Surface

$$A = \frac{1000 \, H}{k \, \theta_m}$$

$$\theta_m = \frac{\theta_f - \theta_r + \theta_2 - \theta_1}{2.3 \log_{10} \dfrac{\theta_f - \theta_1}{\theta_r - \theta_2}}$$

where

A =heating surface of calorifier	(m^2)
H =rate of heating	(kW)
k =heat transmission coefficient	$(W/m^2 \, K)$
θ_m =logarithmic mean temperature difference	(K)
θ_f =primary flow temperature	(°C)
θ_r =primary return temperature	(°C)
θ_1 =secondary inlet temperature	(°C)
θ_2 =secondary final temperature	(°C)

3   Boiler

Boiler rating=Heating capacity of calorifier
Boiler with correct rating to be selected from manufacturers' catalogues.

4   Pipe sizes

Pipes can be sized as for hot water heating systems (see section 8, page 129).

Volume flow through pipes to draw offs is determined by maximum demand. Volume flow through return pipes of circulating system is made sufficient to keep temperature drop between flow and return connections of calorifier down to about 5 K.

For most schemes pipe sizing table on page 159 is satisfactory.

Pump duties can be determined as for hot water heating systems (see section 8, page 128).

Domestic hot water schemes

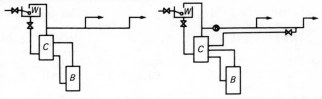

Direct System   Direct System with pumped secondary circulation

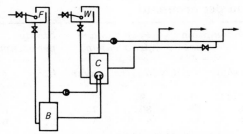

Indirect System with pumped primary and pumped secondary

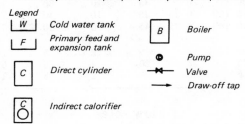

Legend

W	Cold water tank
F	Primary feed and expansion tank
C	Direct cylinder
	Indirect calorifier
B	Boiler
⦿	Pump
⋈	Valve
→	Draw-off tap

Hot water consumption per fitting

Fitting	Consumption		Fitting	Consumption	
	litre/hr	gal/hr		litre/hr	gal/hr
Basin (private)	14	3	Sink	45–90	10–20
Basin (public)	45	10	Bath	90–180	20–40
Shower	180	40			

Hot water consumption per occupant

Type of building	Consumption per occupant		Peak demand per occupant		Storage per occupant	
	litre/day	gal/day	litre/hr	gal/hr	litre	gal
Factories (no process)	22–45	5–10	9	2	5	1
Hospitals, general	160	35	30	7	27	6
mental	110	25	22	5	27	6
Hostels	90	20	45	10	30	7
Hotels	90–160	20–35	45	10	30	7
Houses and flats	90–160	20–35	45	10	30	7
Offices	22	5	9	2	5	1
Schools, boarding	115	25	20	4	25	5
day	15	3	9	2	5	1

Contents of fittings

Fitting	Contents	
	litre	gal
Basin, normal	5	1
Basin, full	9	2
Sink, normal	22	5
Sink, full	45	10
Bath	135–180	30–40

Flow rates

Fitting	Flow rate	
	litre/s	gal/min
Basin	0.08	1
Sink	0.15	2
Bath	0.15	2
Shower	0.5–0.6	7–8

Maximum dead leg of hot water pipe without circulation

Pipe size		Length
Steel	Copper	m
15	15	12
20	22	8
25	28	3

Temperature drop in bare pipes

Flow of water kg/s	Temperature drop K/m for size of pipe								
	15 mm	20 mm	25 mm	32 mm	40 mm	50 mm	65 mm	80 mm	100 mm
0.010	1.03	1.37	1.49	1.83	2.06	2.52	2.88	3.44	4.35
0.012	0.86	1.14	1.24	1.54	1.72	2.10	2.40	2.87	3.63
0.014	0.74	0.98	1.06	1.31	1.45	1.80	2.06	2.43	3.11
0.016	0.65	0.86	0.93	1.14	1.29	1.57	1.80	2.14	2.72
0.018	0.57	0.76	0.83	1.02	1.14	1.40	1.60	1.91	2.42
0.020	0.52	0.69	0.74	0.92	1.03	1.26	1.44	1.77	2.08
0.025	0.41	0.55	0.60	0.72	0.82	1.01	1.16	1.37	1.78
0.030	0.34	0.45	0.50	0.61	0.69	0.84	0.96	1.15	1.45
0.035	0.29	0.39	0.43	0.52	0.59	0.72	0.82	0.98	1.24
0.040	0.26	0.34	0.39	0.46	0.52	0.63	0.72	0.86	1.09
0.045	0.23	0.30	0.33	0.41	0.46	0.56	0.64	0.76	0.97
0.050	0.21	0.27	0.30	0.37	0.41	0.50	0.57	0.69	0.87
0.060	0.17	0.23	0.25	0.31	0.34	0.42	0.48	0.57	0.76
0.070	0.15	0.20	0.21	0.26	0.29	0.36	0.41	0.49	0.62
0.080	0.13	0.17	0.19	0.23	0.26	0.32	0.36	0.47	0.54
0.090	0.11	0.15	0.17	0.20	0.23	0.27	0.32	0.43	0.48
0.100	0.10	0.14	0.15	0.18	0.21	0.25	0.29	0.34	0.44

Flow of water lb/hr	Temperature drop °F/ft for size of pipe								
	$\frac{1}{2}$ in	$\frac{3}{4}$ in	1 in	$1\frac{1}{4}$ in	$1\frac{1}{2}$ in	2 in	$2\frac{1}{2}$ in	3 in	4 in
100	0.45	0.60	0.65	0.80	0.90	1.10	1.25	1.50	1.90
120	0.38	0.50	0.54	0.62	0.75	0.92	1.04	1.21	1.58
140	0.32	0.43	0.46	0.57	0.64	0.79	0.89	1.07	1.36
160	0.28	0.37	0.41	0.50	0.56	0.69	0.78	0.94	1.19
180	0.25	0.33	0.36	0.44	0.50	0.61	0.69	0.83	1.06
200	0.22	0.30	0.33	0.40	0.45	0.55	0.63	0.75	0.95
250	0.18	0.24	0.26	0.32	0.36	0.44	0.50	0.60	0.76
300	0.15	0.20	0.22	0.27	0.30	0.37	0.42	0.50	0.63
350	0.13	0.17	0.19	0.23	0.26	0.31	0.36	0.43	0.54
400	0.11	0.15	0.17	0.20	0.23	0.28	0.32	0.38	0.48
450	0.10	0.13	0.14	0.18	0.20	0.24	0.28	0.33	0.42
500	0.09	0.12	0.13	0.16	0.18	0.22	0.25	0.30	0.38
600	0.075	0.10	0.11	0.14	0.15	0.19	0.21	0.25	0.37
700	0.065	0.085	0.095	0.13	0.13	0.16	0.18	0.22	0.27
800	0.055	0.075	0.083	0.10	0.11	0.14	0.16	0.19	0.24
900	0.050	0.066	0.070	0.089	0.10	0.12	0.14	0.17	0.21
1000	0.045	0.060	0.065	0.080	0.090	0.11	0.13	0.15	0.19

Pipe sizes for domestic cold and hot water service

Nominal bore of pipe			Maximum number of draw offs served		
			Flow pipes		Return pipes
in	Steel pipe mm	Copper pipe mm	Head up to 20 m (70 ft)	Head over 20 m (70 ft)	
$\frac{1}{2}$	15	15	1	1 to 2	1 to 8
$\frac{3}{4}$	20	22	2 to 4	3 to 9	9 to 29
1	25	28	5 to 8	10 to 19	30 to 66
$1\frac{1}{4}$	32	35	9 to 24	20 to 49	67 to 169
$1\frac{1}{2}$	40	42	25 to 49	50 to 79	170 to 350
2	50	54	50 to 99	80 to 153	—
$2\frac{1}{2}$	65	67	100 to 200	154 to 300	—

For the purpose of this table, basins, sinks, showers count as one draw off, baths count as two draw offs.

Cold water storage per occupant

Type of building	Storage per occupant		Type of building	Storage per occupant	
	litres	gal		litres	gal
Factories (no process)	10	2	Offices with canteen	45	10
Hospitals per bed	135	30	without canteen	35	8
per staff on duty	45	10	Restaurant, per meal	7	1.5
Hostels	90	20	Schools		
Hotels	135	30	boarding	90	20
Houses and flats	135	30	day	30	7

Cold water storage per fitting

Type of fitting	Storage per unit		Type of fitting	Storage per unit	
	litres	gal		litres	gal
Shower	450–900	100–200	Sink	90	20
Bath	900	200	Urinal	180	40
W.C.	180	40	Garden watering tap	180	40
Basin	90	20			

Cold water storage systems for tall buildings

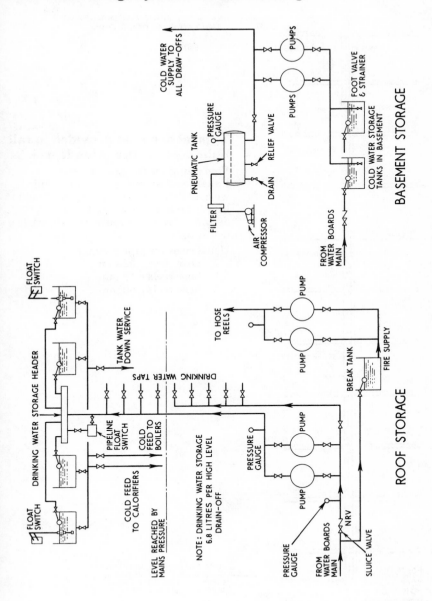

Fire service

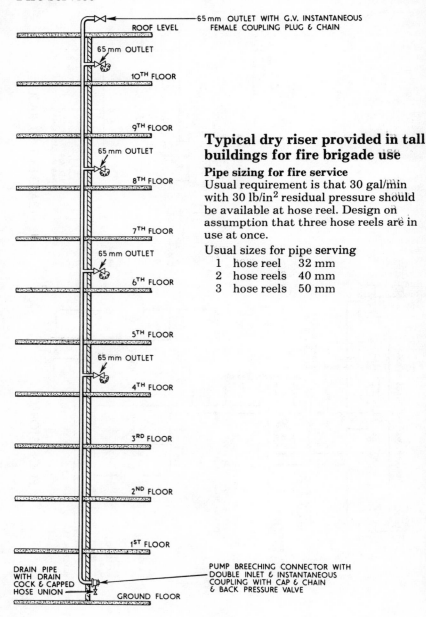

65mm OUTLET WITH G.V. INSTANTANEOUS
FEMALE COUPLING PLUG & CHAIN

ROOF LEVEL

65mm OUTLET

10TH FLOOR

9TH FLOOR

65mm OUTLET

8TH FLOOR

7TH FLOOR

65mm OUTLET

6TH FLOOR

5TH FLOOR

65mm OUTLET

4TH FLOOR

3RD FLOOR

2ND FLOOR

1ST FLOOR

DRAIN PIPE
WITH DRAIN
COCK & CAPPED
HOSE UNION

GROUND FLOOR

PUMP BREECHING CONNECTOR WITH
DOUBLE INLET & INSTANTANEOUS
COUPLING WITH CAP & CHAIN
& BACK PRESSURE VALVE

Typical dry riser provided in tall buildings for fire brigade use

Pipe sizing for fire service

Usual requirement is that 30 gal/min with 30 lb/in^2 residual pressure should be available at hose reel. Design on assumption that three hose reels are in use at once.

Usual sizes for pipe serving
1   hose reel   32 mm
2   hose reels   40 mm
3   hose reels   50 mm

Gas supply. Gas consumption of equipment (natural gas)

	ft^3/h	m^3/s	litre/s
10 gal boiling pan	45	350×10^{-6}	0.35
20 gal boiling pan	60	475×10^{-6}	0.48
30 gal boiling pan	75	600×10^{-6}	0.60
40 gal boiling pan	90	700×10^{-6}	0.70
4 ft hot cupboard	48	375×10^{-6}	0.38
6 ft hot cupboard	54	425×10^{-6}	0.43
Steaming oven	40 to 50	300 to 400×10^{-6}	0.30 to 0.40
Double steaming oven	100	800×10^{-6}	0.80
2-tier roasting oven	50	400×10^{-6}	0.40
Double oven range	400	3200×10^{-6}	1.6
Roasting oven	30	240×10^{-6}	0.24
Gas cooker	75	600×10^{-6}	0.30
Hot cupboard	17	140×10^{-6}	0.14
Drying cupboard	5	40×10^{-6}	0.04
Gas iron heater	5	40×10^{-6}	0.04
Washing machine	20	150×10^{-6}	0.15
Wash boiler	30 to 50	230 to 400×10^{-6}	0.23 to 0.40
Bunsen burner	3	20×10^{-6}	0.02
Bunsen burner, full on	10	80×10^{-6}	0.08
Glue kettle	10	80×10^{-6}	0.08
Forge	15	115×10^{-6}	0.12
Brazing hearth	30	230×10^{-6}	0.23

Flow of gas in steel tubes

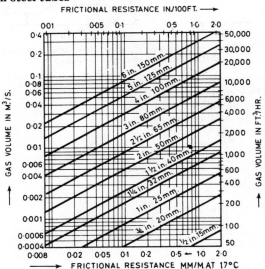

11 Ventilation

Ventilation

Classification by distribution

Central system. A central plant supplies air to the whole building. There can also be a central extract system.

Unit system. Each room or area of the building has its own ventilating unit.

Classification by function

Split system of heating and ventilating. Heat losses through the fabric of the building are supplied by a radiator heating system and the ventilation delivers air at room temperature.

Combined system. A central ventilation plant supplies air above or below room temperature so that in cooling or heating to room temperature it provides the required heating or cooling as well as ventilation.

Schemes of air distribution

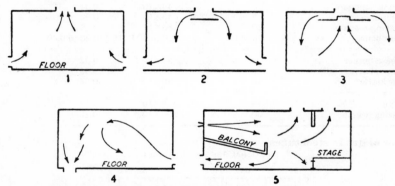

Diagrammatic Views (in Elevation) showing how various systems of Air Distribution are applied in buildings.

1 Upward flow system
2 Downward flow system
3 High-level supply and return system
4 Low-level supply and return system
5 Ejector system

Design procedure for ventilating system

1   Heating or cooling load, including sensible and latent heat.
2   Temperature of air leaving grilles, calculated or assumed.
3   Mass of air to be circulated.
4   Temperature loss in ducts.
5   Output of heaters, washers, humidifiers, coolers.
6   Boiler or heater size.
7   Duct system and duct sizes.

1   Heating and cooling loads
Calculated with data in sections 6 and 7.

2   Supply air temperature
For heating 38°–50°C (100°–120°F).
For cooling, inlets near occupied zones, 6°–8°C below room temperature (10°–15°F).
For cooling, high velocity diffusing jets, 17°C below room temperature (30°F).

3   Air quantity

$$W = \frac{H}{C\,(t_d - t_r)} \qquad V = \frac{H}{C\varrho\,(t_d - t_r)}$$

where

W = mass of air	(kg/s)
V = volume of air	(m³/s)
H = sensible heat loss or gain	(kW)
C = specific heat capacity of air (=1.01)	(kJ/kg K)
ϱ = density of air (=1.21)	(kg/m³)
t_d = discharge temperature of air at grilles	(°C)
t_r = room temperature	(°C)

when moisture content is limiting factor

$$W = \frac{M}{w_2 - w_1}$$

where

W = mass of air	(kg/s)
M = moisture to be absorbed	(g/s)
w_1 = humidity of supply air	(g/kg)
w_2 = humidity of room air	(g/kg)

Alternatively, the air quantity is determined by the ventilation requirements of the occupants or process in the various rooms.

It is a disadvantage of the *Combined System* that the air quantity necessary to satisfy the heating or cooling requirement is not always the same as that necessary to satisfy the ventilation requirement and an acceptable compromise is not always easy to find.

4   Temperature drop in ducts

$$WC\,(t_1-t_2)=Ak\left(\frac{t_1+t_2}{2}-t_r\right)$$

where

W=mass of air flowing   (kg/s)
C=specific heat capacity of air (=1.01)   (kJ/kg K)
A=area of duct walls   (m²)
k=heat loss coefficient of duct walls   (kW/m² K)
t_1=initial temperature in duct   (°C)
t_2=final temperature in duct   (°C)
t_r=surrounding room temperature   (°C)
k=5.68×10⁻³ kW/m² K for sheet metal ducts
  =2.3×10⁻³ kW/m² K for insulated ducts.

For large temperature drops the logarithmic mean temperature should be used. The equation then becomes

$$WC\,(t_2-t_1)=Ak\,\frac{(t_1-t_r)-(t_2-t_r)}{\log_e\dfrac{t_1-t_r}{t_2-t_r}}$$

5   Heaters, washers, humidifiers, coolers

Units with required combination of air quantity, heating or cooling capacity, humidifying or dehumidifying capacity to be selected from manufacturers' catalogues.

6   Boiler

$$B=H\,(1+X)$$

where

B=boiler rating   (kW)
H=total heat load of all heater units in system   (kW)
X=margin for heating up and design uncertainties (0.15 to 0.20)

Boiler with correct rating to be selected from manufacturers' catalogues.

7   Duct sizes

$$v = \frac{Q}{A}$$

$$p_t = p_1 + p_2 + p_3$$

$$p_1 = il$$

$$i = \frac{2f\varrho v^2}{d}$$

$$p_2 = \Sigma \frac{Fv^2\varrho}{2}$$

where

v = air velocity	(m/s)
Q = air volume	(m³/s)
A = cross section of duct	(m²)
p_t = total pressure loss in system	(N/m²)
p_1 = pressure loss in ducts due to friction	(N/m²)
p_2 = pressure loss in fittings	(N/m²)
p_3 = pressure loss in apparatus (filters, heaters, etc.)	N/m²)
i = duct friction resistance per unit length	(N/m² per m run)
f = friction factor, which is a function of Reynolds number	—
F = coefficient of resistance for fitting	—
ϱ = density of air	(kg/m³)
d = diameter of duct	(m)

i can be obtained from Chart 4.

For rectangular ducts the equivalent diameter must be used

$$d = 1.26 \sqrt[5]{\frac{(ab)^3}{a+b}}$$

where

d = equivalent diameter   (m)
a, b = sides of rectangular duct   (m)

For standard air

$$\varrho = 1.21 \text{ kg/m}^3$$

$$p_2 = F \left(\frac{v}{1.29}\right)^2 \text{ N/m}^2 \text{ with } v \text{ in m/s}$$

Ventilation rates, occupancy known

Type of building	Fresh air supply m³/s per person	Type of building	Fresh air supply m³/s per person
Assembly halls	0.014	Schools	0.014
Factories	0.02–0.03	Shops	0.02
Hospitals, general contagious diseases	0.025 0.05	Theatres	0.014

Ventilation rates, occupancy unknown

Type of building	Air changes per hour	Type of building	Air changes per hour
Assembly halls	5–10	Kitchens, small	20–40
Baths	5–8	large	10–20
Boiler rooms	4	Laundries	10–15
Cinemas	5–10	Lavatories	5–10
Engine rooms	4	Offices	3–8
Garages	5–6	Restaurants	5–10
		Swimming pools	5–10

Garage ventilation
Two thirds total extract at high level, one third at low level

Bathroom and W.C. ventilation
Six air changes per hour or 0.018 m³/s per room.

To provide a standby service two fans with an automatic changeover switch are installed.

Proprietary units incorporating two fans with automatic changeover are widely used. Alternatively individual fans can be joined by ducting and the changeover control supplied separately. Typical schemes for this are

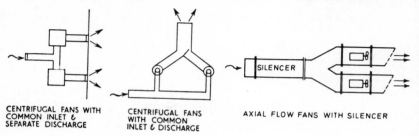

CENTRIFUGAL FANS WITH COMMON INLET & SEPARATE DISCHARGE

CENTRIFUGAL FANS WITH COMMON INLET & DISCHARGE

AXIAL FLOW FANS WITH SILENCER

Filters

Dust load for filters

	mg/m^3
Rural and suburban districts	0.45–1.00
Metropolitan districts	1.0 –1.8
Industrial districts	1.8 –3.5

Types of filter

(a) *Washers*

Overall length	about 20 m
Air velocity through washer	2.5 m/s
Water quantity required	0.5 to 0.8 litre per m^3 air
Water pressure required for spray nozzles	140–170 kN/m^2
Water pressure required for flooding nozzles	35–70 kN/m^2

(b) *Dry filters*

Felt, cloth, cellulose, glass, silk, etc. without adhesive liquid

  (i) Panel type — disposable

       Air velocity   0.1–1.0 m/s

       Resistance   25–250 N/m^2

  (ii) Continuous roll — self cleaning

       Air velocity   2.5 m/s

       Resistance   30–175 N/m^2

(c) *Viscous filters*

  (i) Panel type — cloth with viscous fluid coating — washable or disposable

       Plates about 500 mm×500 mm

       Air velocity   1.5–2.5 m/s

       Resistance   20–150 N/m^2

  (ii) Continuous roll — continuously moving, self cleaning

       Air velocity   2.5 m/s

       Resistance   30–175 N/m^2

(e) *Electrostatic precipitators*

    Cleaned automatically

       Air velocity   1.5–2.5 m/s

       Resistance   negligible

(f) *Absolute*

    Dry panel with special coating — disposable or self cleaning

       Air velocity   2.5 m/s

       Resistance   250–625 N/m^2

Resistance of ducts. (Allowance for surface conditions)

Surface	Chart reading to be multiplied by
Asbestos cement	0.8
Asphalted cast iron	6.0
Aluminium	0.8
Brickwork	4
Concrete	2
Fibreglass	0.8
PVC	0.8
Sheet iron	1.5
Sheet steel	1.0

Coefficients of resistance (for fittings in ventilating systems)

Fitting	F	Fitting	F
90° elbow	1.5	Abrupt\enlargement	$\left(1-\frac{A_1}{A_2}\right)^2$
Rounded 90° elbow	0.5	Exit from duct into room	1.0
Long sweep 90° elbow radius = 2 x diameter	0.1	Gradual reduction	0
45° elbow	0.5	Abrupt reduction	0.3
Rounded 45° elbow	0.2	Entry from room into duct	0.3
Long sweep 45° elbow radius = 2 x diameter	0.05	Grille ratio of free area to total surface	
Gradual enlargement α ⩽ 8°	$0.15\left(1-\frac{A_1}{A_2}\right)^2$	0.6	4
		0.5	6
		0.4	10
Gradual enlargement α > 8°	$\left(1-\frac{A_1}{A_2}\right)^2$	0.3	20
		0.2	50

Resistance for various velocities and values of F

Resistance in N/m^2

Velocity m/s	F 1	2	3	4	5	6	7	8	9
2.0	2.44	4.87	7.32	9.77	12.3	14.6	17.1	19.5	22.0
2.5	3.82	7.64	11.5	15.3	19.1	22.8	26.7	30.5	34.3
3.0	5.49	11.0	16.5	22.0	27.5	33.0	38.5	43.9	50.3
3.5	7.50	15.0	22.4	30.0	36.5	44.9	52.5	59.9	68.4
4.0	9.76	19.6	29.3	39.0	48.8	58.6	68.4	78.1	87.9
4.5	11.8	23.6	35.4	47.3	59.1	70.9	82.7	94.5	106
5.0	15.3	30.6	46.0	73.0	76.5	91.8	107	123	137
6.0	22.0	43.9	65.9	87.9	110	131	154	176	198
7.0	29.9	59.8	89.8	120	150	179	210	239	270
8.0	39.0	78.1	117	156	195	234	274	312	351
9.0	49.4	99.0	148	198	247	296	346	395	445
10.0	61.0	122	183	244	305	366	427	489	638
12.5	95.3	190	286	382	477	572	667	763	858
15.0	137	274	412	549	687	824	961	1100	1240
17.5	187	383	561	767	935	1120	1110	1490	1680
20	244	489	733	977	1230	1460	1710	1950	2200
25	382	783	1140	1530	1910	2290	2670	3050	3430

Resistance in inches w.g.

Velocity ft/min	F 1	2	3	4	5	6	7	8	9
400	0.0099	0.0198	0.0297	0.0396	0.0496	0.0595	0.0694	0.0793	0.0892
500	0.0155	0.0310	0.0465	0.0620	0.0775	0.0929	0.108	0.124	0.139
600	0.0223	0.0446	0.0669	0.0892	0.112	0.134	0.156	0.178	0.201
700	0.0304	0.0607	0.0911	0.121	0.152	0.182	0.213	0.243	0.273
800	0.0396	0.0793	0.119	0.159	0.198	0.238	0.277	0.317	0.357
900	0.0502	0.100	0.151	0.201	0.251	0.301	0.351	0.401	0.452
1000	0.0619	0.124	0.186	0.248	0.310	0.372	0.434	0.496	0.557
1200	0.0892	0.178	0.268	0.357	0.446	0.535	0.624	0.714	0.803
1400	0.121	0.243	0.364	0.486	0.607	0.728	0.850	0.974	1.09
1600	0.151	0.317	0.476	0.634	0.793	0.952	1.11	1.27	1.43
1800	0.201	0.401	0.602	0.803	1.00	1.20	1.41	1.61	1.81
2000	0.248	0.496	0.743	0.991	1.24	1.49	1.73	1.98	2.23
2400	0.357	0.714	1.07	1.43	1.78	2.14	2.50	2.85	3.21
2800	0.486	0.971	1.46	1.94	2.43	2.91	3.40	3.88	4.37
3200	0.634	1.27	1.90	2.54	3.17	3.81	4.44	5.07	5.71
3600	0.803	1.61	2.41	3.21	4.01	4.82	5.62	6.42	7.22
4000	0.991	1.98	2.97	3.96	4.96	5.95	6.94	7.93	8.92

Pressure drop in apparatus. (Usually given by manufacturers)

Apparatus	Average pressure drop (N/m^2)	(in w.g.)
Filters	50 to 100	$\frac{1}{16}$ to $\frac{1}{4}$
Air washers	50 to 100	$\frac{1}{16}$ to $\frac{1}{4}$
Heater batteries	30 to 100	$\frac{1}{8}$ to $\frac{1}{4}$

Recommended velocities for ventilating systems

Service	Velocity			
	Public buildings		Industrial plant	
	m/s	ft/min	m/s	ft/min
Air intake from outside	2.5–4.5	500–900	5–6	1000–1200
Heater connection to fan	3.5–4.5	700–900	5–7	1000–1400
Main supply ducts	5.0–8.0	1000–1500	6–12	1200–2400
Branch supply ducts	2.5–3.0	500–600	4.5–9	900–1800
Supply registers and grilles	1.2–2.3	250–450	1.5–2.5	350–500
Low level supply registers	0.8–1.2	150–250	—	—
Main extract ducts	4.5–8.0	900–1500	6–12	1200–2400
Branch extract ducts	2.5–3.0	500–600	4.5–9	900–1800

Velocities in natural draught extract systems should be 1–3 m/s (200–600 ft/min).

Thickness of ducts

Rectangular

Longest side		Thickness
mm	in	mm
400	15	0.6
600	24	0.8
800	32	0.8
1000	40	0.8
1250	48	1.0
1600	63	1.0
2000	78	1.0
2500	96	1.0
3000	118	1.2

Circular

Diameter		Thickness
mm	in	mm
160	6	0.6
510	20	0.7
630	24	0.8
1020	40	1.0
1525	60	1.2

Ducts outside buildings exposed to atmosphere should be two gauge numbers thicker.

Theoretical velocity of air (due to natural draught)

$$V = 4.48 \sqrt{\frac{h\,(t_c - t_o)}{273 + t_o}}$$

V = theoretical velocity (m/s)
h = height of flue (m)
t_c = temperature of warm air column (°C)
t_o = temperature of outside air (°C)

Height of flue m	Excess of temperature in flue above outside air °C (for $t_o = 2$°C)								
	2	4	6	8	10	15	30	50	80
0.3	0.21	0.30	0.36	0.42	0.47	0.57	0.81	1.0	1.3
1.0	0.39	0.54	0.66	0.77	0.86	1.0	1.48	1.91	2.42
3.0	0.66	0.94	1.15	1.32	1.48	1.81	2.57	3.31	4.19
5.0	0.87	1.22	1.50	1.73	1.93	2.37	3.35	4.31	5.46
6.0	0.94	1.32	1.62	1.87	2.10	2.57	3.63	4.68	5.93
7.5	1.07	1.51	1.85	2.13	2.38	2.92	4.13	5.32	6.75
10	1.21	1.71	2.10	2.42	2.73	3.32	4.69	6.04	7.66
15	1.49	2.10	2.57	2.96	3.31	4.06	5.74	7.40	9.37
20	1.71	2.42	2.97	3.42	3.83	4.69	6.63	8.55	10.8
25	1.91	2.71	3.32	3.83	4.28	5.24	7.42	9.55	12.1
30	2.10	2.96	3.63	4.19	4.69	5.74	8.12	10.5	13.2
35	2.27	3.20	3.92	4.53	5.07	6.20	8.77	11.3	14.3
40	2.42	3.42	4.20	4.84	5.41	6.63	9.33	12.1	15.3
45	2.57	3.63	4.45	5.13	5.74	7.03	9.95	12.8	16.2
50	2.71	3.82	4.69	5.41	6.05	7.41	10.5	13.5	17.1

$$V = 8.02 \sqrt{\frac{h\,(t_c - t_o)}{460 + t_o}}$$

V = in ft/s
h = in ft
t_c = in °F
t_o = in °F

Height of flue ft	Excess of temperature in flue above outside air °F (for $t_o = 35$°F)								
	5	10	15	20	25	30	50	100	150
1	0.8	1.1	1.4	1.6	1.8	2.0	2.5	3.6	4.4
5	1.8	2.5	3.1	3.6	4.0	4.5	5.6	8.1	9.9
10	2.6	3.6	4.4	5.1	5.7	6.6	8.1	11.4	14.0
15	3.1	4.4	5.4	6.3	7.0	7.7	9.9	14.0	17.1
20	3.6	5.1	6.3	7.2	8.1	8.8	11.4	16.1	19.8
30	4.4	6.3	7.8	8.8	9.9	10.9	14.0	19.8	24.2
40	5.1	7.3	8.9	10.2	11.4	12.5	16.1	22.8	27.9
50	5.7	8.1	9.9	11.4	12.8	14.0	18.0	25.5	31.1
60	6.3	8.8	10.8	12.6	14.0	15.3	19.8	27.8	33.3
70	6.8	9.5	11.7	13.6	15.2	16.5	21.4	30.0	36.1
80	7.3	10.2	12.5	14.4	16.2	18.7	22.9	32.2	38.9
90	7.7	10.8	13.3	15.3	17.2	18.8	24.3	34.2	41.6
100	8.1	11.4	14.0	16.2	17.8	19.8	25.6	36.0	45.2
125	9.1	12.8	15.6	18.1	20.1	22.1	28.7	40.3	49.3
150	9.9	14.0	17.2	19.8	22.2	24.3	31.4	44.3	54.3

Air velocities and equivalent pressures

$$p = \frac{V^2 \varrho}{2}$$

$$= 0.6 V^2$$

p = velocity pressure N/m^2
V = velocity m/s
ϱ = density of air = 1.2 kg/m^3

V m/s	p N/m^2	V m/s	p N/m^2	V m/s	p N/m^2
0.25	0.0375	5.0	15.0	15.0	135
0.5	0.150	5.5	18.2	17.5	184
0.75	0.338	6.0	21.6	20.0	240
1.0	0.600	7	29.4	22.5	304
1.25	0.938	8	38.4	25.0	375
1.5	1.35	9	48.6	27.5	454
2.0	2.40	10	60.0	30.0	540
2.5	3.75	11	72.6	32.5	634
3.0	5.40	12	86.4	35.0	735
3.25	6.34	13	101		
4.0	9.60	14	118		

$$h = \frac{V^2 \varrho}{2g} \cdot \frac{1}{18\,720}$$

$$= \frac{V^2}{16\,000\,000}$$

h = velocity head in water gauge
V = velocity ft/min
ϱ = density of air = 0.075 lb/ft^3

V ft/min	h in w.g.	V ft/min	h in w.g.	V ft/min	h in w.g.
60	0.00023	1200	0.0915	3430	0.750
120	0.00092	1250	0.100	3600	0.824
180	0.00206	1500	0.143	4000	1.00
240	0.00366	1770	0.200	4200	1.12
360	0.00824	1800	0.206	4800	1.46
480	0.0146	2000	0.250	4850	1.5
600	0.0229	2100	0.280	5400	1.85
720	0.0329	2400	0.366	5600	2.00
840	0.0448	2700	0.463	6000	2.29
960	0.0586	2800	0.500	6260	2.50
1080	0.0741	3000	0.572	6870	3.00

Circular equivalents of rectangular ducts for equal friction

Duct Sides	100	150	200	250	300	400	500	600	800	1000	1200	1400	1600	1800	2000
100	100														
150	134	165													
200	153	190	219												
250	170	211	245	274											
300	185	230	268	300	329										
400	210	263	307	345	379	439									
500	231	290	340	383	422	490	548								
600	250	315	369	417	460	535	600	658							
800	283	357	420	475	525	613	690	758	878						
1000	311	393	463	525	581	680	767	844	980	1100					
1200	335	424	497	568	629	738	834	920	1070	1200	1320				
1400	358	453	534	607	673	791	895	988	1150	1290	1420	1540			
1600	377	479	565	643	713	839	950	1050	1230	1380	1520	1640	1760		
1800	396	503	594	676	751	884	1000	1110	1300	1460	1610	1740	1860	1970	
2000	414	525	621	707	785	925	1050	1160	1360	1530	1690	1830	1960	2080	2190

$$d = 1.26 \sqrt[5]{\frac{(ab)^3}{a+b}}$$

Thick line encloses standard duct sizes.

Fume and dust removal

Equipment for industrial exhaust systems

A   Suction hoods, booths, or canopies for fume and dust collection, or suction nozzles, or feed hoppers for pneumatic conveying.

B   Conveying, ducting or tubing.

C   Fan or exhauster to create the necessary pressure or vacuum for pneumatic conveying.

D   Dust separator, for separating the conveyed material from the conveying air.

Classification of schemes

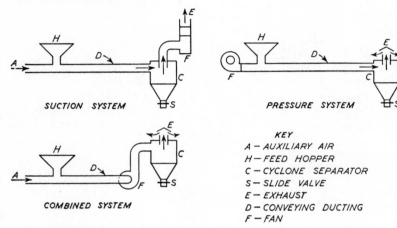

SUCTION SYSTEM

PRESSURE SYSTEM

COMBINED SYSTEM

KEY
A – AUXILIARY AIR
H – FEED HOPPER
C – CYCLONE SEPARATOR
S – SLIDE VALVE
E – EXHAUST
D – CONVEYING DUCTING
F – FAN

Pneumatic conveying plants are suitable for conveyance of material in powdered form or in solids up to 50 mm size, dry: not more than 20% moisture, not sticking.

Efficiency of pneumatic conveying plants is low but compensated by easy handling, free of dust.

Suction type — Distance of conveying up to 300 m difference in heights up to 40 m. Required vacuum 200 to 400 mm mercury.

Pressure type — Distance of conveying above 300 m working pressure up to 40 kN/m^2. Advantage: possibility of conveying material over long distance by connecting more systems in series.

Working pressure above 40 kN/m^2 not suitable, because of high running cost.

Types of hoods

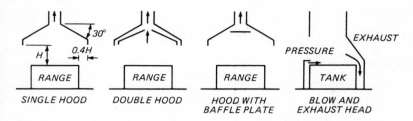

SINGLE HOOD   DOUBLE HOOD   HOOD WITH   BLOW AND
                                    BAFFLE PLATE   EXHAUST HEAD

Single hoods — For removing fumes which rise naturally, for ranges, forge fires, vats, kettles, etc. Projection beyond the range approx. 0.4 m per m of height above range. 0.25 to 1.5 m/s entrance velocity. Duct area about one fifth to one-tenth of hood area.

Double hoods with gap around the perimeter for fume extraction in rooms with cross currents, high velocity of entering air, approximately 5.0 m/s.

Velocity in ducts — Approximately 10 m/s.

Recommended velocities through top hoods and booth, subject to cross draughts in m/s

Canopy hood, open	1.0 –1.5	Canopy hood, double	5.0
Canopy hood, closed 1 side	0.9 –1.0	Booths, through 1 side	0.5 –0.75
Canopy hood, closed 2 sides	0.75-0.9	Laboratory hoods,	
Canopy hood. closed 3 sides	0.5 –0.75	through doors	0.25-0.35

Coefficients of entry and velocity. Pressure loss of duct extraction hoods

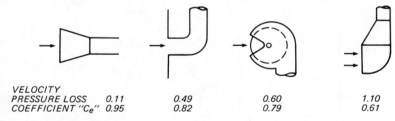

VELOCITY				
PRESSURE LOSS	0.11	0.49	0.60	1.10
COEFFICIENT "C_e"	0.95	0.82	0.79	0.61

Flow of air into a hood

$Q = 1.3\, C_e\, A_t\, \sqrt{h_t}$

Q = Air volume m³/s
C_e = Entrance coefficient
A_t = Area of throat, m²
h_t = Static suction in throat, N/m²

$Q = 4000\, C_e\, A_t\, \sqrt{h_t}$

Q = Air volume ft³/min
C_e = Entrance coefficient
A_t = Area of throat, ft²
h_t = Static suction in throat, inches w.g.

Coefficient of entry

$$C_e = \sqrt{\frac{h_v}{h_t}} \quad (h_v = \text{velocity pressure})$$

Entrance loss into hood

$$C_e h_t = \frac{(I - C_e^2)}{C_e^2}\, h_v$$

The transporting velocity for material varies with the size, specific gravity and shape of the material   (Dalla Valle)

Vertical lifting velocity

$$V = 10.7 \frac{s}{s+1} \times d^{0.57}$$

$$V = 13\ 300 \frac{s}{s+1} \times d^{0.57}$$

Horizontal transport velocity

$$V = 8.4 \frac{s}{s+1} \times d^{0.40}$$

$$V = 6000 \frac{s}{s+1} \times d^{0.40}$$

V = Velocity m/s
s = Specific gravity of material
d = Average dia of largest
    particle in mm

V = Velocity ft/min
s = Specific gravity of material
d = Average dia of largest
    particle in in.

Friction loss of mixture

$$\frac{F_m}{F_a} = 1 + 0.32 \frac{W_s}{W_a}$$

where
  F_m = Friction loss of mixture
  F_a = Friction loss of air
  W_s = Mass of solid
  W_a = Mass of air

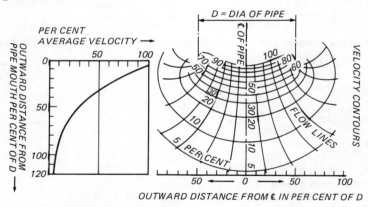

Velocity contours and flow directional lines in radial plane of circular suction pipe.

Carrying velocities. (For dust extraction and pneumatic conveying)

Material	m/s	ft/min
Ashes, powdered clinker	30–43	6500–8500
Cement	30–46	6500–9000
Coal, powdered	20–28	4000–5500
Coffee beans	15–20	3000–4000
Cork	17–28	3500–5500
Corn, wheat, Rye	25–36	5500–7000
Cotton	22–30	4500–6500
Flour	17–30	3500–6500
Grain dust	10–15	2000–3000
Grinding and foundry dust	17–23	3500–4500
Jute	22–30	4500–6500
Lead dust	20–30	4500–6500
Leather dust	8–12	1800–2500
Lime	25–36	5500–7500
Limestone dust	10–15	2000–3500
Metal dust	15–18	3500–4000
Oats	22–30	4500–6500
Plastic moulding powder	15–17	3000–3500
Plastic dust	10–12	2000–2500
Pulp chips	22–36	4500–7000
Rags	22–33	4500–6500
Rubber dust	10–15	2000–3000
Sand	30–46	6000–9000
Sandblast	17–23	3500–4500
Sawdust and shavings, light	10–15	2000–3000
Sawdust and shavings, heavy	17–23	3500–4500
Textile dust	10–15	2000–3500
Wood chips	20–25	4500–5500
Wool	22–30	4500–6000

Minimum particle size for which various separator types are suitable

Gravity	200 microns (1 micron=0.001 mm)
Inertial	50 to 150
Centrifugal, large dia cyclone	40 to 60
Centrifugal, small dia cyclone	20 to 30
Fan type	15 to 30
Filter	0.5
Scrubber	0.5 to 2.0
Electrical	0.001 to 1.0

Size of particles

Outdoor dust	0.5 microns
Sand blasting	1.4
Foundry dust	1.0 to 200
Granite cutting	1.4
Coal mining	1.0
Raindrops	500 to 5000
Mist	40 to 500
Fog	1 to 40
Fly ash	3 to 70
Pulverised coal	10 to 400

Drying

Weight of air to be circulated

$$W=\frac{X}{w_2-w_1}$$

$W=$ Mass of air to be circulated   (kg/s)
$X=$ Mass of water to be evaporated   (kg/s)
$w_1=$ Absolute humidity of entering air   (kg/kg)
$w_2=$ Absolute humidity of leaving air   (kg/kg)

The relative humidity of the air leaving the dryer is usually kept below 75%.

Heat amount

Total heat amount = 1   Heat for evaporating moisture
2   Heat for heating of stock
3   Heat-loss due to air change
4   Heat transmission loss of drying chamber

Water content of various materials

Material	Original per cent	Final per cent	Material	Original per cent	Final per cent
Bituminous coal	40–60	8–12	Hides	45	0
Earth	45–50	0	Glue	80–90	0
Earth, sandy	20–25	0	Glue, air dried	15	0
Grain	17–23	10–12	Macaroni	35	0
Rubber goods	30–50	0	Soap	27–35	25–26
Green hardwood	50		Starch	38–45	12–14
Green softwood	30–50		Starch, air dried	16–20	12–14
Air dried hardwood	17–20	10–15	Peat	85–90	30–35
Air dried softwood	10–15		Yarn, washing	40–50	0
Cork	40–45	10–15			

Drying temperatures and time for various materials

Material	Temperature °C	Temperature °F	Time Hr	Material	Temperature °C	Temperature °F	Time Hr
Bedding	66–88	150–190		Hides, thin	32	90	2–4
Cereals	43–66	110–150		Ink, printing	21–150	70–300	
Coconut	63–68	145–155	4–6	Knitted fabrics	60–82	140–180	
Coffee	71–82	160–180	24	Leather, thick sole	32	90	4–6
Cores, oil sand	150	300	0.5	Lumber:			
Films, photo	32	90		Green, hardwood	38–82	100–180	3–180
Fruits, vegetable	60	140	2–6	Green, softwood	71–105	160–220	24–350
Furs	43	110		Macaroni	32–43	90–110	
Glue	21–32	70–90	2–4	Matches	60–82	140–180	
Glue size on furniture	54	130	4	Milk	120–150	250–300	
Gut	66	150		Paper glued	54–150	130–300	
Gypsum wall board				Paper treated	60–93	140–200	
Start wet	175	350		Rubber	27–32	80–80	6–12
Finish	88	190		Soap	52	125	12
Gypsum blocks	175–88	350–180	8–16	Sugar	66–93	150–200	0.3–0.5
Hair goods	66–88	150–190		Tannin	120–150	250–300	
Hats, felt	60–82	140–180		Terra cotta	66–93	150–200	12–96
Hops	49–82	120–187					

Defogging plants

The defogging of rooms is carried out by blowing in dry, hot air and exhausting humidified air.

Mass of water evaporated from open vats

$$W = 1.25 \times 10^{-2} \times Ac \frac{(P_S - P_A)}{P}$$

W = Mass of water evaporated kg/s

A = Surface of vats, m^2.

P_S = Partial pressure of water vapour of saturated air at the temperature of the water, mm Hg

P_A = Partial pressure of water vapour of surrounding air, mm Hg

P = Atmospheric pressure mm Hg

c = 0.55 for still air
0.71 for slight air movement
0.86 for fast air movement

$$W = 9.4 \, Ac \frac{(P_S - P_A)}{P}$$

W = Weight of water evaporated lb/hr

A = Surface of vats, ft^2

P_S = Partial pressure of water vapour of saturated air at the temperature of the water, in Hg

P_A = Partial pressure of water vapour of surrounding air, in Hg

P = Atmospheric pressure, in Hg

c = 0.55 for still air
0.71 for slight air movement
0.86 for fast air movement

Mass of air to be circulated

$$G = \frac{W}{(w_2 - w_1)}$$

G = Mass of air, kg/s
W = Mass of water vapour to be removed, kg/s
w_1 = Original absolute humidity of air, kg/kg
w_2 = Final absolute humidity of air, kg/kg

Amount of heat

$$H = Gc \, (t_i - t_o)$$

H = Amount of heat, without fabric loss of room or other losses, W
G = Mass of air (see above), kg/s
t_i = Inside air temperature, °C
t_o = Outside air temperature, °C
c = Specific heat capacity of air = 1.012×10^3 J/kg °C

12 Air conditioning

Design procedure for air conditioning
1 Cooling load calculation
  (a) Sensible heat load due to
      (i) heat gain through walls, etc.
      (ii) solar radiation.
      (iii) heat emision of occupants.
      (iv) infiltration of outside air.
      (v) heat emission of lights and machinery.
  (b) Latent heat load due to
      (i) moisture given off by occupants.
      (ii) infiltration of outside air.
      (iii) moisture from process machinery.
2 Selection of air treatment process. For processes and psychrometric chart see pages 92, 93 and Chart 5.
3 Determination of air quantities.
4 Layout and sizing of ducts.
5 Determination of capacities of air treating units, allowing for heat gains in ducts.
6 Determination of refrigerator and boiler duties.
7 Determination of pump and fan duties.

Methods of cooling air
1 Spray type washer.
2 Surface type cooler
  (i) Indirect. By heat exchange with water which has been cooled by a refrigerant.
  (ii) Direct. By heat exchange in evaporator of a refrigerator system.

Methods of refrigeration
1 Compression system
  Hot compressed vapour leaves a compressor and is liquefied in a condenser by heat exchange with cooling water or air. The liquid refrigerant then passes through an expansion valve and the low pressure liquid enters the evaporator. It absorbs heat from the medium to be cooled and is vapourised. The vapour enters the compressor and is raised to a higher pressure.
2 **Absorption system**
  Low pressure refrigerant is dissolved in water in a generator and vapour at high pressure is driven out of the solution by heat. The vapour is liquefied in a condenser and expanded through an expansion valve, as in a compression system. The low pressure liquid enters the evaporator and absorbs heat from the medium to be cooled. It vapourises and returns to the generator.

183

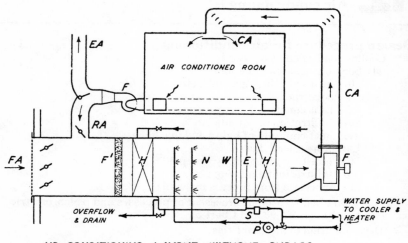

AIR-CONDITIONING LAYOUT WITHOUT BYPASS

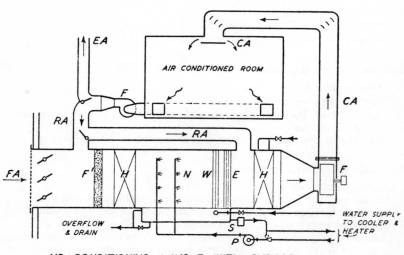

AIR-CONDITIONING LAYOUT WITH BYPASS

FA = Fresh air	F = Fan	P = Pump
CA = Conditioned air	F' = Filter	S = Strainer
RA = Recirculated air	H = Heater	W = Wet scrubber
EA = Exhaust air	N = Spray nozzles	E = Eliminator plates

Refrigerant	Symbol	Boiling Temp.	Critical Temp.	Properties	Inflammability	Use
Ammonia	NH_3	−28°F −33°C	271°F 133°C	Penetrating odour soluble in water, harmless in concentration up to 1/30%	Non-inflammable explosive	Large plants
Sulphur dioxide	SO_2	14°F −10°C	311°F 155°C	Colourless vapour, unpleasant to breathe but not poisonous	Not combustible or corrosive if not in contact with water	Small plants
Carbon dioxide	CO_2	−108.4°F −78°C	87.8°F 30°C	Heavy, colourless odourless gas, harmless to breathe	Not inflammable	Large plants
Ethyl chloride	C_2H_5Cl	55°F 12.8°C	—	Colourless, very volatile, sweet taste	Inflammable; non-corrosive with steel, iron, copper	—
Methyl chloride	CH_3Cl	−10.7°F −23.7°C	289.6°F 143°C	Colourless, sweet smelling vapour	Inflammable, explosive, non-corrosive with steel, iron, copper	Small plants
Dichloro-difluoro-methane, F-12 'Freon'	CCl_2F_2	−21.7°F −30°C	222.7°F 106°C	Odourless, non-toxic	Not inflammable not explosive; non-corrosive	Small plants
Carrene methylene chloride	$CHCl$	103.6°F 39.8°C	473°F 245°C	Colourless liquid at atmospheric conditions, sweet, pleasant odour, similar to chloroform	Not explosive	—
Dieline dichloro-ethylene	$C_2H_2Cl_2$	122°F 50°C	470°F 243°C	Colourless liquid odourless, non-toxic	Inflammable non-corrosive with steel, iron, nickel, copper, aluminium	Small plants
Trieline Trichlor-ethylene	C_2HCl_3	−126°F −87.8°C	188°F 86.6°C	Heavy, colourless liquid, pleasant odour	Non-inflammable; non-explosive; non-corrosive	—
Water	H_2O	212°F 100°C	706°F 374°C	See data on page 79	—	Steam jet and centri-fugal plants

Units

Cooling is expressed in the same units as heating, namely kW or Btu/hr.
Another unit much used formerly was the Ton of Refrigeration. This
was the cooling produced when one American ton of ice melted at 32°F in
24 hours. Since the latent heat of melting ice at 32°F is 144 Btu/lb

1 ton of refrigeration $=$ 2000 lb$\times$144 Btu/lb in 24 hours
$$=288\ 000 \text{ Btu in 24 hours}$$
$$=12\ 000 \text{ Btu/hr}$$
$$=3.517 \text{ kW}$$

Air washer

Air washers are sheet metal, or sometimes brick or concrete chambers, in
which air is drawn through a mist caused by spray nozzles and then
through eliminators to remove particles of water not evaporated into the
air. The water for the spray nozzles is recirculated by a pump and can be
heated or cooled. A tempering heater is installed before, and a reheating
battery after the air washer.

General data

Cleaning efficiency	70% on fine dust
	98% on coarse dirt
Air velocity through washer	2–3 m/s 450–550 ft/min
Resistance	50–140 N/m^2 0.2–0.5 in water gauge
Water pressure for sprays	100–170 kN/m^2 15–25 lb/in^2
Water quantity	0.45–0.55 l/m^3 air 3–3.5 gal per 1000 ft^3 air

Humidifying efficiency

$$E=\frac{t_1-t_2}{t-t_w}\times100\%$$

where

$t_1 =$ initial dry bulb temperature
$t_2 =$ final dry bulb temperature
$t_w =$ initial wet bulb temperature.

Typical efficiencies obtained are

60–70% with one bank of nozzles downstream
65–75% with one book of nozzles upstream
85–100% with two banks of nozzles.

Shell and tube cooler

Shell and tube coolers consist of plain or finned tubes in an outer shell. Air flows through the shell and a liquid coolant (water, brine or refrigerant) flows through the tubes. The air can be dehumidified as well as cooled by being cooled below its dew point so that part of the moisture is condensed.

Surface area of cooler

$$A = \frac{H}{U\,(t_a - t_m)}$$

where

A = area of cooling surface	(m^2)
H = cooling rate	(kW)
U = heat transfer coefficient	$(kW/m^2\ K)$
$t_a - t_m$ = log mean temperature difference	
between air and coolant	(K)

Direct dehumidification

Classification
1 Adsorption type.
2 Absorption type.

Adsorption type

In adsorption systems the humidity is reduced by adsorption of moisture by an adsorbent material such as silica gel or activated alumina. Adsorption is a physical process in which moisture is condensed and held on the surface of the material without any change in the physical or chemical structure of the material. The adsorbent material can be reactivated by being heated, the water being driven off and evaporated.

The adsorption system is particularly suitable for dehumidification at room temperature and where gas or high pressure steam or hot water is available for reactivation.

Temperature for reactivation	160–175°C 325–350°F
Heat required for reactivation	4800–5800 kJ/kg water removed
	2100–2500 Btu/lb water removed

Silica gel SiO_2, is a hard, adsorbent, crystalline substance; size of a pea; very porous.

Voids are about 50% by volume.
Adsorbs water up to 40% of its own mass
Bulk density 480–720 kg/m^3
Specific heat capacity 1.13 kJ/kg K

Activated alumina is about 90% aluminium oxide, AL_2O_3; very porous
Voids about 50–70% by volume
Adsorbs water up to 60% of its own mass
Bulk density 800–870 kg/m^3
Specific heat capacity 1.0 kJ/kg K

Absorption type

In absorption systems the humidity is reduced by absorption of moisture by an absorbent material such as calcium chloride solution. Absorption involves a change in the physical or chemical structure of the material and it is not generally practicable to reactivate the material.

Design temperatures and humidities for industrial processes

Industry	Process		Temperature °C	Relative humidity %
Textile	Cotton	carding	24–27	50
		spinning	15–27	60–70
		weaving	20–24	70–80
	Rayon	spinning	21	85
		twisting	21	65
	Silk	spinning	24–27	65–70
		weaving	24–27	60–70
	Wool	carding	24–27	65–70
		spinning	24–27	55–60
		weaving	24–27	50–55
Tobacco	Cigar and cigarette making		21–24	55–65
	Softening		32	85
	Stemming and strigging		24–30	70
Paint	Drying oil paints		15–32	25–50
	Brush and spray painting		15–27	25–50
Paper	Binding, cutting, drying, folding, gluing		15–27	25–50
	Storage of paper		15–27	34–45
	Storage of books		18–21	38–50
Printing	Binding		21	45
	Folding		25	65
	Pressing, general		24	60–78
Photographic	Development of film		21–24	60
	Drying		24–27	50
	Printing		21	70
	Cutting		22	65
Fur	Storage		−2 to +4	25–40
	Drying		43	—

High velocity air conditioning

Basic systems   1   Single duct system
                2   Dual duct system
                3   Induction system

Single duct system

A central plant delivers conditioned air through high velocity ducting to attenuator boxes throughout the building. The distribution boxes have sound attenuators.

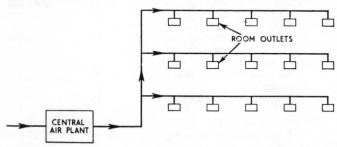

Advantages
   Space saving through use of high velocity small diameter ducts.
   Low initial cost.
   Zone control can be used.

Disadvantages
   Large volume of air to be treated in central plant.
   Individual room control not possible.
   Recirculating system necessary.

Dual duct system

A central plant delivers two streams of air through two sets of high velocity ducting to attenuator mixing boxes in the various rooms. The two streams are at different temperatures and humidities, and the ratio in which they are mixed can be set at each mixing box independently of all others in the building.

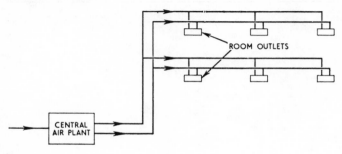

Advantages

Space saving through use of high velocity small diameter ducts.
Individual room control — zoning not necessary.
Flexible in operation.
Units are available for mounting under window-sills or in ceilings.
Suitable for use where large air volumes are required.

Disadvantages

Two sets of air ducting are needed, using more space.
More air has to be treated in central plant.
Recirculating system is necessary.

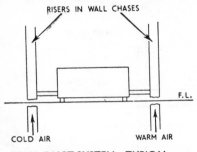

DUAL DUCT SYSTEM—TYPICAL
CONNECTIONS TO ROOM UNIT

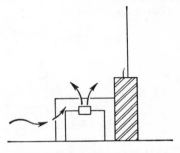

TYPICAL ARRANGEMENT OF
UNIT UNDER WINDOW SILL

Control

An individual pneumatic or electric room thermostat adjusts the ratio in
which air streams are mixed.

Each stream is kept at constant temperature and humidity by
automatic controls in plant room.

Induction system

A central air plant delivers conditioned air through high velocity ducting
to induction units in the rooms. Water from a central plant is also supplied
to the induction units. The conditioned, or primary, air supplied to the
units induces room, or secondary, air through the unit. This induced
secondary air passes over the water coil and is thus heated or cooled.

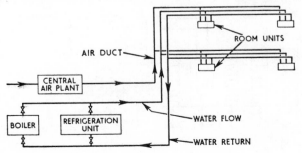

Advantages

Space saving through use of high velocity small diameter ducts.
Low running costs.
Individual room control.
Very suitable for modular building layouts.
Central air plant need handle only part of the air treated.
Particularly applicable to perimeter zones of large buildings — hotels, hospitals, schools and flats, etc.
Suitable for large heat loads with small air volumes.

Disadvantages

High capital cost.

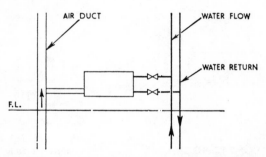

INDUCTION SYSTEM — TYPICAL CONNECTIONS TO ROOM UNIT

Primary air plant

Central air handling plant consists of

1 Intake louvres.
2 Air filters.
3 Preheater.
4 Humidifier or dehumidifier.
5 Reheater.
6 Fan.
7 Silencer or sound absorber.

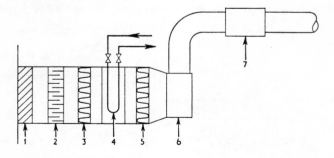

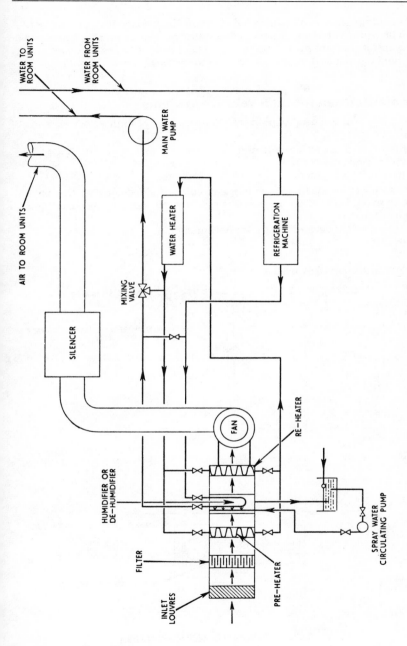

SCHEME OF CENTRAL PLANT FOR INDUCTION SYSTEM

Air-handling plant can be installed either in the basement or on the roof.

To provide heated water and chilled water for the air plant a boiler and a refrigerator unit are provided. For reasons of weight these are usually installed in the basement; they need not necessarily be near the air-handling plant.

Air distribution for high velocity systems

High pressures are used to obtain the advantages of high velocities and small ducts.

Pressure at inlet to farthest unit $100-250$ N/m^2
Typical pressures at fan $1250-1500$ N/m^2
Air velocities in ducts $15-20$ m/s

Ducts for these systems are always circular. Welded construction is used to avoid leaks at the higher air pressures. Spirally wound ducting is also available.

Alternatively special fittings are obtainable.

Ducts must be insulated.

Room distribution units

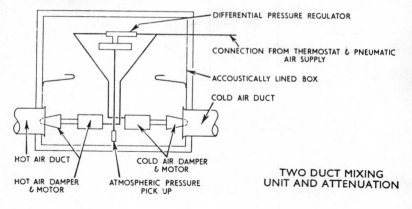

TWO DUCT MIXING
UNIT AND ATTENUATION

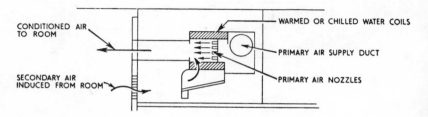

CEILING MOUNTED INDUCTION UNIT

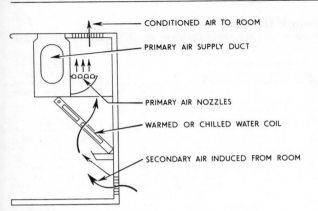

CONDITIONED AIR TO ROOM

PRIMARY AIR SUPPLY DUCT

PRIMARY AIR NOZZLES

WARMED OR CHILLED WATER COIL

SECONDARY AIR INDUCED FROM ROOM

Design procedure for induction units

1 Calculate heat gain.
2 Select suitable room unit from manufacturers' catalogues.
3 Determine temperature of chilled water according to dew point of room air.
4 Determine primary air quantity.
5 Design ducting, using equivalent length method.
6 Design water pipes, as for radiator system, see section 8.

Design data

Air heater
4–6 m/s over free area
2.5–3.0 m/s over total area

Supply of primary fresh air
0.010 m³/s per person
0.015 m³/s per person where heavy smokers are present

Air velocities in primary ducts
15-20 m/s

Induction units
Ratio: secondary air/primary air   3:1
Pressure of primary air   200 N/m²

Friction loss through fittings

The following table takes into account static regain. EL=Eqivalent length of pipe.

Fitting		4 in 100 mm	6 in 150 mm	8 in 200 mm	10 in 250 mm	12 in 300 mm	14 in 350 mm	16 in 400 mm	18 in 450 mm	20in 500 mm
	EL ft	−9	−15							
	EL m	−3	−5							
	EL ft	12	21							
	EL m	4	7							
90°	LE ft	3	4	7	10	12	15	18	21	24
	LE m	1	1.2	2	3	4	5	6	7	8
45°	LE ft	1	2	4	5	6	8	9	10	12
	LE m	0.3	0.6	1.2	1.5	1.8	2.4	3	3	4
30°	LE ft	1	1	2	3	4	5	6	7	8
	LE m	0.3	0.3	0.6	1	1.2	1.5	1.8	2	2.4
	LE ft	−5	−9	−13	−17	−22	−26	−31	−36	−42
	LE m	−1.5	−3	−4	−5	−7	−8	−10	−11	−13
	LE ft	12	21	30	40	52	63	75	87	100
	LE m	4	6	10	12	16	19	22	25	30
	LE ft	−13	−22	−32	−42	−54	−66	−78	−91	−105
	LE m	−4	−7	−10	−13	−16	−20	−24	−28	−32
	LE ft	13	22	32	42	54	66	78	91	105
	LE m	4	7	10	13	16	20	24	28	32
$\frac{d}{b} < 0.4$	LE ft	−8	−10	−11	−13	−17	−20	−24	−28	−32
	LE m	−2.4	−3	−3.3	−4	−5	−6	−7	−9	−10
	LE ft					−9	−9	−10	−10	−10
$\frac{d}{b} \leqslant 0.4$	LE m		−3	−3	−3	−3	−3	−3		−3
	LE ft	13	22	32	42	54	56	78	91	105
	LE m	4	7	10	13	16	20	24	28	32
	LE ft		−21	−30	−40	−52	−63	−75	−87	−100
	LE m		−6	−10	−12	−16	−19	−22	−25	−30
	LE ft	13	22	32	42	54	66	78	91	105
	LE m	4	7	10	13	16	20	24	28	32
	LE ft	14	23	37	49	62	76	90	106	121
	LE m	4	7	11	15	19	23	27	32	

Air curtains

Heated air is blown across a door opening to prevent or reduce ingress of cold atmospheric air.

Applications
   Door-less shop fronts.
   Workshop entrances.
   Doors of public buildings which are frequently opened.

Temperatures
Discharge Temperature: for small installation   35–50°C
                        for large installation   25–35°C
                        Suction Temperature   5–15°C

Air velocity
   Flow from above   5–15m/s
            below   2–4 m/s
            side   10–15 m/s

Air quantity:
Quantity required depends on too many variable factors for exact calculation to be possible. The quantity should be made as large as possible consistent with practicable heat requirements. Suggested values: 2000–5000 m^3/m^2 hr of door opening. In very exposed situations or other difficult cases this can be increased to 10 000 m^3/m^2 hr.

Let V_o=quantity of air entering in absence of curtain
   V=quantity blown by curtain
   For one-sided curtain $V=0.45\ V_o$
   For two-sided curtain $V=0.9\ V_o$

Example: Width of door 4 m. Height of door 2 m. Speed of outdoor air 2 m/s.

$\therefore V_o=4\times2\times2=16\text{ m}^3\text{/s}$
$\therefore V =0.45\times16=7.2\text{ m}^3\text{/s}$

Discharge velocity, say 10 m/s.

$\therefore$ Grille area$=\dfrac{7.2}{10}=0.72\text{ m}^2$

Height of grille=height of door=2 m.

$\therefore$ Width of grille$=\dfrac{0.72}{2}=0.36\text{ m}$

13 Pumps and fans

Flow in pipes

Bernoulli's Equation can be applied between points in a pipe through which fluid is flowing, with the addition of a term to allow for energy lost from the fluid in overcoming friction.

$$\frac{p_1}{\varrho g}+\frac{U_1^2}{2g}+z_1=\frac{p_2}{\varrho g}+\frac{U_2^2}{2g}+z_2+h_f$$

$$h_f=\frac{p_f}{p_g}$$

where
    Subscript 1 refers to values at point 1.
    Subscript 2 refers to values at point 2.
    p = pressure   (N/m^2)
    ϱ = density   (kg/m^3)
    g = weight per unit mass
      = acceleration due to gravity (m/s^2)
    U = velocity   (m/s)
    z = height above arbitrary
        datum   (m)
    h_f = friction head from point 1
        to point 2   (m)
    p_f = pressure necessary to
        overcome friction between
        points 1 and 2   (N/m^2)

Fluid statics

For a liquid in equilibrium
$$p + \varrho g z = \text{const.}$$
If the datum from which z is measured is taken as the free surface of the liquid
$$z = -h$$
and
$$p = \varrho g h$$

$\dfrac{p}{\varrho g} = h$ and is termed *pressure head*

$\dfrac{p}{\varrho g} + z = \text{const.}$ and is termed *piezometric head*

where

p = pressure of liquid	(N/m^2)
ϱ = density	(kg/m^3)
g = weight per unit mass	
= acceleration due to gravity	(m/s^2)
z = height above arbitrary datum	(m)
h = depth below free surface	(m)

Fluid motion

The total energy per unit weight of a liquid in steady flow remains constant. This is expressed in *Bernoulli's Equation:*

$$\frac{p}{\varrho} + \frac{U^2}{2} + gz = \text{const.}$$

or

$$\frac{p}{\varrho g} + \frac{U^2}{2g} + z = \text{const.}$$

$\dfrac{p}{\varrho g}$ is the pressure head per unit weight of fluid.

$\dfrac{U^2}{2g}$ is the velocity head per unit weight of fluid.

z is the gravitational head above datum per unit weight of fluid.

where
U = velocity of fluid (m/s).

Other symbols as above.

Venturimeter

A venturimeter is inserted in a pipe to measure the quantity of water flowing through it.

$$Q = \frac{C_d A_2}{\sqrt{1 - \left(\dfrac{A_2}{A_1}\right)^2}} \sqrt{2 \frac{p_1 - p_2}{\varrho}}$$

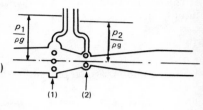

where

Q = quantity of water flowing   (m³/s)
C_d = coefficient of discharge
   = 0.96 to 0.99
A = area   (m²)
p = pressure   (N/m²)
ϱ = density   (kg/m³)

Subscripts 1 and 2 refer to values of sections 1 and 2 respectively.

Discharge of water through small orifice

$$Q = v a_o$$
$$v = C_v \sqrt{2gh}$$
$$Q_o = C_c a_1$$
$$Q = C_v C_c a_1 \sqrt{2gh}$$

where

Q = quantity of water discharged   (m³/s)
v = velocity at section of minimum area of jet   (m/s)
a_o = area at section of minimum area of jet   (m²)
a_1 = area of orifice   (m²)
h = height of free surface above orifice   (m)
g = weight per unit mass
   = acceleration due to gravity   (m/s²)
C_v = coefficient of velocity
   $= \dfrac{\text{actual velocity}}{\text{theoretical velocity}} = 0.96$ to 0.99

C_c = coefficient of contraction
   $= \dfrac{a_o}{a_1} = 0.6$ to 0.7

Velocity heads and theoretical velocities of water

$$h=\frac{v^2}{2g}$$

$h=$Head in m
$v=$Velocity in m/s
$g=$Gravity of earth$=9.81$ m/s^2

v m/s	h m	v m/s	h m	v m/s	h m	v m/s	h m
0.01	0.0000051	0.80	0.0326	1.60	0.130	2.40	0.293
0.05	0.000127	0.85	0.0368	1.65	0.139	2.45	0.306
0.10	0.00051	0.90	0.0413	1.70	0.147	2.50	0.318
0.15	0.00115	0.95	0.046	1.75	0.156	2.55	0.331
0.20	0.00204	1.0	0.0510	1.80	0.165	2.60	0.344
0.25	0.00319	1.05	0.0561	1.85	0.174	2.65	0.358
0.30	0.00459	1.10	0.0617	1.90	0.184	2.70	0.371
0.35	0.00624	1.15	0.0674	1.95	0.194	2.75	0.385
0.40	0.00815	1.20	0.0734	2.0	0.204	2.80	0.400
0.45	0.0103	1.25	0.0797	2.05	0.214	2.85	0.414
0.50	0.0127	1.30	0.0862	2.10	0.225	2.90	0.429
0.55	0.0154	1.35	0.0930	2.15	0.236	2.95	0.444
0.60	0.0183	1.40	0.100	2.20	0.246	3.0	0.459
0.65	0.0125	1.45	0.107	2.25	0.258		
0.70	0.0250	1.50	0.115	2.30	0.269		
0.75	0.0287	1.55	0.122	2.35	0.281		

$$h=\frac{v^2}{2g}$$

$h=$Head in ft
$v=$Velocity in ft/s
$g=$Gravity of earth$=32.2$ ft/s^2

v ft/s	h ft	v ft/s	h ft	v ft/s	h ft	v ft/s	h ft
0.1	0.0002	2.1	0.068	4.1	0.261	6.1	0.578
0.2	0.0006	2.2	0.075	4.2	0.274	6.2	0.597
0.3	0.0014	2.3	0.082	4.3	0.289	6.3	0.616
0.4	0.0025	2.4	0.089	4.4	0.301	6.4	0.636
0.5	0.0039	2.5	0.097	4.5	0.314	6.5	0.656
0.6	0.0056	2.6	0.105	4.6	0.329	6.6	0.676
0.7	0.0076	2.7	0.113	4.7	0.343	6.7	0.697
0.8	0.0099	2.8	0.122	4.8	0.358	6.8	0.718
0.9	0.0126	2.9	0.131	4.9	0.373	6.9	0.739
1.0	0.0155	3.0	0.140	5.0	0.388	7.0	0.761
1.1	0.019	3.1	0.149	5.1	0.404	7.1	0.783
1.2	0.022	3.2	0.159	5.2	0.420	7.2	0.805
1.3	0.026	3.3	0.169	5.3	0.436	7.3	0.827
1.4	0.030	3.4	0.179	5.4	0.453	7.4	0.850
1.5	0.035	3.5	0.190	5.5	0.470	7.5	0.874
1.6	0.040	3.6	0.201	5.6	0.487	7.6	0.897
1.7	0.045	3.7	0.212	5.7	0.505	7.7	0.921
1.8	0.050	3.8	0.224	5.8	0.522	7.8	0.945
1.9	0.056	3.9	0.236	5.9	0.541	7.9	0.969
2.0	0.062	4.0	0.248	6.0	0.559	8.0	0.994

Centrifugal pumps

The action of pumps is most conveniently expressed in terms of head. The rotor gives the liquid a head.

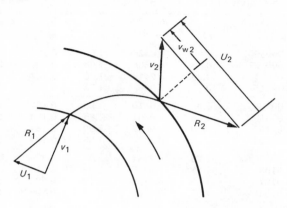

Notation

v_1=absolute velocity of water at inlet   (m/s)
v_2=absolute velocity of water at outlet   (m/s)
U_1=tangential velocity of blade at inlet   (m/s)
U_2=tangential velocity of blade at outlet   (m/s)
V_{w1}=tangential velocity of water at inlet   (m/s)
V_{w2}=tangential velocity of water at outlet   (m/s)
R_1=velocity of water relative to blade at inlet   (m/s)
R_2=velocity of water relative to blade at outlet   (m/s)
g=weight per unit mass=9.81   (m/s^2)
ϱ=density   (kg/m^3)
p_1=pressure of water at inlet   (N/m^2)
p_2=pressure of water at outlet   (N/m^2)
H_i=ideal head developed by pump   (m)
H_a=manometric head
   =actual head developed by pump   (m)
η_m=manometric efficiency   (%)
η_o=overall efficiency   (%)

Normally for a pump V_{w1}=o
Then

$$H_i=\text{work done on water per unit weight}=\frac{U_2V_{w2}}{g}$$

When the output of a pump is expressed as head of working liquid it is independent of the density of the liquid.

$$H_m = \frac{p_2 - p_1}{\varrho g} + \frac{v_2^2}{2g}$$

Actual head is less than ideal because of friction losses within pump.

$$\eta_m = \frac{H_m}{H_i} \times 100$$

Overall efficiency is lower again because of mechanical losses in bearings, etc.

$$\eta_o = \frac{H_m Q \varrho g}{S} \times 100$$

where
Q = quantity of water flowing (m^3/s)
S = power input at shaft (Nm/s)

The specific speed of a centrifugal pump is the speed at which the pump would deliver $1 \ m^3/s$ of water at a head of 1 m.

$$N_s = \frac{n \ Q^{1/2}}{H^{3/4}}$$

where
N_s = specific speed
n = speed   (rev/min)
Q = volume delivered (m^3/s)
H = total head developed   (m)

Pump laws

1   Volume delivered varies directly as speed $\dfrac{Q_1}{Q_2} = \dfrac{N_1}{N_2}$

2   Head developed varies as the square of speed $\dfrac{H_1}{H_2} = \left(\dfrac{N_1}{N_2}\right)^2$

3   Power absorbed varies as the cube of speed $\dfrac{S_1}{S_2} = \left(\dfrac{N_1}{N_2}\right)^3$

Characteristic curves of pumps

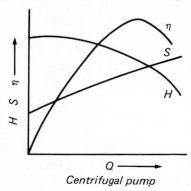

Centrifugal pump

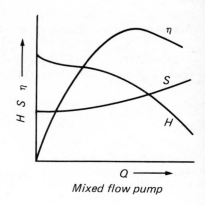

Mixed flow pump

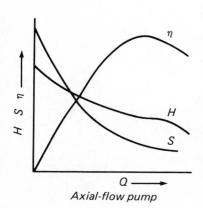

Axial-flow pump

Q = quantity flowing $\quad m^3/s$
H = head developed $\quad\quad m$
S = power absorbed $\quad\quad W$
η = efficiency $\quad\quad\quad\quad$ %

A centrifugal pump takes the least power when the flow is zero. It should therefore be started with the delivery valve shut.

An axial flow pump takes the least power when the flow is greatest. It should therefore be started with the delivery valve open.

Fans

1   Propeller fans and axial flow fans

Pressure for single stage up to about 300 N/m².

Suitable for large volumes at comparatively low pressures.

Characteristic curve for axial flow fan

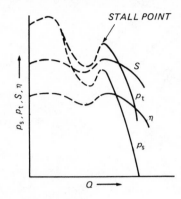

$$Q = \text{volume flowing} \quad m^3/s$$
$$p_s = \text{static pressure} \quad N/m^2$$
$$p_t = \text{total pressure} \quad N/m^2$$
$$S = \text{power absorbed} \quad W$$
$$\eta = \text{efficiency} \quad \%$$

2   Centrifugal fans

Types of blade

STRAIGHT
STEEL PLATE
PADDLE WHEEL

FORWARD
MULTIVANE
MULTIBLADE

BACKWARD
TURBOVANE

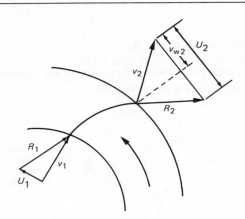

Notation

Suffix 1 refers to inlet.
Suffix 2 refers to outlet.

v=absolute velocity of air (m/s)
u=tangential velocity of blade (m/s)
v_w=tangential velocity of air (m/s)
R=velocity of air relative to blade (m/s)
g=weight per unit mass
=9.81 (m/s^2)
ϱ=density of air (kg/m^3)
p_t=total pressure (N/m^2)
p_g=static pressure (N/m^2)
P_i=theoretical total pressure developed by fan (N/m^2)
P_a=actual total pressure developed by fan (N/m^2)
Q=volume of air (m^3/s)
S=power input to fan (W)
η=efficiency (%)

Normally

$$P_\mathrm{i}=U_2 v_\mathrm{w2}\varrho \qquad v_\mathrm{w1}=0$$

$$p_\mathrm{t}=p_\mathrm{s}+\frac{v^2\varrho}{2}$$

$$p_\mathrm{a}=p_\mathrm{t2}-p_\mathrm{t1}=p_\mathrm{s2}-p_\mathrm{s1}+\frac{(v_2^2-v_1^2)\varrho}{2}$$

$$\eta=\frac{P_\mathrm{a}Q}{S}\times100$$

Characteristic curve for centrifugal fan

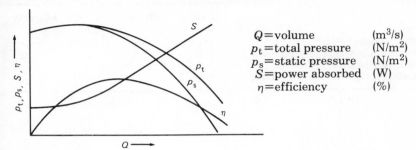

Q = volume   (m³/s)
p_t = total pressure   (N/m²)
p_s = static pressure   (N/m²)
S = power absorbed   (W)
η = efficiency   (%)

Typical efficiencies
Small fans   0.40
Medium fans   0.60
Large fans   0.80

Fan laws

1 Volume varies directly as speed

$$\frac{Q_1}{Q_2} = \frac{N_1}{N_2}$$

2 Total pressure varies as the square of speed

$$\frac{P_{t1}}{P_{t2}} = \left(\frac{N_1}{N_2}\right)^2$$

3 Power absorbed varies as the cube of speed

$$\frac{S_1}{S_2} = \left(\frac{N_1}{N_2}\right)^3$$

Selection of fans
1 Air volume to be moved.
2 Static pressure or resistance.
3 Noise level permissible.
4 Electric supply available.

Pressures commonly used for typical systems

Public buildings, ventilation only	90–150 N/m²
Public buildings, combined heating and ventilation	150–250 N/m²
Public buildings, combined heating and ventilation with air cleaning plant	170–300 N/m²
Factories, heating only	170–400 N/m²
Factories, combined heating and ventilation	300–500 N/m²

Fan discharge velocities for quiet operation

	Supply systems m/s	Extract systems m/s
Sound studios, churches, libraries	4–5	5–7
Cinemas, theatres, ballrooms	5–7.5	6–8
Restaurants, offices, hotels, shops	6–8	7–9

14 Sound

Sound. (Energy travelling as a pressure wave)

One decibel is equal to ten times the logarithm to base 10 of the ratio of two quantities.

$$I=\frac{W}{A}=\frac{p^2}{\varrho c}$$

Sound power level

$$PWL=10 \log_{10} \frac{W}{W_{\mathrm{o}}}$$

Sound intensity

$$IL=10 \log_{10} \frac{I}{I_{\mathrm{o}}}$$

Sound pressure level

$$SPL=10 \log_{10} \frac{p^2}{p_{\mathrm{o}}^2}$$

$$=20 \log_{10} \frac{p}{p_{\mathrm{o}}}$$

where

I	=intensity of sound	(W/m²)
I_{o}	=reference intensity	(W/m²)
W	=power	(W)
W_{o}	=reference power	(W)
A	=area	(m²)
p	=root mean square pressure	(N/m²)
p_{o}	=reference pressure	(N/m²)
ϱ	=density	(kg/m³)
c	=velocity of sound	(m/s)

The usual reference levels are

$W_{\mathrm{o}}=10^{-12}$ watts
$I_{\mathrm{o}}=10^{-12}$ W/m²
$p_{\mathrm{o}}=0.0002 \, \mu\text{bar}=20\times10^{-6}$ N/m²

At room temperature and at sea level $SPL=IL+0.2$ decibels

Measurement of noise

Method of adding levels expressed in decibels

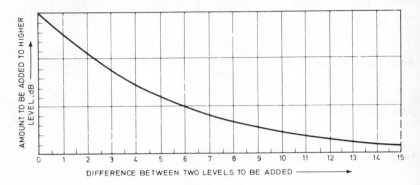

Noise rating Graphs are plotted of Sound Pressure Level (SPL) v frequency, to show how the acceptable sound level varies with frequency. What is acceptable depends on the use to which the room will be put, and so a different curve is obtained for each type of use. Each such curve is designated by an NR number.

NR No.	Application
NR 25	Concert halls, broadcasting and recording studios, churches
NR 30	Private dwellings, hospitals, theatres, cinemas, conference rooms
NR 35	Libraries, museums, court rooms, schools, hospital operating theatres and wards, flats, hotels, executive offices
NR 40	Halls, corridors, cloakrooms, restaurants, night clubs, offices, shops
NR 45	Department stores, supermarkets, canteens, general offices
NR 50	Typing pools, offices with business machines
NR 60	Light engineering works
NR 70	Foundries, heavy engineering works

NR levels (SPL, dB re 0.00002 N/m^2)

Noise rating	Octave band mid-frequency, Hz							
	62.5	125	250	500	1000	2000	4000	8000
NR10	42	32	23	15	10	7	3	2
NR20	51	39	31	24	20	17	14	13
NR30	59	48	40	34	30	27	25	23
NR35	63	52	45	39	35	32	30	28
NR40	67	57	49	44	40	37	35	33
NR45	71	61	54	48	45	42	40	38
NR50	75	65	59	53	50	47	45	43
NR55	79	70	63	58	55	52	50	49
NR60	83	74	68	63	60	57	55	54
NR65	87	78	72	68	65	62	61	59
NR70	91	83	77	73	70	68	66	64
NR75	95	87	82	78	75	73	71	69
NR80	99	91	86	82	80	78	76	74

Sound obeys the Inverse Square Law

$$p^2 = K \frac{W}{r^2}$$

where

p = root mean square pressure
K = constant
W = power
r = distance from source

or SPL = PWL $- 20 \log_{10} r + K'$. $K' = \log_{10} K$ = constant.

In air with source near ground, $K' = -8$.

For a continuing source in a room, the sound level is the sum of the direct and the reverberant sound and is given by

$$SPL = PWL + 10 \log_{10} \left[\frac{Q}{4\pi r^2} + \frac{4}{R} \right] \text{ dB}$$

where

$$Q = \frac{\text{SPL at distance } r \text{ from actual source}}{\text{SPL at distance } r \text{ from uniform source of same power}}$$

R = Room constant = $\dfrac{S\alpha}{1-\alpha}$ m^2

S = Total surface area of room m^2
α = Absorption coefficient of walls
r in m

Coefficient of absorption α

For range of frequencies usual in ventilation applications

Plaster walls	0.01–0.03	25 mm wood wool cement	
Unpainted brickwork	0.02–0.05	on battens	0.6–0.7
Painted brickwork	0.01–0.02	50 mm slag wool or glass	
		silk	0.8–0.9

3-plywood panel	0.01–0.02	12 mm acoustic belt	0.5–0.6
6 mm cork sheet	0.1–0.2	Hardwood	0.3
6 mm porous rubber sheet	0.1–0.2	25 mm sprayed asbestos	0.6–0.7

12 mm fibreboard on		Persons, each	2.0–5.0
battens	0.3–0.4	Acoustic tiles	0.4–0.8

Sound insulation of walls

Transmission coefficient $\tau = \dfrac{\text{transmitted energy}}{\text{incident energy}}$

Sound reduction index

$$SRI = 10 \log_{10} \frac{1}{\tau} \quad dB$$

Empirical formula is
$$SRI = 15 \log (\sigma f) - 17$$
where
$\sigma =$ mass per unit area of wall   (kg/m^2)
$f =$ frequency   (Hz)

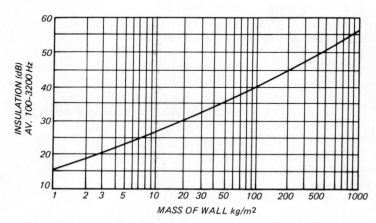

SOUND INSULATION OF SOLID WALLS ACCORDING TO MASS

Transmission through walls

$$(SPL)_1 - (SPL)_2 = SRI - 10 \log_{10} \frac{S_p}{S_2 \alpha_2} \text{ dB}$$

where $(SPL)_1$ = sound pressure in sending room
$(SPL)_2$ = sound pressure in receiving room
SRI = sound Reduction Index
$S_2 \alpha_2$ = equivalent Absorption in receiving room
S_p = area of partition wall

Sound insulation of windows

Single/ double window	Type of window	Type of glass	Sound reduction in dB
Single	Opening type (closed)	Any glass	18-20
Single	Fixed or opening type with air-tight weather strips	24/32 oz sheet glass	23-25
		6 mm polished plate glass	27
		9 mm polished plate glass	30
Double	Opening type (closed) plus absorbent material on sides of air space	24/32 oz sheet glass 100 mm space	28
		24/32 oz sheet glass 200 mm space	31
		6 mm polished plate glass 100 mm space	30
		6 mm polished plate glass 200 mm space	33
Double	Fixed or opening type with air-tight weather strips	24/32 oz sheet glass 100 mm space	34
		24/32 oz sheet glass 200 mm space	40
		6 mm polished plate glass 100 mm space	38
		6 mm polished plate glass 200 mm space	44

Attenuation by building structure

Structure	Attenu- ation dB	Structure	Attenu- ation dB
9 in brick wall	50	Double window 50 mm spacing	30
6 in (150 mm) concrete wall	42	12 mm T & G boarded partition	26
Wood joist floor and ceiling	40	2.5 mm glass window	23
Lath and plaster partition	38		

Transmission through ducts

$$\frac{\text{Attenuation}}{\text{Duct length}} = 3.5 \alpha^{1.4} \frac{P}{A} \text{ dB per ft}$$

$$= 3.5 \alpha^{1.4} \frac{P}{A} \text{ dB per m}$$

where α = coefficient of absorption
P = perimeter of duct
A = cross sectional area of duct

Approximate attenuation of round bends or square bends with turning vanes in dB

Frequency Hz	20–75	75–150	150–300	300–600	600–1200	1200–2400	2400–4800	4800–10 000
Diameter								
5 to 10 in 125 to 250 mm	0	0	0	0	1	2	3	3
11 to 20 in 251 to 500 mm	0	0	0	1	2	3	3	3
21 to 40 in 501 to 1000 mm	0	0	1	2	3	3	3	3
41 to 80 in 1001 to 2000 mm	0	1	2	3	3	3	3	3

Attenuation due to changes in area in dB

Ratio of Area S_2/S_1	Attenuation dB	Ratio of Areas S_2/S_1	Attenuation dB
1	0.0	3	1.3
2	0.5	4	1.9
2.5	0.9	5	2.6

Attenuation at entry to room (end reflection loss)

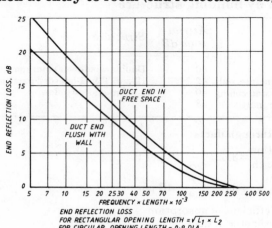

END REFLECTION LOSS
FOR RECTANGULAR OPENING LENGTH = $\sqrt{L_1 \times L_2}$
FOR CIRCULAR OPENING LENGTH = 0·9 DIA.
LENGTHS IN MM.

Sound power level (PWL) of fans

Exact data for any particular fan is to be obtained from the manufacturer. In the absence of this the following approximate expressions may be used.

$PWL = 90 + 10 \log_{10} s + 10 \log_{10} h$
$PWL = 55 + 10 \log_{10} q + 20 \log_{10} h$
$PWL = 125 + 20 \log_{10} s - 10 \log_{10} q$

where

s = rated motor power   (hp)
h = fan static head   (in water gauge)
q = volume discharged   (ft^3/min)

$PWL = 67 + 10 \log_{10} S + 10 \log_{10} p$
$PWL = 40 + 10 \log_{10} Q + 20 \log_{10} p$
$PWL = 94 + 20 \log_{10} S - 10 \log_{10} Q$

where

S = rated motor power   (kW)
p = fan static pressure   (N/m^2)
Q = volume discharged   (m^3/s)

Typical curves of fan frequency distribution

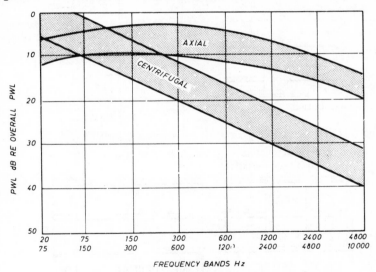

SOUND POWER LEVEL SPECTRA OF FANS

Sound absorption

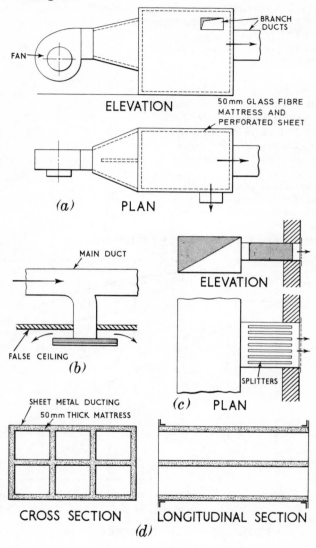

(a) Sound absorption by increase of duct area.
(b) Ceiling air outlet with sound-absorbing plate.
(c) Sound absorption in branch duct with splitter.
(d) Arrangement of splitters in main duct.

15 Labour rates

The following schedules give basic times for installation and erection of heating and ventilating equipment.

Included. Haulage of all parts into position, erection on site, surveying of builder's work, testing.

Not included. Delivery to site, travelling time, addition for overtime working.

Additions to basic time

The basic time given should be increased

For jobs under 1 week	by 40%
For jobs under 2 weeks	20%
For jobs under 3 weeks	8%
For work in existing buildings, unoccupied	5%
For work in existing buildings, occupied	15%
For work in existing building, with concealed pipes	20%

Plant	Time in hr
Boilers. Including all fittings	
Cast iron sectional	
up to 36 kW	20
37–75 kW	25
76–150 kW	35
151–220 kW	50
221–300 kW	60
301–450 kW	70
451–580 kW	75
581–750 kW	80
Unit construction steel boilers	
up to 110 kW	6
111–300 kW	12
301–600 kW	20

Plant	Time in hr
Oil burners, Pressure jet gas burners	
up to 75 kW	8
76–150 kW	12
151–300 kW	20
301–500 kW	25
Combination boiler — Calorifier sets. Including all fittings	
Boiler rating	
up to 110 kW	20
111–300 kW	25
301–600 kW	35
Calorifiers, Indirect cylinders, Direct cylinders	
Storage capacity	
up to 250 litres	9
251–550 litres	12
551–900 litres	20
901–1300 litres	30
1301–2250 litres	35
2251–3500 litres	40
3501–5000 litres	45
Electric water heaters	
up to 3 kW	4
F and E tanks, Cold water tanks	
Capacity	
up to 90 litres	6
91–225 litres	9
226–450 litres	12
451–900 litres	15
901–2000 litres	20
2001–4000 litres	30

Plant		Time in hr
Pumps. Complete with motor		
Direct coupled or belt driven, with supports		
Flow	Nominal size	
up to 1.5 litre/s	up to 32	10
1.6–2.5 litre/s	40–50	14
2.6–25 litre/s	65–100	18
over 25 litre/s	over 100	24
In-line pipeline pumps		
Flow	Nominal size	
up to 0.7 litre/s	up to 32	6
0.8–1.5 litre/s	40–80	10
over 1.5 litre/s	over 80	14

Flue pipes. Steel or Asbestos		
Pipes		
150 dia	(per m)	1
300 dia	(per m)	2
over 300 dia	(per m)	3
Elbows		
150 dia		0.3
300 dia		0.6
over 300 dia		1.0

Valves, Taps, Cocks	
Nominal bore	
15–32	0.5
40–50	1.0
65–100	2
over 100	3

Mixing Valves, Diverting Valves, Two-way Valves. With	
Actuators	
Nominal bore	
up to 32	8
40–50	10
65–100	12
over 100	15

Plant	Time in hr
Electric Starters	
All ratings	2
Three-way Cocks. For venting	
Nominal bore	
up to 50	2
65–100	3
over 100	4
Pressure Gauge. With Cock	2
Thermometer	1
Thermostat	2
Safety Valves	
Nominal bore	
up to 32	1
40–50	2
over 50	4
Radiators. Complete with 2 valves	
Heating surface	
up to 2.5 m^2	4
2.6–4.5 m^2	6
4.6–10 m^2	8
Remove and refix one radiator (for painting and decorating)	1.5
Natural Draught Convectors	
Length	
up to 1 m	6
1.1–1.5 m	7
over 1.5 m	8
Fan Convectors	
Floor standing 700 mm high	5
recessed 700 mm high	7
recessed 1800 mm high	10

Plant	Time in hr
Industrial Type Unit Heaters	
up to 6 kW	10
7–15 kW	15
16–30 kW	20
Gas Fired Room Heaters	
up to 2 kW	5
2.1–10 kW	7
11–18 kW	12
over 18 kW	15
Centrifugal Fans	
Complete with motor, direct coupled or belt driven, with	
supports	
Impeller diameter	
up to 300 mm	15
301–600 mm	20
601–1000 mm	28
1001–1200 mm	45
1201–1525 mm	50
Axial Flow Fans. Complete with casing and motor	
Diameter	
up to 300 mm	5
301–600 mm	8
601–1500 mm	10
1501–2400 mm	20
Cooling Towers. For air conditioning	
Plan area	
up to 2 m^2	15
2.1–3.5 m^2	20
3.6–6.0 m^2	45
6.1–8.0 m^2	60
8.1–15 m^2	100
15.1–20 m^2	140
20.1–25 m^2	160

Plant	Time in hr
Dry or Throw-away Filters	
Capacity	
up to 0.7 m³/s	1
0.71–2.0 m³/s	2
Self-cleaning Viscous Filters	
Capacity	
up to 1 m³/s	5
1.1–1.8 m³/s	7
1.9–6 m³/s	15
6.1–12 m³/s	20
12.1–22 m³/s	30
22.1–30 m³/s	40
Grease Filters	
Capacity	
up to 0.5 m³/s	1
0.6–1.0 m³/s	2
1.1–1.3 m³/s	3.5
1.4–3.0 m³/s	5
Package Air Handling Units. Consisting of filter, preheater, cooler, humidifier, reheater, fan and silencer	
Capacity	
up to 0.15 m³/s	6
0.16–0.3 m³/S	10
0.4–0.5 m³/s	15
0.6–0.8 m³/s	20
0.9–2 m³/s	30
2.1–3 m³/s	43
3.1–4.5 m³/s	70
4.6–6 m³/s	110
6.1–8 m³/s	150

Plant	Time in hr
Grilles and Registers	
Long side	
up to 100 mm	1
101–450 mm	2
over 450 mm	3
Air Dampers. In ventilation ducting	
Diameter (or equivalent diameter for rectangular dampers)	
up to 100 mm	1
101–200 mm	2
201–500 mm	3
501–1000 mm	5
1001–1700 mm	8
1701–2000 mm	10
Actuator or Motor for Motorised Dampers	
All ratings	7.5

	Time in hr/m
Pipes. Including brackets and fittings	
Nominal bore	
up to 20 mm	0.5
25–32 mm	0.75
40–100 mm	1
150 mm	1.8
200 mm	2.5
250 mm	3
Pipe Lagging. Rigid or flexible sectional	
Nominal bore of pipe	
up to 150 mm	0.5
over 150 mm	0.75

	Time in hr/m²
Equipment Lagging	
Flat	0.5

Plant	*Time in hr/m*
Steel Ducts for ventilation systems, including supports and brackets and all fittings Diameter (or equivalent diameter for rectangular ducts)	
up to 200 mm	3
201–300 mm	6
301–500 mm	10
501–750 mm	18
751–1000 mm	25
1001–1200 mm	40
1201–1700 mm	50
1701–2000 mm	70

Time in hours/tonne

Ventilation and Air Conditioning Equipment Not separately detailed, or as alternative to times given above	90

16 Bibliography

The following list is intended as a guide for readers who require more theoretical treatment of the topics on which data is presented in this book. It is a selection of books which are both useful and generally accessible, but does not claim to be exhaustive. Some of the books mentioned are out of print; they are included because they are available in libraries and contain material which is still useful.

Handbooks

Guide to Current Practice, Chartered Institution of Building Services, London

Handbook of Air Conditioning Design, Carrier Air Conditioning Co., Croydon, Surrey

Kempe's Engineering Yearbook, Morgan-Grampian (Publishers), London

Machinery's Handbook, The Industrial Press, New York

Mark's Standard Handbook for Mechanical Engineers, McGraw-Hill, New York & London

Parrish, A., *Mechanical Engineers' Reference Book,* Butterworths, London (1973)

Powell, M. J. V., *House Builder's Reference Book,* Butterworths, London (1979)

Heating, Ventilating, Air Conditioning

Barton, J. J., *Small Bore Heating and Hot Water Supply for Small Dwellings,* 2nd ed, Newnes-Butterworths, London (1970)

Barton, J. J., *Electric Floor Warming,* Newnes-Butterworths, London (1967)

Bedford, Thomas, *Bedford's Basic Principles of Ventilation and Heating,* ed F. A. Chrenka, 3rd ed, H. K. Lewis, London (1974)

Burckhardt, C. H., *Residential and Commercial Air Conditioning,* McGraw-Hill, New York & London (1959)

Carrier, W. H., *Modern Air Conditioning, Heating and Ventilation,* Pitman, London (1959)

Cheremisinoff, P. N. and Regina, T. C., *Principles and Applications of Solar Energy* (1978)

Croome-Gale, D. J. and Roberts, T. M., *Air Conditioning and Ventilation of Buildings* (1975)

Geiringer, P. J., *High Temperature Water Heating,* Wiley, New York & London (1963)

Gosling, C. T., *Applied Air Conditioning and Refrigeration,* Applied Science Publishers, London (1974)

Haines, R. W., *Control Systems for Heating, Ventilating and Air Conditioning,* 2nd ed, Van Nostrand Reinhold (1974)

Harris, N. C. and Conde, N. F., *Modern Air Conditioning Practice,* McGraw-Hill, New York & London (1974)

Hutchinson, F. W., *Design of Air Conditioning Systems,* Industrial Press, New York (1958)

Jones, W. P., *Air Conditioning Engineering,* 2nd ed, Edward Arnold, London (1973)

Jones, W. P., *Air Conditioning Applications and Design* (1980)

Kell, J. R. and Martin, P. L., *Heating and Air Conditioning of Buildings* (by Faber and Kell), 6th ed, The Architectural Press, London (1979)
Kimura, K. I., *Scientific Basis of Air Conditioning*, Applied Science Publishers, London (1977)
Kovach, E. G., *Thermal Energy Storage* (1976)
Kut, D., *Heating and Hot Water Services in Buildings*, Pergamon Press, Oxford (1968)
Kut, D., *Warm Air Heating*, Pergamon Press, Oxford (1970)
Mackenzie-Kennedy, C., *District Heating*, Pergamon Press, Oxford (1979)
McQuislon, F. C. and Parker, J. D., *Heating, Ventilating and Air Conditioning* (1977)
Miles, V. C., *Thermostatic Control*, 2nd ed (1975)
Shaw, E. W., *Heating and Hot Water Services: Selected Subjects with Worked Examples*, 4th ed, Crosby-Lockwood, London (1980)

Heat pumps
Ambrose, E. R., *Heat Pumps and Electric Heating*, Wiley, New York & London (1966)
Heap, R. D., *Heat Pumps* (1979)
Reay, D. A. and MacMichael, D. B. A., *Heat Pumps: Design and Application* (1979)
von Cube, Hans Luckrig and Steimle, Fritz, *Heat Pump Technology*, Butterworths, London (1980)

Heat, Heat Transfer and Thermodynamics
Chapman, A. J., *Heat Transfer*, 3rd ed, Collier-Macmillan, London (1974)
Dunn, P. D. and Reay, D. A., *Heat Pipes*, 2nd ed (1978)
Fishenden, M. and Saunders, O. A., *An Introduction to Heat Transfer*, Oxford University Press (1950)
Holman, J. P., *Heat Transfer*, 4th ed (1976)
Jakob, M. and Hawkins, G. A., *Elements of Heat Transfer and Insulation*, 3rd ed, Chapman & Hall, London (1957)
Lewitt, E. H., *Thermodynamics Applied to Heat Engines*, 6th ed, Pitman, London (1965)
McAdams, W. H., *Heat Transmission*, 3rd ed, McGraw-Hill, New York & London (1954)
Robinson, W. and Dickson, S. M., *Applied Thermodynamics*, Pitman, London (1954)
Schmidt, E., *Thermodynamics: Principles and Applications to Engineering*, translated from 3rd German edition, Dover and London (Reprinted 1966)
Walshaw, A. C., *Thermodynamics for Engineers*, 5th ed, Longmans, London (1963)

Refrigeration
Dossat, R. J., *Principles of Refrigeration*, 2nd ed (1978)
King, G. R., *Modern Refrigeration Practice* (1971)
Langley, B. C., *Refrigeration and Air Conditioning* (1978)

Hydraulics
Hansen, A. G., *Fluid Mechanics*, Wiley, New York & London (1967)
Lewitt, E. H., *Hydraulics and Fluid Mechanics*, Pitman, London (1966)
Massey, B. S., *Mechanics of Fluid*, 4th ed, Van Nostrand, London (1979)
Walshaw, A. C. and Jobson, D. A., *Mechanics of Fluids*, 2nd ed,
  Longmans, London (1972)

Combustion
Brame and King, *Fuels, Solid, Liquid and Gaseous*, Edward Arnold,
  London (1967)
Gilchrist, J. D., *Fuels, Furnaces and Refractories*, Pergamon Press, Oxford
  (1977)

Fans
Buffalo Forge Co, *Fan Engineering*, 7th ed, New York (1970)
Eck, I. B., *Fans*, translated from German, Pergamon Press, Oxford (1973)
Osborne, W. C., *Fans*, 2nd ed, Pergamon Press, Oxford (1977)
Wood's, *Practical Guide to Fan Engineering*, 3rd ed, Woods of Colchester
  Ltd (1978)

Pumps
Addison, H., *Centrifugal and other Rotodynamic Pumps*, 3rd ed, Chapman
  Hall, London (1966)
Anderson, H. H., *Centrifugal Pumps*, Trade & Technical Press, Morden,
  Surrey (1971)
British Pump Manufacturers' Association, *Pump Users' Handbook*, Trade
  & Technical Press, Morden, Surrey (1978)
De Kovats, A. and Desmur, G., *Pumps, Fans and Compressors*, translated
  from French by R. S. Eaton (1958)
Hicks, T. G. and Edwards, T. W., *Pump Application Engineering*,
  McGraw-Hill, London (1971)
Karassik, I. J., *Engineers' Guide to Centrifugal Pumps*, McGraw-Hill,
  New York & London (1964)
Pumping Manual, Trade & Technical Press, Morden, Surrey (1975)
Walker, R., *Pump Selection: A Consulting Engineer's Manual* (1972)

Sound
Croome, D. J., *Noise, Buildings and People* (1977)
Ghering, W. L., *Reference Data for Acoustic Noise Control* (1978)
Iqbal, M. A., *The Control of Noise in Ventilation Systems* (1977)
Porges, G., *Applied Acoustics*, Edward Arnold, London (1977)
Sharland, I., *Wood's Practical Guide to Noise Control*, Wood's of
  Colchester Ltd (1972)

Piping
Holman, E., *Handbook of Industrial Pipework Engineering* (1973)
M. W. Kellog Co, *Design of Piping Systems*, Wiley, New York & London
  (1965)
Littleton, C. T., *Industrial Piping*, 2nd ed, McGraw-Hill, New York &
  London (1962)
Pearson, G . H., *Valve Design*, Pitman, London (1972)

Welding

American Welding Society, *Welding Handbook,* 7th ed, Macmillan, London (1970–78)

Davies, A. C., *The Science and Practice of Welding,* 7th ed, Cambridge University Press (1977)

Giachino, J. W. and Weeks, W., *Welding Skills and Practices,* 5th Technical Press, London (1976)

Giachino, J. W., *Welding Technology,* 2nd ed, Technical Press, London (1973)

Gourd, L. M., *Principles of Welding Technology* (1980)

Manko, H. H., *Solders and Soldering,* 2nd ed. (1979)

17 British Standards

The following list of British Standards relevant to Heating, Ventilating and Air Conditioning is based on information available in May 1980. For the latest details reference should be made to the current BSI Yearbook which is published annually.

10: 1962   Flanges and bolting for pipes, valves and fittings (Obsolescent)
Flanges in grey cast iron, copper alloy and cast or wrought steel for $-328°F$ ($-200°C$) to $975°F$ ($524°C$) and up to 2800 lb/in^2. Materials and dimensions of flanges, bolts and nuts. Ten tables cover plain, boss, integrally cast or forged, and welding neck types.

21: 1973   Pipe threads for tubes and fittings where pressure-tight joints are made on the threads
A range of jointing threads, size $\frac{1}{16}$ to 6, where pressure-tight joints are made by mating taper internal and external threads, or taper external and parallel internal threads. Longscrew threads for use with connectors specified in BS 1387 are included. Thread forms, dimensions and tolerances together with method of designating each type of thread.

41: 1973   Cast iron spigot and socket flue or smoke pipes and fittings
Material, dimensions and tolerances of pipes, bends and offsets up to 300 mm nominal bore and nominal weight of pipes.

66 & 99: 1970   Cast copper alloy pipe fittings for use with screwed copper tubes
Materials and dimensions for banded or beaded cast copper alloy pipe fittings and three piece unions for use with screwed copper tubes suitable for working pressures of up to 125 lbf/in^2 (0.86 MN/m^2) for steam, air, water, gas and oil.

78: ——   Cast iron spigot and socket (vertically cast) and spigot and socket fittings

78: Part 2: 1965   Fittings
Dimensions and weights of bends. elbows, tees, angle branches, crosses, condensate receivers, hatchboxes, plugs and caps for water, gas, sewage, etc. Grades A, B, C and D; internal diameters 3 in to 48 in. Quality of metal, mode of casting, test requirements, coating, testing facilities.

143 & 1256: 1968   Malleable cast iron and cast copper alloy screwed pipe fittings for steam, air, water, gas and oil
Materials, test and dimensions of plain and reinforced fittings suitable for working pressures of up to 200 lbf/in^2 (1380 MN/m^2) for water and 150 lbf/in^2 (1.035 N/m^2) for steam, air, gas and oil.

350: ——   Conversion factors and tables

350: Part 1: 1974   Basis of tables. Conversion factors

Conversion factors for metrology, mechanics, heat. Extended basic information units including SI, metric technical, imperial. Tables of conversion factors showing inter-relationship of units. Letter symbols for every unit. Does not deal with purely electrical units.

350: Part 2: 1962   Detailed conversion tables

Metrology, mechanics, heat, with the numerical basis of each table given at the head and tabulated values expressed for the most part to the nearest 6th significant figure. Summary of tables of conversion factors.

Supplement No. 1: 1967   (PD 6203) to BS 350: Part 2 Additional tables for SI conversions

Contains 36 additional tables for conversions to and from SI units.

416: 1973   Cast iron spigot and socket soil, waste and ventilating pipes (sand cast and spun) and fittings

Deals with one grade of pipe with alternative spigots and sockets and a range of cast iron fittings for use above ground. Quality of materials, finish, testing and marketing. Tables of dimensions to cover pipes, bends, offsets, branches, traps, access doors, roof outlets, inspection pieces, sockets, shoes, holderbats, wire balloons and sanitary connections.

417: ——   Galvanized mild steel cisterns and covers, tanks and cylinders

417: Part 1: 1964   Imperial units

Cold and hot water storage vessels for domestic purposes, as follows:
Cisterns: 20 sizes, from 4 to 740 gallons capacity, in two grades: with covers.
Tanks: 5 sizes, from 21 to 34 gallons capacity, in two grades.
Cylinders: 10 sizes, from 16 to 97 gallons capacity, in three grades.
Materials, workmanship, design and construction, dimensions and tolerances; provision for pipe connections and electric immersion heater and gas circulator connections. Optional internal coating of cisterns with bitumen, testing and marking requirements, test pressures and working heads.

417: Part 2: 1973   Metric units

Metric verson of Part 1

499: ——   Welding terms and symbols

499: Part 1: 1965   Welding, brazing and thermal cutting glossary

Seven sections: terms common to more than one section; relating to welding with pressure, fusion welding, brazing, testing, weld imperfections, thermal cutting. Appendices: typical information to appear on welding and cutting procedure sheets.

499: Part 2: 1965   Symbols for welding

Type, size, location and finish of a weld for a variety of welding processes. Table of standard symbols: illustrations of application of the scheme. Appendices: typical information to be given on welding and cutting procedure sheets.

499C: 1965   Chart of British Standard welding symbols (based on BS 499:Part 2)

Type, size and position of welds, with examples of their use.

499: Part 3: 1965   Terminology of and abbreviations for fusion weld imperfections as revealed by radiography

Definitions for imperfections, descriptions of their appearances in radiographs, typical radiographs. Coding system for reporting defects and their location in a radiograph.

526: 1961   Definitions of the calorific value of fuels

Two sets of definitions (solid and liquid fuels and gaseous fuels) of four calorific values: gross calorific value at constant pressure and at constant volume, net calorific value at constant pressure and at constant volume. Calculation from the basic, e.g. experimentally determined, calorific value of any other of the four calorific values for a fuel.

567: 1973   Asbestos-cement flue pipes and fittings, light quality

Diameters 50 mm, 75 mm, 100 mm, 125 mm and 150 mm, for use with gas fired appliances of input-rating up to 45 kW.

599: 1966   Methods of testing pumps

Testing performance, efficiency of pumps for fluids which behave as homogeneous liquids.

602 & 1085: 1970   Lead and lead alloy pipes for other than chemical purposes

Lead pipes in three different compositions in sizes up to 125 mm bore (BS 602) and for lead-silver-copper pipes in sizes up to 40 mm bore (BS 1085). Suitable for use as service and distributing pipes laid underground; service, cold water and hot water pipes fixed above ground; soil, waste and soil-and-water ventilating, flushing and warning pipes; gas pipes in heavier and lighter weights. See CP 310 for further information on use.

699: 1972   Copper cylinders for domestic purposes

Cylinders for heating and storage of hot water. Grades 1, 2 and 3 for maximum working heads of 25 m, 15 m and 10 m; 14 sizes (from 14 litres to 450 litres). Dimensions from 350 mm to 600 mm external diameter, 675 mm to 1800 mm height. Materials, manufacture, dimensions, connections for pipes and heaters. Tests, marking requirements.

715: 1970   Sheet metal flue pipes and accessories for gas fired appliances

Single- and twin-wall flue pipes, fittings and accessories with welded orfolded seams, finished as necessary to resist heat and minimize corrosion. Tabulated dimensions with appendices on testing certain coatings, measurement of U value and typical assembly.

749: 1969   Underfeed stokers

Stokers rated up to 550 kg of coal per hour for all furnaces except metallurgical or other high temperature; requirements, installation, maintenance (see also CP 3000).

759: 1975   Valves, gauges and other safety fittings for application to boilers and to piping installations for and in connection with boilers

Requirements for steam and water fittings where the steam pressure exceeds 1 bar or, in the case of hot water boilers, the rated capacity exceeds 45 kW.

779: 1976   Cast iron boilers for central heating and indirect hot water supply (44 kW rating and above)

Minimum performance requirements, materials, manufacture, mountings and fittings, automatic controls inspection, hydraulic testing and marking, electrical wiring.

799: ——   Oil burning equipment

799: Part 2: 1964   Vaporizing burners and associated equipment

Fully automatic, semi-automatic and hand-controlled burners and associated equipment for boilers, heaters, furnaces, ovens and other similar static flued plant (free standing space-heating appliances for single family dwellings) suitable for oil to classes C and D of BS 2869.

Performance requirements, timings for controls and safety devices on ignition failure and flame failure for fully automatic and semi-automatic types, construction and plate thicknesses of oil storage tanks up to 750 gallons capacity, integral tanks and barometric tanks, filling pipes and connections, filters and other items of equipment forming part of the oil burner assembly. Smoke test appended.

799: Part 3: 1970   Automatic and semi-automatic atomizing burners up to 36 litres per hour and associated equipment

Includes pressure jet and semi-automtic burners for boilers, space heating and cooking appliances, and similar static and mobile plant suitable for burning Classes C and D fuel complying with BS 2869

799: Part 4: 1972   Atomizing burners over 36 litres/hour and associated equipment for single and multi-burner installations

For land and marine purposes. Suitable for liquid fuels to BS 2869 and BS 1469

799: Part 5: 1975   Oil storage tanks

Requirements for mild steel integral tanks forming part of a complete oil-fired unit for service and storage tanks of unlimited capacity with 10 m maximum height, used for the storage of liquid fuel used with oil burning equipment as specified in BS 799: Parts 2 to 4

835: 1973   Asbestos-cement flue pipes and fittings, heavy quality

Diameters from 75 mm to 600 mm for use with solid fuel and oil burning appliances of output rating not exceeding 45 kW, for gas fired appliances, and for incinerators not exceeding 0.09 m³ capacity.

845: 1972   Acceptance tests for industrial type boilers and steam generators

Methods, and data required for simple efficiency test at minimum cost on hot water and steam raising plant using solid, liquid or gaseous fuel. Not for large power station trials.

848: —— Methods of testing fans for general purposes, including mine fans

848: Part I: 1963   Performance

Nine methods for performance and efficiency of axial flow, centrifugal and propeller fans, including site testing of fans in mines and tunnels. Terms, definitions, symbols, formulae for use in fan testing; procedure, instruments for measuring pressure, air velocity, air volume under test conditions; tolerances on fan performance. Selection of test methods for particular fans; illustrations of layout for each test.

848: Part 2: 1966   Fan noise testing

In-duct, free-field and reverberant field test methods from which sound output of fan may be derived; semi-reverberant test method and methods for site testing. Definitions, symbols formulae. Procedure and instruments for measuring fan sound output. Illustrations of modification to test airway (in BS 848: Part 1) for sound measurement.

853: —— Calorifiers for central heating and hot water supply

853: Part 1: 1960   Mild steel and cast iron

For operating pressures and temperatures in the shell not exceeding 65 lb/sq in and 250°F respectively and for design pressures in the tube battery not exceeding 250 lb/sq in; applies to steam heated calorifiers of any output and also to water-to-water and electrically heated calorifiers exceeding 50 gallons holding capacity. Materials; workmanship; rules for scantlings; weldings, mountings and appliances; inspection tests; marking and certification.

853: Part 2: 1960   Copper

For operating pressures and temperatures in the shell not exceeding 65 lb/sq in and 250°F respectively, and for design pressures in the tube battery not exceeding 250 lb/sq in; applies to steam heated calorifiers of any putput and also to water-to-water and electrically heated calorifiers exceeding 50 gallons holding capacity; for calorifiers for pressures above 65 lb/sq in, see BS 3274. Material; construction; rules for scantlings; mountings and appliances; inspection testing and certification. Appendices give the calculated thickness of the shells and ends, and the equivalent or next heavier SWG for each calculated thickness.

855: 1976   Specifications for welded steel boilers for central heating and indirect hot water supply (rated output 44 kW to 3 MW)

Hot water boilers with maximum operating pressure of 0.45 N/mm^2 and temperature of $132°C$. Steam boilers limited to output of 1500 kW with max operating pressure of 0.2 N/mm^2 and temperature of $132°C$. Specifies min efficiencies for oil, gas and solid fuel firing. Materials, design stress and manufacture, workmanship, inspection, hydrostatic testing, mounting and fittings, automatic controls and electrical wiring requirements.

864: —— Capillary and compression tube fittings of copper and copper alloy

864: Part 2: 1971 Metric units

For use with copper tubes to BS 2871: Part 1: Tables X, Y and Z. Commonly used types of fitting sizes 6 mm to 67 mm. Design, construction, hydraulic test, porosity test, maximum cooling temperatures and pressures.

864: Part 3: 1975 Compression fittings for polyethylene pipes

Fittings for pipes complying with BS 1972, BS 1973, BS 2384 and BS 3796 for cold water services. Range of nominal sizes 3/8 to 2 for working pressures and temperatures up to 12 bar at 20°C

1010: —— Draw-off taps and stopvalves for water srvices (screwdown pattern)

1010: Part 1: 1959 (1977) Imperial units

Requirements for sizes $\frac{1}{4}$ in to 2 in, also for rising spindle/rising top, rising spindle/non-rising top, non-rising spindle types. Material, workmanship for casting and hot pressing. Component parts; waterways, screw threads, spindle and head threads, tap bodies, washers and washer plates, gland packing, union connections. Hydraulic test. Ends suitable for direct connection to copper tubing or to lead or iron piping. 'Easy clean' taps and valves ($\frac{1}{2}$ in and $\frac{1}{4}$ in, non-rising spindles with 'O' ring seals) are covered in PD 5432 (design, dimensions, performance tests for ring materials). (Confirmed 1977)

1010: Part 2: 1973 Draw-off taps and above-ground stopvalves

Dimensions, test requirements for screw-down pattern draw-off taps and above-ground stopvalves $\frac{1}{4}$ in to 2 in nominal sizes. Material (mainly metal), design, dimensions of components and union ends.

1042: —— Methods for the measurement of fluid flow in pipes

1042: Part 1: 1964 Orifice plates, nozzles and Venturi tubes

Geometrical shape, relative dimensions, construction, accuracy of manufacture of square-edged, conical-entrance, quarter-circle orifice-plates, nozzles (of ISA 1932 profile), Venturi nozzles and tubes. Calculation of rate of flow of homogeneous fluids in pipes of inside diameter over 1 in; calculation of dimensions of device for metering given rate of flow. Applicable to compressible and incompressible fluids, to flow of viscous liquids at low Reynolds number, to flow at high pressure differences (initial flow); not to fluids exhibiting non-Newtonian behaviour, to suspensions of solids in liquids or gases, to non-steady or pulsating flow or to flow in partially filled pipelines.

1042: Part 2A: 1973 Pitot tubes. Class A accuracy

Rate of flow of a liquid or gas in a pipe, within a specified range of velocities, using a pitot-static tube (or any tube whose coefficient is known). Conditions for which a total-pressure tube may be used with a wall-static pressure tapping in place of a combined pitot-static tube are described. Shape, relative proportions, limits of size, constructional requirements of a family of pitot-static tubes. Restricted to fluid flow in pipes of circular cross section.

1042: Part 3: 1965   Guide to the effects of departure from the methods in Part 1
Effects of non-compliance with the requirements laid down in Part 1. Additional tolerances or corrections which cannot, however, compensate for deviation from Part 1.

1181: 1971 (1977)   Clay flue linings and flue terminals
Materials, workmanship, design, construction, dimensions, tests for clay flue linings, bends, flue terminals for heating appliances and incinerators and for ventilation.

1192: 1969   Building drawing practice
Sizes, layout of drawing sheets, scales, dimensions of drawings, drawing materials and reproduction, various types of projection, symbols and graphic representation, examples of schedules. Drawings included.

1211: 1958   Centrifugally cast (spun) iron pressure pipes for water, gas and sewage
Pipes with spigot and socket joints cast in either metal or sand moulds. Class B, field test pressure 400 ft head of water; Class C, 600 ft head of water; Class D, 800 ft head of water. Standard lengths, internal diameters, hydraulic tests and tests for straightness.

1212: —— Specification for float operated valves (excluding floats)

1212: Part 1: 1953   Piston type
Seven sizes, for attachment of floats to BS 1968, BS 2456, $\frac{1}{8}$, $\frac{1}{2}$, $\frac{1}{4}$, 1, $1\frac{1}{4}$, $1\frac{1}{2}$ and 2 in. Provision for removable seats, different sized orifices for different pressure and flow. Materials, quality, workmanship, dimensions, performance test, mechanical strength test of levers. Computed flow through seat orifices at various heads of water appended.

1212: Part 2: 1970   Diaphragm type (brass body)
Material, workmanship, design, construction, sizes, tolerances, performance of diaphragm operated ballvalves in two sizes ($\frac{1}{8}$ in and $\frac{1}{2}$ in) having four seat sizes ($\frac{1}{8}$ in, $\frac{1}{16}$ in, $\frac{1}{4}$ in, $\frac{1}{8}$ in bore)

1212: Part 3: 1979   Diaphragm type (plastics body) for cold water services
Materials, workmanship, dimensions and performance requirements of $\frac{1}{2}$ nominal size float operated valves.

1250: —— Domestic appliances burning town gas

1250: Part 1: 1966   General requirements
Construction, performance. Test gases; conditions, test methods common to all appliances appended.

1250: Part 3: 1963   Water-heating appliances
Design, performance for other than laundering appliances; test methods appended.

1250: Part 4: 1965   Space heating appliances
Design, performance, test methods.

1289: 1975   Precast concrete flue blocks for domestic gas appliances
Materials, workmanship, dimensions, tolerances, strength and drying shrinkage. Tests include one for performance of completed flues.

1294: 1946 (1954)   Soot doors for domestic buildings
Five sizes for use in concrete and brickwork flues. Quality of materials, workmanship, construction, finish. Drawings fully detailed in table of dimensions (Confirmed 1954).

1339: 1965   Definitions, formulae and constants relating to the humidity of the air
Includes tables of saturation vapour pressures and bibliography.

1387: 1967   Steel tubes and tubulars suitable for screwing to BS 21 pipe threads
Materials, dimensions, testing of welded and seamless screwed and socketed steel tubes and tubulars, plain end steel tubes suitable for screwing to BS 21 pipe threads, nominal bores $\frac{1}{8}$ in (3.2 mm) to 6 in (150 mm) in medium and heavy thickness and up to 4 in (100 mm) in light thickness. Dimensions, weight per foot and per metre run. Marking. Testing for galvanizing.

1394: ——   Power driven circulators

1394: Part 1: 1971   Glanded and glandless pumps
Centrifugal glanded pumps and glandless pumps 200 W to 2000 W input at maximum voltage (single and three phase electrical supply), used on heating and domestic hot water supply piping systems. Design, construction, performance, testing: specific electrical requirements.

1394: Part 2: 1971   Domestic glandless pumps
Power input up to 200 W at maximum rated voltage (single phase electrical supply), for small bore domestic heating and hot water installations. Design, construction, performance, testing electrical requirements.

1415: ——   Mixing valves

1415: Part 1: 1976   Non-thermostatic, non-compensating mixing valves
Performance requirements, materials and method of specifying size of $\frac{1}{2}$ and $\frac{1}{4}$ nominal size valves.

1563: 1949 (1964)   Cast iron sectional tanks (rectangular)
Bolted tanks up to 40 ft square nad 12 ft deep excluding supporting structures not subject to pressure other than static head with internal or external flanges and open or closed tops, and made from unit plates 2, 3 or 4 ft square. Mild steel tie rod ends and turnbuckles, sizes and thicknesses of unit plates. Illustrations of typical tanks, tables of scantlings and of approximate weights and nominal capacities (Confirmed 1964).

1564: 1975 Pressed steel sectional rectangular tanks

Working under a pressure not exceeding the static head corresponding to the depth of the tank, built up from pressed steel plates 1220 mm square. The sectional dimensions are interchangeable with the imperial dimensions of the 1949 edition of the standard.

1565: —— Galvanized mild steel indirect cylinders, annular or saddle-back type

1565: Part 1: 1949 Imperial units

Seven sizes in two grades, maximum working heads 60 ft and 30 ft. Minimum thickness of material, minimum heating surfaces, methods of manufacture, radius of curvature, bolted ends and handholes, method of galvanizing, screwed connections for pipes and for auxiliary electric heating. Test requirements for primary heaters and complete cylinders. Marking. Dimensions in a table, drawings illustrate method of measuring.

1565: Part 2: 1973 Metric units

Materials, manufacture, design, dimensions, testing, marking. Cylinders in 8 sizes (109 to 455 litres), 2 grades (max. working heads 18 and 9 m). Screwed connections for pipes, electric immersion heaters, thermostats; hand holes, draining taps, gas circulators.

1566: —— Copper indirect cylinders for domestic purposes

1566: Part 1: 1972 Double feed indirect cylinders

Two grades, for max. working heads 15 m and 10 m, 14 sizes (72 litres to 440 litres). Dimensions 350 mm to 600 mm external diameter, 675 mm to 1800 mm height. Materials, manufacture, dimensions, connections for pipes and heaters. Tests, marking.

1566: Part 2: 1972 Single feed indirect cylinders

Self-venting type. Two grades, max. working heads 15 m and 10 m, 6 sizes (86 litres to 180 litres). Dimensions 400 mm to 500 mm external diameter, 750 mm to 1200 mm height. Materials, manufacture, dimensions, connections for pipes and heaters. Tests, marking.

1586: 1964 Methods for testing of refrigerant condensing units

Electrically driven units of power up to 25 hp. Four primary and three confirming test methods, results of primary test being accepted if those of confirming test agree to within ±3 per cent. Group rating conditions appended, applicable to units for use in temperate tropical climates.

1608: 1966 Electrically-driven refrigerant condensing units

Units up to 25 hp using di- and monochlorodifluoromethane; may be applied to use of other halogenated refrigerants. Construction, mechanical and electrical equipment, testing for rating. Nine groups of rating conditions for temperate and tropical climates appended.

1710: 1975 Identification of pipelines

Colours for identifying pipes conveying fluids in liquid or gaseous condition in land installations and on board ships.

1740: ——   Wrought steel pipe fittings (screwed BSP thread)

1740: Part 1: 1971   Metric units
Welded and seamless fittings 6 mm to 150 mm, for use with steel tubes to BS 1387, screwed BSP thread to BS 21

1756: ——   Methods for sampling and analysis of flue gases

1756: Part 1: 1971   Methods of sampling

1756: Part 2: 1971   Analysis by the Orsat apparatus
Apparatus, reagents, method, sample analysis, calculation, reporting of results.

1756: Part 3: 1971   Analysis by the Haldane apparatus
Apparatus, reagents, method, sample analysis, calculation, reporting of results.

1756: Part 4: 1977   Miscellaneous analyses
Determination of moisture content, sulphuric acid dew-point, carbon monoxide, oxides of sulphur and oxides of nitrogen.

1756: Part 5: 1971   Semi-routine analyses
Carbon dioxide, carbon monoxide and total oxides of sulphur. Mainly for combustion performance of domestic gas appliances.

1846: ——   Glossary of terms relating to solid fuel burning equipment

1846: Part 1: 1968   Domestic appliances
Appendices deal with natural and manufactured fuels.

1846: Part 2: 1968   Industrial water heating and steam raising installations
Includes installations fired with pulverized fuel.

1894: 1952   Electrode boilers of riveted, seamless, welded and cast iron construction for water heating and steam generating
Steel water-heating boilers, steel steam boilers, cast iron water-heating boilers. Design temperatures not exceeding 650°F; water heated by resistance to passage of alternating electric current. Materials, construction, workmanship, scantlings, inspection, testing. Safety valves, electrical safety devices.

1952: 1964   Copper alloy gate valves for general purposes
Rating, design and manufacture, materials, dimensions, tests, marking for Classes 100, 125, 150, 200 and 250, with flanged or screwed ends; $\frac{1}{4}$ in to 3 in, operated by inside screw, rising or non-rising stem, or by outside screw, rising stem. Wedge gate, either solid or split; double disk; parallel slide.

1953: 1964   Copper alloy check valves for general purposes

Rating, design and manufacture, materials, dimensions, tests, marking for Classes 100, 125, 150, 200 and 250, with flanged or screwed ends; $\frac{1}{4}$ in to 3 in. Swing (for horizontal or vertical use); lift (i) piston (for horizontal or angle use), (ii) disk (for horizontal, vertical or angle use), (iii) ball (for horizontal, vertical or angle use).

1972: 1967   Polythene pipe (Type 32) for cold water services

Requirements for extrusion compound, pipe material, classification and dimensions of pipes, physical and mechanical characteristics, sampling, marking, and stocking and transport. Test methods for toluene extract of carbon black and antioxidant content in appendices.

2051: ——   Tube and pipe fittings for engineering purposes

2051: Part 1: 1973   Copper and copper alloy capillary and compression tube fittings for engineering purposes

Applies to capillary and compression fittings, Types A and B, in sizes ranging from 4 mm to 42 mm inclusive. These fittings are intended primarily for use with tubes of the outside diameters given in BS 2871: Part 2

2456: 1973   Floats (plastics) for ballvalves for hot and cold water

Gives the requirements for floats of 102 mm, 114 mm, 127 mm and 152 mm diameter manufactured from plastics materials for attachment to ball valves specified in BS 1212: Parts 1 and 2. Performance tests are specified for impact, strength and deflection of boss, cold embrittlement and resistance to hot water up to 90°C

2740: 1969   Simple smoke alarms and alarm metering devices

Requirements for the construction and operation of instruments designed to give an alarm when smoke emission from a chimney exceeds a chosen Ringelmann shade.

2741: 1969   Recommendations for the construction of simple smoke viewers

Advice on the construction of simple smoke viewers, particularly suitable for fitting to individual flues to supplement information provided by more complex instruments installed in a common flue.

2742: 1969   Notes on the use of the Ringelmann and miniature smoke charts

Explains the purpose and method of use of these charts for the visual assessment of the darkness of smoke emitted from chimneys.

2742C: 1957   Ringelmann chart

2742M: 1960   Miniature smoke chart

A chart, printed in shades of grey matt lacquer, which when held at about 5 ft from the observer gives readings of the density values of smoke from chimneys. These are comparable with those obtained from the BS Ringelmann Chart (BS 2742C). The method of use is explained in BS 2742

Addendum No. 1: 1972   The calibration of instruments in Ringelmann numbers

Provides a relationship for the conversion of measurements of optical density of smoke to 'standard' Ringelmann numbers.

2767: 1972   Valves and unions for hot water radiators

The revision now covers the inclusion of non-rising stem angle valves; the extension of the service conditions for which certain valves and unions, when specially tested, may be used; the incorporation of Y-pattern straight valves: the inclusion of requirements for materials for toroidal sealing rings and the alignment of minimum stem diameters, and body and bonnet wall thickness with the once-designated Class 100 valves in the latest revisions of BS 1952 and BS 2060

2777: 1979   Asbestos-cement cisterns

Specifies requirements for twelve types of cistern with waterline capacities from 17 to 701 litres. Gives sizes and approximate weights together with sizes of co-ordinating spaces. Includes a system of referencing and test requirements.

2811: 1969   Smoke density indicators and recorders

Requirements of construction and operation of instruments designed to measure the optical density of or percentage obscuration caused by smoke emitted from chimneys.

2831: 1971   Methods of test for air filters used in air conditioning and general ventilation

Two tests are included: the first, applicable to any filter, deals with the determination of methylene blue efficiency; the second, concerning the determination of the dust-holding capacity, does not apply to designs which preclude accurate weighing before and after collection. Does not specify performance standards.

2852: 1970   Rating and testing room air-conditioners

Prescribes three sets of standard rating conditions for the statement of performance of room air-conditioners employing air-cooled or water-cooled condensers, when used for cooling duties only and gives the corresponding test conditions and test procedures based on the use of a room calorimeter.

2869: 1970   Petroleum fuels for oil engines and burners

Four classes of fuel for internal combustion engines and seven classes of fuel for oil burners including a class (identified by a distinctive symbol) intended for use with free-standing domestic appliances not connected to flues. Minimum temperatures for storage and for outflow from storage and for handling are given for those burner fuels requiring heating facilities. Includes a viscosity conversion chart and a nomograph for calculated cetane index.

2871: ——   Copper and copper alloys. Tubes

2871: Part 1: 1971   Copper tubes for water, gas and sanitation

2871: Part 2: 1972   Tubes for general purposes

Composition, condition, dimensions, mechanical properties, non-destructive tests.

2879: 1957   Draining taps (screw-down pattern)

Specifies the design, materials and dimensions of, and tests for, the screw-down pattern non-ferrous taps used for draining hot and cold water and heating systems. It covers $\frac{1}{2}$ in, $\frac{3}{4}$ in, and 1 in nominal size taps, operated by loose keys, and gives a range of loose key square sizes.

3048: 1958   Code for the continuous sampling and automatic analysis of flue gases. Indicators and recorders

Automatic instruments for direct indication or record of composition of flue gases from industrial plant. Thermal conductivity instruments, instruments depending on chemical absorption and chemical reaction, viscosity and density instruments, oxygen meters, infra-red absorption instruments. Determination of dew point.

3063: 1965   Dimensions of gaskets for pipe flanges

'Plan' dimensions for 'inside bolt circle' and 'full face' gaskets for pipe flanges in accordance with BS 10 and BS 2035, and 'full face' gaskets for flanges to BS 1770. The tables giving dimensions bear the same designation as the flange tables in the appropriate pipe flange standard. Marking of gaskets for purchasing and identification.

3198: 1960   Combination hot water storage units (copper) for domestic purposes

Gives general requirements and tests for both direct and indirect types of hot water storage unit of 25 gallons capacity, made in copper.

3250: ——   Methods for the thermal testing of domestic solid fuel burning appliances

3250: Part 1: 1973   Flue loss method

Describes a method of performance testing in which the heat content of the flue gases and the ashpit loss are determined and subtracted from the total heat content of the fuel consumed. Radiation and, where applicable, boiler output are also determined and convection output is obtained by difference.

3250: Part 2: 1961   Hood method

Describes a method of performance testing in which the convection warm air from the appliance is collected by means of a hood and measured directly.

3276: 1960   Thermometers for measuring air cooling power

Specifies essential requirements of a series of thermometers for measuring low wind speeds or the efficiency of ventilation in ships, factories, hospitals, mines, etc. Standard charts are included, from which the 'cooling power' of the atmosphere and hence the air speed can be read off.

3284: 1967   Polythene pipe (Type 50) for cold water services

Requirements for extrusion compound, pipe material, classification and dimensions of pipes, physical and mechanical characteristics, sampling, marking, and stocking and transport. Test methods for toluene extract of carbon black and antioxidant content in appendices.

3300: 1974   Kerosine (paraffin) unflued space heaters, cooking and boiling appliances for domestic use

Construction, safety, performance, marking and methods of test.

3323: 1978   Glossary of coal terms

Covers terms in general use dealing with petrography, classification, analysis, marketing and utilization of coal but not those terms specific to coal preparation.

3416: 1975   Black bitumen coating solutions for cold application

Bitumen coating solutions. Type I being general purpose for protection of iron and steel, the classes A and B differing only in flashpoint classification, and Type II for coating drinking water tanks, etc.

3505: 1968   Unplasticized PVC pipe for cold water services

Requirements for material, classification and dimensions of pipes, physical and mechanical characteristics, sampling, marking and stocking and transport. Test methods.

3528: 1977   Specification for convection type space heaters operating with steam or hot water

Equipment and procedure for determining thermal output of heating appliances, including radiators, operating with steam or water. Brief references to materials and construction.

3561: 1962   Non-domestic space heaters burning town gas

Specifies constructional and performance requirements for non-domestic space heaters burning town gas; includes general requirements and those specific to fan-assisted air heaters, radiant type overhead heaters, flued convector heaters and room-sealed heaters. Test gases and methods of test are described in appendices.

3899: 1965   Refrigerated room air-conditioners

Room air-conditioners for all climates defined as 'encased assemblies primarily for mounting in a window or through a wall, or as a console'. Prescribes the construction requirements for cooling capacities generally up to 3 ton — refrigeration (36 000 Btu/h). Specifies a type test to be carried out by the room calorimeter method described in BS 2852, and production tests for the electrical equipment.

3974: ——   Pipe supports

3974: Part 1: 1974   Pipe hangers, slider and roller type supports

Covers requirements for the design and manufacture of components for pipe hangers, slider and roller type supports for uninsulated and insulated steel and cast iron pipes of nominal size 15 mm to 160 mm used for transporting fluids within the temperature range −20°C to +470°C

3974: Part 2: 1978 Pipe clamps, cages, cantilevers and attachments to beams

Requirements for design and manufacture. Applies to insulated and uninsulated pipes of nominal size 100 mm to 600 mm for transporting fluids within the temperature range $-20\,°C$ to $+470\,°C$

4076: 1978 Specification for steel chimneys

Structural design and construction for chimneys (with or without linings) and their supports. Applications of linings or cladding. Insulation, maintenance, protective treatments, inspection. Effects of wind.

4118: 1967 Glossary of sanitation terms

Water supply, from connection with water undertaker's main or from private natural supply; storage and distribution within the curtilage, including hot water supply but not hot water central heating. Sanitary appliances and their associated water fittings and waste fittings. Above-ground drainage of sanitary appliances, roofs and yards. Below-ground drainage, including small private sewage treatment and disposal works and connection to a local authority's sewerage system.

4127: —— Light gauge stainless steel tubes

4127: Part 2: 1972 Metric units

Covers stainless steel tubes supplied in straight lengths and suitable for connection by means of capillary and compression type fittings. The tubes are suitable for bending and can be used in plumbing and heating applications when the working pressure does not exceed 13 bar

4213: 1975 Cold water storage cisterns (polyolefin or olefin copolymer) and cistern covers

Material requirements, dimensions, mechanical requirements, sampling and testing; special requirements for expansion cisterns.

4256: —— Oil-burning air heaters

4256: Part 1: 1972 Non-domestic, transportable, fan-assisted heaters

Construction, operation, performance and safety requirements for flued and unflued heaters designed for use with distillate oils such as kerosine, gas oil and domestic fuel oil.

4256: Part 2: 1972 Fixed, flued, fan-assisted heaters

Construction, operation, performance and safety requirements for heaters designed for use with dillate oils such as kerosine, gas oil and domestic fuel oil.

4256: Part 3: 1972 Fixed, flued, convector heaters

Construction, operation, performance and safety requirements for heaters designed for use with distillate oils such as kerosine, gas oil and domestic fuel oil.

4433: —— Solid smokeless fuel boilers with rated outputs up to 45 kW

4433: Part 1: 1973   Boilers with undergrate ash removal
Deals with constructional requirements, controllability tests, performance at rated output and at low load, ability to withstand accidental over-run. Supersedes BS 758: Parts 1 and 2

4433: Part 2: 1969   Gravity feed boilers designed to burn small anthracite
Deals with constructional requirements and testing for controllability performance at rated output and low load, ability to withstand accidental over-run.

4485: —— Water cooling towers

4485: Part 1: 1969   Glossary of terms
Defines general terms, together with specific terms used in the testing of natural draught and mechanical draught water cooling towers.

4485: Part 2: 1969   Methods of test and acceptance testing
Performance and efficiency of natural draught and mechanical draught water cooling towers. Definitions, symbols and formulae; performance, test procedure, instruments, methods of measurement, computation and evaluation of results, conditions of validity and technical guarantees. Worked examples, evaluating test results and guidance on drift nuisance and determination of cooling tower noise.

4485: Part 3: 1977   Thermal and functional design of cooling towers
Design principles, siting and spacing of natural draught and mechanical draught towers. Guidance on operational and hydraulic requirements, mechanical equipment and environmental aspects.

Addendum No. 1 (1978)   to BS 4485: Part 3: 1977   Factory prefabricated cooling towers
For towers transported from factory to site in parts or whole. Design, materials, maintenance and testing. Includes layouts for presentation of basic data to be provided by client and manufacturer.

4485: Part 4: 1975   Structural design of cooling towers
Applicable to the design and construction on site of natural draught hyperbolic concrete shell and mechanical draught concrete and timber structure towers.

4504: —— Flanges and bolting for pipes, valves and fittings. Metric series

4504: Part 1: 1969   Ferrous
Specifies circular flanges of steel and grey and malleable cast iron with associated pressure/temperature ratings in the range 2.5 bar to 400 bar.

4504: Part 2: 1974   Copper alloy and composite flanges
Extends BS 4504 to give coverage for integral bossed and composite flanges in nominal pressures 6 to 40 bar and for nominal sizes up to 1800 mm.

4508: — — Thermally insulated underground piping systems

4508: Part 1: 1969   Steel cased systems with air gap

Requirements for construction, installation and testing of pipe-in-pipe thermal insulation systems for underground piping systems with a welded steel casing, enclosing the thermally insulated service or product pipe and an air gap, suitable for conveying fluids with any temperature exceeding 5°C in either wet or dry sites.

4508: Part 2: 1973   Asbestos-cement cased systems with air gap

Requirements for construction, installation and testing of pipe-in-pipe thermal insulation systems for underground piping systems with an asbestos-cement casing, enclosing the thermally insulated service or product pipe and an air gap, suitable for conveying fluids with any temperature exceeding 15°C in either wet or dry sites.

4508: Part 3: 1977   General requirements for cased systems without air gap

Construction and installation of pipe-in-pipe distribution systems with an insulated service or product pipe enclosed in a pressure-tight casing.

4508: Part 4: 1977   Specific testing and inspection requirements for cased systems without air gap

Testing, inspection and certification of pipe-in-pipe distribution systems with an insulated service or product pipe enclosed in a pressure-tight casing.

4543: — — Factory-made insulated chimneys

4543: Part 1: 1976   Methods of test for factory-made insulated chimneys

For chimneys supplied in sections with associated fittings for site assembly. Suitable for solid fuel and oil-fired appliances up to 45 kW rated output. Apparatus and procedures for testing chimney support, joint leakage, draught, thermal shock, thermal insulation and strength.

4543: Pat 2: 1976   Specification for chimneys for solid fuel fired appliances

Materials, construction, erection, finish, firestops and spacers, support assemblies, wind resistance, terminal assembly and rain cap, joints, cleaning trap, dimensions, test sequences and requirements, inspection, manufacturer's particulars, marking. For appliances up to 45 kW rated output.

4543: Part 3: 1976   Specification for chimneys for oil fired appliances

Materials, construction, erection, finish, firestops and spacers, support assemblies, wind resistance, terminal assembly and rain cap, joints, cleaning trap, dimensions, test sequences and requirements, inspection, manufacturer's particulars, marking. For appliances up to 45 kW rated output.

4788: 1972   Rating and testing of refrigerated dehumidifers

Specifies test conditions for determining performance characteristics of dehumidifiers of the refrigerated type. Prescribes standard conditions on which ratings are based together with methods of testing to be applied.

4814: 1976   Specification for expansion vessels using an internal diaphragm, for sealed hot water heating systems

Construction, mounting, marking, testing, etc., of expansion vessels constructed in carbon steel up to 1000 litres in volume and operating at pressures up to 7 bar (grade 1) or 3 bar (grade 2); these two grades also reflect the mode of construction.

4856: ——   Methods for testing and rating fan coil units — unit heaters and unit coolers

4856: Part 1: 1972   Thermal and volumetric performance for heating duties: without additional ducting

Deals with methods of carrying out thermal and volumetric tests on forced convection units containing fluid-to-air heat exchangers and incorporating their own fans. The units are for heating applications and the tests are to be carried out on units in an essentially clean condition.

4856: Part 2: 1975   Thermal and volumetric performance for cooling duties: without additional ducting

Coolers as used for cooling and dehumidifying under frost-free conditions, the medium used being water or other heat transfer fluid (excluding voltatile refrigerants). Range of approx. air volume flow rates between 25×10^{-3} m³/s and 5 m³/s

4856: Part 3: 1975   Thermal and volumetric performance for heating and cooling duties: with additional ducting

Units for use with additional ducting containing fluid to air heat exchangers and incorporating their own electrically powered fan system. For heating or cooling applications, the latter with or without dehumidifcation under frost-free conditions. Air volume flow rate shall lie within the range 25×10^{-3} m³/s to 5 m³/s

4856: Part 4: 1978   Acoustic performance: without additional ducting

Testing and rating for sound power emission from equipment defined in BS 4856: Parts 1 and 2, when used directly in the conditioned space, i.e. without ducting. Instructions for calculations and for presentation of test results.

4856: Part 5: 1979   Acoustic performance: with ducting

Methods of testing and rating sound power emission resulting from the operation of air-moving parts of fan coil units, unit heaters and coolers as defined in Part 3, when used with ducting. Instructions for calculations and for presentation of test results comprising sound power radiated from the outlet, the inlet or the casing of a unit.

4857: —— Methods for testing and rating terminal reheat units for air distribution systems

4857: Part 1: 1972 Thermal and aerodynamic performance

Describes methods of thermal and aerodynamic testing and rating for high pressure terminal reheat units with or without flow rate controllers. It describes the equipment required and gives instructions for the calculation, interpretation and interpolation of results.

4857: Part 2: 1978 Acoustic testing and rating

Methods of testing and rating for static terminal attenuation; sound generation, upstream and downstream of the unit; radiation of sound from the casing.

4876: 1972 Performance requirements and test procedures for domestic flued oil burning appliances

Applies to flued oil burning appliances, up to and including 44 kW capacity, used for hot water and for space heating purposes.

4954: —— Methods for testing and rating induction units for air distribution systems

4954: Part 1: 1973 Thermal and aerodynamic performance

Specifies methods of test for induction units with water coils for heating and/or sensible cooling duties. It gives instructions for the calculation, interpretation and interpolation of the test results for the thermal and aerodynamic rating of the units.

4954: Part 2: 1978 Acoustic testing and rating

Methods of acoustic testing and rating of induction units for sound power emission and terminal attenuation

4979: —— Methods for testing and rating air control devices for air distribution systems

4979: Part 1: 1973 Aerodynamic testing of constant flow rate assemblies without a heat exchanger

Deals with a constant flow rate controller characteristics, the performance of the proportioning damper fitted to a dual duct box and the degree of temperature mixing achieved by this latter, as well as with casing leakage. Both single and dual duct boxes are covered, also single duct units.

4979: Part 2: 1974 Aerodynamic testing of variable flow rate assemblies without a heat exchanger

Deals with the testing of the variable flow rate control characteristics (using a simulated external signal) and casing and damper leakage, as well as (in the case of dual duct variable flow rate boxes) the efficiency of mixing following the transition from variable flow rate, and the flow proportioning damper.

4994: 1973 Vessels and tanks in reinforced plastics
Specifies requirements for design, materials, construction, inspection and testing of vessels (pressure and vacuum service) and tanks in reinforced plastics, consisting of a polyester or epoxide resin system reinforced with glass fibres, manufactured by the wet lay-up process. Includes constructions both with and without a lining of thermoplastics. Limited pressure and volume for vessels but no size limitation for tanks subjected only to hydrostatic head of liquid contents. Appendices include examples of design calculations and methods of test.

5041: —— Fire hydrant systems equipment

5041: Part 1: 1975 Landing valves for wet risers
Requirements for copper alloy screw down stop valves suitable for fitment on wet rising mains, also requirements for high and low pressure installations including design, manufacture, materials, dimensions, tests and marking.

5041: Part 2: 1976 Landing valves for dry risers
Requirements for copper alloy gate valves of nominal $2\frac{1}{2}$ in bore for use on dry rising mains and fitted with an instantaneous female outlet complying with the requirements of BS 336

5041: Part 3: 1975 Inlet breechings for dry riser inlets
Requirements for 2- and 4-way inlet breechings on a dry rising water main for fire fighting. Max. overall size to ensure ready accommodation in the boxes specified in BS 5041: Part 5, test requirements to ensure that no valve or part of the body will leak water.

5041: Part 4: 1975 Boxes for landing valves for dry risers
Dimensions to provide clearances and ensure that valves are easily accessible. Constructional details, requirements for hingeing, glazing, marking, locking of doors.

5041: Part 4: 1974 Boxes for foam inlets and dry risers
Standard sizes according to the number of inlets for foam or to the size of the riser. Choice and thickness of materials. Dimensions of glass in the door frame and marking thereon. May also be used for other purposes, e.g. fuel oil inlets and drencher systems.

5141: —— Air heating and cooling coils

5141: Part 1: 1975 Method of testing for rating of cooling coils
Duct-mounted cooling coil rating rest with chilled water as the cooling medium within specified ranges of variables for inlet air and water temperatures and for water flow and air velocity.

5141: Part 2: 1977 Method of testing for rating of heating coils
Rating test for duct-mounted air heating coils with hot water or dry saturated steam as the heating medium. Supersedes BS 2619 and BS 3208

5258: —— Safety of domestic gas appliances

5258: Part 1: 1975 Central heating boilers and circulators

Safety requirements and associated methods of test for boilers of rated heat inputs up to and including 60 kW and for circulators burning 1st, 2nd and 3rd family gases.

5258: Part 4: 1977 Fanned-circulation ducted-air heaters

Safety requirements and associated methods of test for appliances burning 1st, 2nd and 3rd family gases and having an input rating not exceeding 60 kW

5258: Part 5: 1975 Gas fires

Safety requirements and associated methods of test for open flued gas fires burning 1st, 2nd and 3rd family gases.

5258: Part 7: 1977 Storage water heaters

Safety requirements and associated methods of test for appliances burning 1st, 2nd and 3rd family gases and having an input rating not exceeding 20 kW

5376: Part 2: 1976 Boilers of rated input not exceeding 60 kW

Recommendations on the selection of boilers for use with open and sealed systems and on their installation in domestic and commercial premises. Does not cover the heating system as a whole.

5384: 1977 Guide to the selection and use of control systems for heating, ventilating and air conditioning installations

5410: —— Code of practice for oil firing

5410: Part 1: 1978 Installations up to 44 kW output capacity for space heating and hot water supply purposes

Applies, where relevant, to oil fired cookers where these are connected to flues. Does not apply to oil firing in marine and transportable installations, or in flueless heaters.

5410: Part 2: 1978 Installations of 44 kW or above output capacity for space heating, hot water and steam supply purposes

Deals with the provision of new—or modernizing of existing—oil burning systems for petroleum oil fuel as applied to boiler and warm air heater plants and associated oil tanks. Does not apply to marine installations or flueless heaters.

5422: 1977 Specification for the use of thermal insulating materials

Insulation of metallic surfaces of process plant, vessels, tanks, ducts, pipelines, boilers, ancillary plant. Domestic and industrial applications for heating fluids and raising steam for ventilation and for refrigeration and air conditioning in the temperature range $-40\,°C$ to $+650\,°C$

5433: 1976 Specification for underground stopvalves for water services

Copper alloy screwdown stopvalves, nominal sizes ½ to 2, for installation on underground water service pipes.

5440: —— Code of practice for flues and air supply for gas appliances of rated input not exceeding 60 kW (1st and 2nd family gases)

5440: Part 1: 1978   Flues

Choice and installation of flues forming parts of installations for domestic or commercial purposes but excluding industrial and specialist applications. Complete flue equipment, from point of issue of the combustion products from the appliance to their discharge to outside air. Materials, components and appliances, design considerations, installation constructional work, inspection and testing.

5440: Part 2: 1976   Air supply

Air supply requirements for domestic and commercial gas appliances installed in rooms and other internal spaces and in purpose-designed compartments. Air vent areas are specified where appropriate.

5449: —— Code of practice for central heating for domestic premises

5449: Part 1: 1977   Forced circulation hot water systems

Includes sealed systems and microbore systems. Unless otherwise stated, all types of forced circulation hot water heating systems are covered.

5491: 1977   Specification for rating and testing unit air conditioners of above 7 kW cooling capacity

Covers air conditioners employing air- or water-cooled condensers and the use of air conditioners for cooling, but does not cover the performance of such conditioners when used for heating or humidification. Test conditions and methods for determining performance characteristics. Conditions on which ratings are based and test methods for determining ratings.

5494: 1978   Specification for gas taps for domestic and catering appliances

Requirements for design, materials and performance of gas taps of size not exceeding 25 mm, for use with appliances operating on 1st/2nd and 3rd family gases at nominal pressures up to 20 mbar and 37 mbar respectively.

5502: —— Code of practice for the design of buildings and structures for agriculture

5502: Part 1   General considerations

Written in performance terms for designers and users. Defines where buildings must comply totally with Building Regulations and where they need not comply. Interpretation of existing statutory documents.

5502: Part 1: Section 1.5: 1978   Services

5601: —— Code of practice for ventilation and heating of caravans

5601: Part 1: 1978 Ventilation

Recommends minimum ventilation requirements for touring trailer, permanent (static) residential and holiday caravans. Includes a new formula for the effective total fixed free area of ventilation and a method of testing that does not involve expensive equipment or complicated calculations.

5601: Part 2: 1978 Installation of solid fuel fired heating appliances

Guidance on installation in caravans of smokeless solid fuel heating appliances and independent boilers for any central heating and/or hot water services designed to be associated with them. Safety precautions necessary and performance figures.

5601: Part 3: 1979 Installation of oil fired heating appliances

Recommendations for the installation of fixed, flued heating appliances burning oil fuels in touring trailer, permanent (static) residential and permanent (static) holiday caravans.

5615: 1978 Specification for insulating jackets for domestic hot water storage cylinders

Requirements and a method of test for the determination of the standing heat loss which sets a minimum performance for insulating jackets of different sizes.

5643: 1979 Glossary of refrigeration, heating, ventilating and air conditioning terms

Definitions of technical terms used in industry.

5803: —— Thermal insulation for pitched roof spaces in dwellings

5803: Part 1: 1979 Specification for man-made mineral fibre thermal insulation mats

Codes of Practice

New and revised Codes and Practice are being issued with BS numbers. Use of the separate CP series will be gradually discontinued, but the following were still current when this edition was prepared.

CP 3: —— Code of basic data for the design of buildings

CP 3: Chapter I Lighting

CP 3: Chapter I(C): 1950   Ventilation

This chapter deals with the ventilation of buildings for human habitation. The recommended rate of fresh air supply for different types of occupation are tabulated. The appendix advises on the choice between natural and mechanical ventilation to meet individual circumstances. For natural ventilation, formulae are given for calculating the rates of air flow due to wind through openings and to temperature differences. Mechanical ventilation is advised when a satisfactory standard cannot be obtained by natural means. The different types are referred to.

CP 3: Chapter II: 1970   Thermal insulation in relation to the control of environment

Deals with the use of material to control internal environment of buildings and structures. Does not deal with use for fire protection or for construction of cold stores.

CP 3: Chapter VIII: 1949   Heating and thermal insulation

This chapter points out that heating and insulation should be considered together in the early stages of design. It examines the conditions affecting the temperature in dwellings, and recommends standards of warmth for rooms and for indoor places of public assembly. It indicates a method of calculating the degree of insulation appropriate to a building in terms of cost of structure, of heating and of expenditure on fuel, and sets out maximum permissible thermal transmittances for external parts of structure.

CP 99: 1972   Frost precautions for water services

Includes recommendations for minimizing frost effects on water services generally, methods of locating pipes and fittings to obtain maximum frost protection (both for water supply pipes and for soil and waste pipes). Types and efficiency of insulating materials and advice on draining facilities.

CP 131: 1974   Chimneys and flues for domestic appliances burning solid fuel

Deals with the design and construction of natural draught chimneys and flues built of brick, stone, concrete and hollow blocks and the installation of factory-made chimneys and insulated flue pipes serving appliances with a maximum heat output of 45 kW

CP 310: 1965   Water supply

Deals with the supply of water to houses, schools, offices, public buildings and industrial buildings; the scope extends from the source of supply to the point where the water is drawn off for use. In addition to the statutory water undertakings, other sources of supply such as wells, springs, rivers, ponds and lakes are discussed. Also covers water treatment; distribution; storage; insulation of all parts of the water system; inspection, testing and maintenance. An appendix and four figures deal with pipe sizing.

CP 331: —— Installation of pipes and meters for town gas

CP 331: Part 1: 1973   Service pipes

Deals with materials, design considerations, workmanship, inspection and testing of service pipes conveying first and second family gases (town gas) from gas main to meter control at pressures up to 7 bar.

CP 331: Part 2: 1974   Low pressure metering

Siting and fixing of meters and associated controls and arrangements for meter bypasses for manufactured and natural gas of 1st and 2nd families at low pressure.

CP 331: Part 3: 1974   Low pressure installation pipes

Materials, design, installation and commissioning of these pipes for manufactured and natural gas of 1st and 2nd families.

CP 332: —— Selection and installation of town gas space heating

CP 332: Part 1: 1961   Independent domestic appliances

This code gives comprehensive guidance on the selection and installation of radiant or convector fires to provide degrees of thermal comfort according to calculated standards, by full heating, background, or supplementary heating. Tables are provided for calculation purposes. In an appendix the methods of calculating heat requirements are explained, and a method of fitting gas fires to existing brick chimneys is discussed as well as use of precast flue blocks for hearth and panel fires and converted flue systems for tall buildings. The code concludes with illustrations of fixing details.

CP 332: Part 3: 1970   Boilers of more than 150 000 Btu/h (44 kW) and up to 2 000 000 Btu/h (586 kW) output

Deals with the selection, siting and installation of gas-fired boilers for central heating and/or hot water supply for commercial and industrial premises.

CP 332: Part 4: 1966   Ducted warm air systems

Air heaters not exceeding 150 000 Btu/h output for warming domestic premises. Guidance on selection of air heaters, heater accommodation, supply of combustion and ventilation air to the heater compartment, room ventilation mounting, return air arrangements, ducting and duct connections, positioning of warm air registers, gas supply, electrical controls and connections, controls, flues, inspection, testing, commissioning and servicing. Appendices contain notes on flues, tables of pipe sizing data and notes on noise.

CP 333: —— Selection and installation of town gas hot water supplies

CP 333: Part 1: 1964   Domestic premises

This code deals with both instantaneous water heaters and storage water heating appliances. It defines the particular types of appliances under each group and sets out the conditions under which the various types of installations are best used together with the ancillary equipments required to complete the installation. Particular attention is given to ventilation requirements and installations in bedrooms, bathrooms, airing cupboards and confined spaces. Also included is information on the use of gas water heaters for showers for bathing purposes. Tables of flow rates are provided for both water and gas. Also a table of equivalent ventilating areas required for various room size and 'fits'. The code concludes with a series of illustrations of typical installations.

CP 341.300-307: 1956   Central heating by low pressure hot water

The code comprises a head-code and seven sub-codes incorporated in one document, the subcodes having the following titles: Boilers and calorifiers; Storage vessels; Pipework, fittings, valves, taps and cocks; Appliances (column radiators, surface panels, convectors); Unit heaters; Power driven circulating pumps for low pressure hot water heating installations; and Thermal insulation. The head-code 341.300 deals with the general aspects of central heating by low pressure hot water, whilst the sub-codes cover in detail the subjects indicated in their titles. Each sub-code includes a list of the relevant British Standards.

CP 342: —— Centralized hot water supply

CP 342: Part 1: 1970   Individual dwellings

Deals with the planning, designing, installation and commissioning of centralized hot water supply systems in individual dwellings.

CP 342: Part 2: 1974   Buildings other than individual dwellings

Design, planning, installation, inspection and testing of hot water supply systems in commercial, industrial or multiple-dwelling buildings, including district or group schemes.

CP 352: 1958   Mechanical ventilation and air conditioning in buildings

This code deals with the work involved in the general design, planning, installation, testing and maintenance of mechanical ventilating and air conditioning installations whereby air is forced into or extracted from buildings. It consists of a head code and eight sub-codes having the following titles: Fans, motors and starting gear; Air heaters; Air distribution system; Air cleaning devices: Thermal insulation; Sound-proofing and anti-vibration devices; Temperature and humidity controls; Cooling and dehumidification. The head code deals with the general aspect of the subject while the sub-codes cover in detail the subject indicated by their title. The code carries fourteen tables and ten illustrations.

CP 413: 1973 Ducts for building services

Deals with the design and construction of subways, crawlways, trenches, casings and chases for the accommodation of services within buildings and external ducts. Position, dimensions, safety precautions and control of hazards. Fire precautions in builders' or structural ducts and, as an appendix, fire precautions for ventilation ductwork.

CP 3000: 1955   Installation and maintenance of underfeed stokers

In addition to the installation, care and maintenance of underfeed stokers used with domestic, sectional, shell and small-tube boilers, this code makes recommendations on the design of boiler room, fuel storage, flues and chimneys, and on the provision of automatic safety controls.

CP 3009: 1970   Thermally insulated underground piping systems

Deals with the work involved in the general designing, planning, pre-fabrication, transport, installation, maintenance and testing of thermally insulated underground piping systems for conveying or circulating steam, hot or chilled water, heated oil and other fluids.

Index